# CHARLES DARWIN

## Evolution and Natural Selection

Ch. Darwin

[*From the Century Magazine.*

# CHARLES DARWIN

## Evolution and Natural Selection

*Edited*
*with an introductory essay*
*by*
Bert James Loewenberg

BEACON PRESS Beacon Hill BOSTON

Library of Congress catalog card number: 59-6682

Printed in the United States of America

*To commemorate*

The Hundredth Anniversary
of the
Meeting at the
Linnean Society, July 1, 1858
and the Papers of
Charles Darwin and Alfred Russel Wallace
which were read there
and the
Centennial of the Publication
of the
ORIGIN OF SPECIES

November 24, 1859

For My Wife

ANNE LOEWENBERG

Bert James Loewenberg, Professor of History at Sarah Lawrence College, was educated at Clark and Harvard universities. His lifelong interest in Charles Darwin originated in 1930 and since this time he has done extensive research both in this country and abroad, with particular emphasis on the Darwin papers in England. Among the author's other works on the subject are DARWINISM: REACTION OR REFORM?, DARWIN, WALLACE, AND THE THEORY OF NATURAL SELECTION, and the preface to CALENDAR OF THE LETTERS OF CHARLES ROBERT DARWIN TO ASA GRAY. At present he is serving as chairman of the Darwin Anniversary Committee.

# *Contents*

# *Table of Illustrations*



The illustrations, unless otherwise noted, are from the original editions of Darwin's works or from related sources contemporary with the text. The woodcut illustrations are from *Darwin, Wallace, and The Theory of Natural Selection,* designed by Gerald E. Cinamon, and are reproduced by permission of Arlington Books.

# CHARLES DARWIN:

## Evolution and Natural Selection

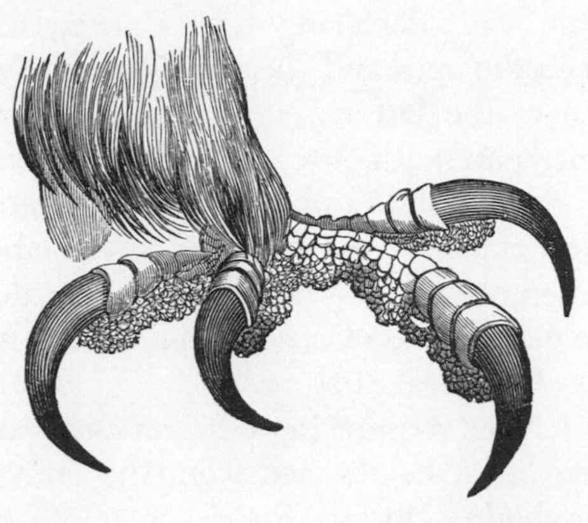

On the twenty-fourth of November, 1859, the London publishing house of John Murray issued a small green-backed volume. The volume was entitled *On the Origin of Species by Means of Natural Selection, or the Preservation of Favoured Races in the Struggle for Life.*[1] Charles Robert Darwin, the author, was a scientist who had written on geological and zoological topics with monographic competence. He had also written an interesting travel account which had reached a much wider public. As a naturalist on H. M. S. *Beagle,* an admiralty vessel engaged in a routine survey, he had reported findings in many areas of natural history and had also recorded his experiences in foreign lands.[2]

The *Origin of Species,* however, created a sensation. Darwin was condemned by powerful bishops, and his works were consigned to the perdition of inconsequence. He had denied the biblical account of creation and was accordingly accused of attacking religion, the church, and God. Secular scholars protested that he had violated the law of reason and had transgressed the proprieties of science. The Darwinian controversy invaded the discussions of Parliament, and one noble lord, declaring that Darwin had forced a choice between the apes and the angels, publicly announced his allegience to the latter. Nevertheless, Charles Darwin became an international figure, and his name was borrowed to describe a cosmic philosophy. Scientists, theologians, and men of letters came to his defence, and elaborate praise paralleled intemperate condemnation. Darwin was celebrated as the Copernicus of a new science and was hailed as "the Newton of Natural History."[3]

But great ideas require periodic infusions of relevance, and great men must be rescued from the oblivion of fame. "Almost everybody," Josiah Royce once remarked of the Hegelian philosophy, "has forgotten what it means and has therefore come to accept it as true."[4] Charles Darwin has become a symbol, and the doctrine of evolution has become a cliché.

Charles Darwin came of a family distinguished for achievement. His grandfather, Erasmus Darwin, enjoyed so favorable a medical reputation that King George III invited him to become physician at court. As a natural philosopher, Erasmus Darwin wrote speculative verse in the best eighteenth-century manner. He wrote of life, of love, and of evolution. His views of the development of species bore considerable resemblance to those of Lamarck, and after his grandson had made evolution scientifically respectable Erasmus Darwin emerged as an indubitable precursor. Achievement of a different kind marked the activities of members of the maternal line. On both sides there was sustained and unpretentious effort. Few purple patches colored the family history, but a large share of talent progressively augmented its claim to renown.

Charles Robert Darwin was born in Shrewsbury on February 12, 1809. Robert Waring Darwin, his father, like

Erasmus was a successful physician equally revered by his patients and by his children. Susannah Wedgwood, Darwin's mother, bore a name as familiar then as it is now. The daughter of the second Josiah Wedgwood, who inherited a flourishing business and a cherished tradition, her character mirrored the happy household in which she matured. Her formal education, more extended than was customary for females, was supplemented by affectionate contact with Dr. Erasmus Darwin, a close friend of the first Josiah. From him Susannah Wedgwood acquired an appreciation of nature and some insight into its meanings. Darwin's childhood interest in natural objects, not unusual in English country lads, was never marred by maternal displeasure. She died when Charles was barely eight, but he always retained warm, if vague, recollections of her.

The Darwins and the Wedgwoods were a single family almost from the beginning. The Darwin brood was as much at home at the Wedgwood estate at Maer as were the Wedgwoods at the Darwin home in Shrewsbury. These intimate relations became even closer when Charles Darwin's sister married one of her Wedgwood cousins. Charles later married Emma Wedgwood, further uniting the two families. Yet it was Darwin's father who exercised a preponderating influence, for Robert Waring Darwin was a formidable man. Dr. Darwin had plans for his children, which, like most parental plans, were easier to devise than to execute.

Except for the untimely death of his mother, Charles Darwin was a happy, carefree boy. He accomplished the usual amount of mischief and the usual amount of study. With his brother and other companions, he roamed the countryside, explored forbidden places, and amassed collections with typical adolescent passion. In August, 1818, he was enrolled in the Shrewsbury Grammar School, a venerable institution with a curriculum appropriate to its age. A brilliant young Cantabridgian, the Reverend Samuel Butler, had been appointed headmaster in 1798 and was still in absolute command when Darwin matriculated. If the Reverend Dr. Butler impressed Darwin no more than headmasters ever impress English schoolboys, the future contrived to provide him with a history. The headmaster of Shrewsbury turned out to be the grandfather of another Samuel Butler, author of *Erewhon* and *The Way of All Flesh,* who undertook to refute the *Origin of Species* in exquisitely acrid prose.[5]

Charles Darwin survived the Shrewsbury experience with comparative ease. The school was close to home, and even as a boarder he was not actually separated from his beloved family. He made friends, enjoyed Horace and Scott, practiced chemistry on the sly, and caught rats openly. Dr. Butler did not regard him with favor and publicly ridiculed him for his deficiencies in scholarship. Dr. Darwin was not pleased with the academic performance of his offspring. A sixteen-year-old boy's interest in rats might have been condoned and his chemical experiments might have been forgiven if young Charles had shown some concern about the serious business of life. In any case, plans for Darwin's future had been made. He was shipped off to the University of Edinburgh to study medicine. Erasmus Darwin and Robert Waring Darwin were both doctors — reason enough for the Darwin boys to seek no further. Darwin's brother was already a medical student at Edinburgh, where an uncle had preceded him. It was now Charles's turn to follow the Darwin way.

Darwin's career as a medical student was an unqualified failure. Though he had served a brief apprenticeship to his father, he found the formal study of medicine intellectually bleak. His professors were dull and their classes duller. The properties of rhubarb, presented on cold mornings before breakfast, were not intriguing to a boy in his teens. He never wanted to hear of *materia medica* again, and even the lectures on geology and zoology — subjects which were later central to his existence — were a bore. The operating theater frightened him, and at his first encounter he ran away before the demonstration was completed. What he witnessed of an operation on a child, performed before the use of chloroform was in practice, haunted him forever. He could never endure the sight of blood after this.

If the university was lacking in inspiration, Edinburgh itself was not without charm. The Scots appealed to Darwin, and he expanded in response to their warmth. Men whose devotion to science was as great as his later became were attracted to a young man who listened well and asked intelligent questions. One of them told him about Lamarck and the Lamarckian theory of evolution. Lamarck reminded him of his grandmather whose works he had already read. When Audubon lectured on birds at the Natural History Society, Darwin went to listen. This was the sort of fare on which he throve, and he found someone to teach him the elements of taxidermy. He went to the Royal Society and could scarcely take his eyes from the presiding officer, who was Sir Walter Scott. He collected marine animals and was given specimens of rare shells by a museum curator. These things stirred him and helped him grow. Everything, his father must have thought, stirred him except medicine. Yet Darwin was far from unhappy. He was a contented seventeen-year-old unworried by the future, but he was harried by the thought that his father was displeased.

Darwin was right. His father was distraught but lacked any clear notion of what to do next. What did one do with a normal son who simply refused to respond to his duty? What could a conscientious father propose? He had already warned Charles that he would disgrace himself and his family — an outcome of his earlier shooting and rat catching. And now more profitless time in Scotland had to be added to the debit side of the doctor's parental account book.

The doctor, however, believed he understood his responsibility as clearly as he understood psychosomatic symptoms in his patients. If Charles would not be a doctor, he would be a preacher. And Charles, not without some remorse, went to Christ's College, Cambridge, as docilely as he had gone to Edinburgh. He would try again to obey his father's wishes. He would take holy orders.

Cambridge, at least in retrospect, seemed as aimless as Edinburgh. When he allowed himself to think of it, Darwin realized that the Episcopal priesthood was simply a temporary answer to his own irresolution. In the interim, he enjoyed himself thoroughly. These were the years which he later described as "the most joyful in my happy life; for I was then in excellent health, and almost always in high spirits." Whatever his silent misgivings, they were years of exuberant undergraduate living. He hunted, practiced marksmanship, and played cards. He belonged to what he called a riotous set — a set given to epicurean dining and expert wine drinking. Characteristically, he later half begrudged himself these youthful pleasures. "I know that I ought to feel ashamed of days and evenings thus spent . . ."; but they were good years, "some of my friends were very pleasant, and we were at all times in the highest of spirits. . . ."[6]

Although Darwin was resigned to the life of a curate, he thought more of a quiet parsonage and the joys of rural living than of ministerial obligations. For at that time he trembled with anticipation in advance of a hunt and left his boots at the bedside so as to lose no time when dawn finally broke on a shooting day. But the round of undergraduate chores was performed routinely. The logic of Paley's *Evidences of Christianity* evoked some admiration, but he really preferred to wander in the Cambridge fields catching butterflies or beetles. In 1831 he qualified for the B.A. degree, without honors, tenth on the Christ College list.

He still had two terms of residence to complete before he could leave Cambridge and take up his calling. It was a fortunate interlude, for events postponed the decision he would otherwise have been obliged to make.

Darwin accounted the Cambridge period a futile one. It was, he said, as barren as the Edinburgh period. He felt that he had wasted his time and that he had learned nothing. Darwin's appraisal was not strictly accurate. Up to that point Cambridge was unquestionably his most important experience. At Cambridge he came to know and admire the Reverend John Steven Henslow, teacher of science at the university and unofficial guide to promising undergraduates. Darwin attended Henslow's lectures on botany and walked with him along the Cambridge "backs." He "botanized" with Henslow's classes on numerous expeditions and listened to scientific talk with fellow students in Henslow's hospitable home. A great teacher, Henslow answered Darwin's elementary questions with patience and treated Darwin's student discoveries with respect and understanding. Here was a man who combined learning with pleasure and religion with natural philosophy. To Darwin he was, and always remained, the ideal personality — wise, generous, and companionable. Henslow communicated his zest for knowledge to the young Darwin and taught him his first real lesson in the meaning of science. Darwin could hardly help loving him, and he could hardly permit himself to doubt that he was worthy of Henslow's pedagogical care.[7] It was Henslow who offered Darwin the opportunity to participate in an exciting voyage of scientific exploration. Darwin's appointment as naturalist on H. M. S. *Beagle* was the most crucial event of his early years, for it was the *Beagle* experience which enabled Darwin to discover himself.

Darwin's father did not respond to the *Beagle* prospect with ardor. He had all manner of reservations, and it was only as a result of the intervention of old Uncle Jos —

Josiah Wedgwood — that Robert Darwin reluctantly acquiesced. With his father's consent, however grudgingly given, Charles Darwin was able to devote himself to preparations for the voyage. For the first time, he was wholeheartedly absorbed in the future and was completely immersed in plans of his own. On December 27, 1831, the *Beagle* put out from Plymouth with Charles Darwin, naturalist, on board. Five long years were to pass before Darwin was to see his father, his family and England again. Those five years of exploration altered Darwin's intellectual life. As a result, they altered the intellectual life of the Western world.

The *Beagle* voyage took Darwin virtually around the globe. Voyages of scientific exploration were not uncommon except for the Darwins. The Darwins occasionally undertook conventional excursions, never global tours. Charles Darwin had been to Edinburgh, to Cambridge, and to London. The *Beagle* took him to Brazil, to Argentina, and to Peru. He rode with the gauchos in Maldonado, he observed the effect of cattle on vegetation near Monte Video, and he marveled at the natives of Tierra del Fuego. He traveled on horseback, on river boats, and on foot. He climbed over South American mountains and swung his geological hammer with a discoverer's gusto. Virgin paleontological beds yielded their treasures of skeletons and bones, and he studied fauna and flora everywhere. Fish and birds, crustaceans and insects now enticed him more than the hunt ever had. Differences among species and varieties puzzled him only slightly less than their similarities. Lonely though he was for his family and for England, his curiosity kept him eager for each new day and each new adventure. Half-formed questions took shape in his mind, and every fresh experience underscored his growing doubts about the immutability of species. He complained only that there were too many new objects to preserve and to classify. His shipmates called him the "Flycatcher,"[8] and so he was, for he was forever littering the deck with his nets and specimens. His cabin was as neat as a nautical zoologist could keep it, but it was crammed with bottles, books, and a naturalist's hoardings. Case after case of specimens was shipped to England, and page after page of observations filled his diaries, letters, and journals. As the ports of the Western world led him inland — Lima, Valparaiso, the Galapagos — there were more specimens, more notes, and more letters home.

Darwin returned to Shrewsbury on the fourth of October, 1836. He was happily reunited with his family, and Dr. Darwin, looking intently at his son, remarked that his head had quite changed. Darwin's head had indeed changed, but the change was internal. The *Beagle* voyage, as Darwin himself later assessed it, was "by far the most important event" in his life.[9] The voyage of the *Beagle* made Darwin a scientist and provided him with an absorbing purpose. In July, 1837, Darwin opened his first research notebook on species.[10] On January 29, 1839, he married his cousin Emma Wedgwood. These two events blocked out the course of the future. His wife, his children, and his home filled Darwin's heart; nature and species filled his mind. Despite illness, almost chronic, which impeded his progress and marred his joy, he realized his aspirations and fulfilled his goals. No barriers separated his life from his work. He was completely identified with his scientific labors, and his wife and children were completely identified with him.

The problem of the origin of species was the focus of Darwin's mental life. He did not discover the idea of evolution; he provided mankind with the factual and conceptual data for believing it. Two separate factors provide the key for an understanding of Darwin's accomplishment. He placed the idea of evolution in a new framework of data, and he presented a reasonable hypothesis to explain how the process of evolution worked. The *Origin of Species* established the fact of evolution; the hypothesis of natural selection demonstrated how evolution operated. Darwin was personally involved with the hypothesis of natural selection, but his main objective was to validate the concept of derivation — the descent by transmutation of all forms of life. Natural selection, he told the American botanist Asa Gray, was "utterly unimportant, compared with the question of Creation *or* Modification."[11]

Charles Darwin's life is divisible into five creative periods: early youth, from 1809 to 1831; on the *Beagle,* from 1831 to 1836; the beginnings of evolutionary research, from 1837 to 1842; the evolution of the *Origin of Species,* from the first pencil sketch of 1842 until its publication in 1859, and the period of the exemplification of evolutionary doctrine from the appearance of the *Origin of Species* in 1859 until his death in 1882.

The voyage of the *Beagle* behind him, Darwin's clear objectives permitted him to glimpse the rim of his own future. At last he was free to make his life in the image of his own urges. He moved in scientific circles, read papers before learned societies, and began the preparation of the *Beagle* materials for publication. Geology intrigued him, and he undertook studies on coral reefs, volcanoes, and Chilean elevation, always conscious of the connections between geology and organic life. He immersed himself in the zoological data accumulated during his travels, but species were never far from the surface of his mind. In one way or another the direction of every research converged on the species question.

The mosaic of Darwinian thought was a tightly-wedged pattern of purpose and idea. Five years after Darwin opened his first notebook on species, in 1842, he sketched out a brief outline of his theory of evolution. A 231-page draft was ready in 1844, which, in the event of his premature death, Darwin intended to have edited and published as a resumé of his views.[12] Thereafter, one experiment followed another in a reasoned sequence of objective. There were problems in abundance — tantalizing, stubborn problems that robbed him of conviction and forced him to probe further. He sought aid and encouragement wherever he could find them: from Sir Charles Lyell, eminent geologist; from Dr. Joseph D. Hooker, Director of the Botanical Gardens at Kew; from Thomas Henry Huxley, brilliant and informed naturalist; and from Asa Gray, expert botanist of the United States. As his data mounted to staggering proportions and the cast of his thought etched itself in the minds of his friends, they urged him to publish.[13] Darwin listened appreciatively to all such advice and patiently went on with his work. There was always another line of investigation to pursue, always another enigma to unravel. Darwin did not procrastinate. He was keenly aware of the magnitude of his task. He was also fully conscious that his conclusions were so unorthodox that every conceptual stage of the argument demanded full analysis, every factual gap required complete explanation.[14] He wrote — and he found writing hard [15] — yet he had no precise vision of how the book would ultimately emerge from his churning thought. That it would be a "big book"[16] he was sure, but he had to stop constantly in order to explore a vital suggestion or to mine a newly discovered vein of fact.

On the morning of June 18, 1858, Darwin received a letter from Alfred Russel Wallace, a young naturalist then collecting species in far-off Malaya. Darwin had previously corresponded with Wallace and had been much impressed by what he had seen of his work. The letter contained a copy of Wallace's essay "On the Tendency of Varieties to depart indefinitely from the Original Type," which Wallace asked Darwin to read and, if he found it interesting enough, to forward to Lyell. It was not only interesting, it was devastating. Wallace's essay set forth Darwin's ideas on transmutation so exactly that his leading terms, as Darwin wrote Lyell, "now stand as heads of my chapters."[17] The repeated warnings of Darwin's friends that he might be forestalled had come true with the vengeance of reality. Deeply and understandably perturbed, Darwin was unsure what course to follow. The prospect of losing his priority momentarily destroyed his equanimity, although he was certain that to publish himself would be unfair to Wallace and thus dishonorable. The dilemma was resolved by Lyell and Hooker, who skillfully arranged that a series of Darwin's writings and Wallace's essay be jointly presented at a meeting of the Linnean Society. On July 1, 1858, the papers were read under the sponsorship of the two noted scientists and Darwin's theory — along with Wallace's — was for the first time presented to the public.

Relieved of anxieties about priorities, Darwin dedicated himself to the completion of his book. In less than a year he was reading the proof sheets of the *Origin of Species* and in November it finally appeared. Actually, as Darwin later admitted, the *Origin* gained from the circumstances dictating its creation.[18] If it was not quite the book the author intended, it was probably a better one. It was certainly shorter, and it profited from the condensation, which tightened its logic and heightened its dramatic appeal. Each argument and each illustration were enhanced by the realization that either was but a single selection chosen from many comparable examples. Yet, for Darwin, the *Origin* was never more than an "Abstract," and he devoted the rest of his life to an elaboration of the grand idea.[19]

One volume pursued another, once Darwin's heresy on the immutability of species was announced to the world. The year after the appearance of the *Origin* came a second and revised edition, the first having been exhausted on the day of its publication. A third edition was published in 1861, a fourth in 1866, a fifth in 1869, and the sixth and final edition in 1872.[20] While the revisions were in progress, he struggled over his orchid volume and over the preparation of *Animals and Plants under Domestication,* which was issued in 1869. Of the former, *On the Various Contrivances by which Orchids are Fertilized by Insects,* he wrote John Murray, his publisher, that it would "serve to illustrate how natural history may be worked under the belief of the modification of species." The book, he believed, would help the *Origin,* "as it will show I have worked hard at details."[21] Darwin worked hard, but he worked even harder on his *Domestication* volume, a two-volume expansion of the *Origin.* Not only was it an elaboration of the *Origin,* but it was a documentation of its first chapter, "Variation under Domestication," and each volume was larger than the *Origin* itself. Darwin planned to supply similar evidence for variation in nature, but this book as such was never written. The work on domestication grew voluminously and cost him "four years and two months of hard labor." Darwin was vexed. The size, he felt, was "quite ludicrous in relation to the subject. I am ready to swear at myself and at every fool who ever writes a book."[22]

Darwin's self-criticism was far too extreme. Nevertheless, the *Domestication* demonstrated that his original plan, altered by the unheralded arrival of the Wallace essay, could not have been successfully carried out. Radical pruning made the *Origin* a great book. The initial design, unprefaced by the *Origin,* would have resulted in the "big book" of Darwin's conjecture — a book bristling with novelty and crammed with documentation. Such a book, Hooker frankly stated, would "have choked any naturalist of the nineteenth century."[23]

The pages of the *Domestication* are far less tedious than Darwin imagined. He was always at his best when describing his own intimate observations, and he had observed dogs, pigeons, horses, and plants closely. The language is direct and personal, never pedantic and hardly ever remote. Darwin talks to his readers and shares his confidences with them. His writings never suggest the professor still lecturing from his classroom notes. The *Domestication* volumes are noteworthy for the introduction of a provisional theory of inheritance — the hypothesis of pangenesis. "The great god Pan," as Darwin jocularly referred to it, was a response to an insistent and deeply felt need. He had to account for the fact of variation itself and for the transmission of individual difference. Wallace expressed Darwin's feelings precisely. "I read the chapter on pangenesis first, for I could not wait. I can hardly tell you how much I admire it. It is a positive comfort to me to have any feasible explanation of a difficulty that has always been haunting me, and I shall never be able to give it up till a better one supplies its place. . . ."[24]

After working with animals and plants, Darwin found relaxation in struggling with human origins.[25] *The Descent of Man* stemmed from an early interest in the expression of emotion, and it was on this aspect of the subject that he was actively engaged after he had finished the *Domestication.* A study of man was so far beyond his intent that as late as 1864 he offered his materials to Wallace in the belief that he would never have use for them.[26] Four years after, he changed his mind, irritated because he believed he was being "taunted" for concealing his views.[27] Darwin reached his literary stride with *The Descent of Man* (1871), which he finished in three years. Actually, the *Descent* was two books under a single title, as both his friends and critics were quick to point out. More than half of the two volumes was reserved for a discussion of the hypothesis of sexual selection.

The *Expression of the Emotions in Man and Animals* followed *The Descent of Man* after the lapse of a year. Darwin had hoped to treat the emotions, man, and sexual selection in a single essay, but there was simply too much he needed to say. Emotion had long fascinated him, and he began his observations with the birth of his own first child.

"My attention was called to this subject many years ago," he wrote, "by Sir Charles Bell's admirable work. This illustrious anatomist maintains that man is endowed with certain muscles solely for the sake of expressing his emotions. As this view is obviously opposed to the belief that man is descended from some other and lower form, it was necessary for me to consider it. I likewise wished to ascertain how far the emotions are expressed in the same manner by different races of man."[28]

Darwin was more interested in the analysis and classication of the emotions than in the emotions as such. Still pertinent, however, are the questions he raised and the methods he employed. He studied infants and the mentally diseased. He made use of photographs that he submitted for appraisal to a variety of experts. Art forms depicting types of emotional expression were compared and classified, and comparative data of diverse peoples and groups were collected. Animal gestures and behavior were also investigated. Only the projective testing devices of modern psychology were missing from the catalogue of methodological techniques. Designed as an amplification of *The Descent of Man,* the *Expression of the Emotions* more than served its purpose. Although it had an initial sale, it did not require a second edition; thus Darwin's corrections and additions were never incorporated. Ingenious and informative though it is, it does not bear comparison with either the *Origin* or *The Descent of Man.*

Darwin was sixty-three when the *Expression of the Emotions* was published in 1872. Most of the reservations he entertained about himself were stilled by a crescendo of honors which came to him from all over the world.[29] Converts to evolution, especially among younger naturalists, assured him that the cause which he had made his own would eventually triumph. Above all, he was weary and was loath to engage in further speculative analysis. But

Charles Darwin could not remain idle. In his own words, he was "never comfortable except when at work". To Hooker, always his confidant, he lamented, "The word holiday is written in a dead language for me, and much I grieve at it."[30] The last decade of his life was just as crowded with intellectual excitement as any period after the *Beagle* expedition. A second edition of *The Descent of Man* appeared in 1874, this time in a single volume. Other fundamental Darwinian books were also revised: *Domestication* (1875), the *Geological Observations* of the *Beagle* voyage (1876), and the *Orchids* (1877). Fresh work in geology and botany was begun and older work continued.[31]

Darwin remained an active research naturalist as long as he was able to work, and he was blessed by being able to work until almost the end. Darwin papers were read before the Linnean Society in March, 1882; *Nature* carried a notice written by Darwin in April; and, on the eighteenth, the very day before he died, a paper on Syrian dogs by W. Van Dyck with a preliminary notice by Charles Darwin was read to the Zoological Society.[32]

*The Formation of Vegetable Mould Through the Action of Earth-Worms,*[33] Darwin's final book, symbolized his dominant intellectual traits. More experimentally oriented than some of his other works, it suggested the catholicity of his interests. These ranged from geological formations and the chain of organic life to flowers, insects, and earthworms. Nothing, including the earthworm, was too lowly. Nothing was lacking in significance to engage his enthusiasm and to enlist his painstaking care. In this spirit he observed the earthworm and studied vegetable mold. He watched, he measured, he computed. A contemporary reviewer concluded that it was an important and fascinating study: "The earthworm steps forth . . . as an intelligent and beneficent personage, a worker of vast geological changes, a planer down of mountain sides . . . a friend of man . . . and an ally of the Society for the preservation of ancient monuments."[34]

Natural history held the mind of Charles Darwin captive from the days of the *Beagle,* but Emma Darwin was the keeper of his spirit. She spent a lifetime protecting him from himself and from the intrusion of others. She nursed him when he was sick and tended him when he was well. She entertained his friends and was hostess to scores of visitors. She bore his children, and they reared them together. She filled the house at Down with quiet pleasure, familial gaiety, and respect for work. She shared his pleasures and assuaged his defeats; she read his proofs and was with him when he died. And Charles Darwin spent his life appreciating her. He was never quite able to understand why Emma Wedgwood had agreed to marry him.[35]

Of ten Darwin children eight survived. Three of the Darwin sons were knighted. One became a Cambridge professor of astronomy and a Fellow of the Royal Society. Another, a manufacturer of scientific instruments, was mayor of Cambridge. A third, a botanist, was also an assistant to his father and the editor of his letters. A fourth son was a successful banker; a fifth became president of the Royal Geographical Society and also of the Eugenics Society. The Darwin children were a source of constant pleasure throughout their parents' lives. Darwin adored them, and he adored them unabashedly. When his first-born was five months old, he exulted: "I defy any one to flatter us on our baby, for I defy any one to say anything in its praise of which we are not already fully conscious."[36]

Darwin's responses to most experiences were as human as his demands of life were normal. He needed approbation, and he was not impervious to fame. No one could have been more completely identified with an idea than Darwin was identified with the idea of evolution. Nor was he indifferent to his reputation, either as a man or as a scholar. Hostile critics frequently angered him, not, it must be added, without due cause. "There has been a plethora of reviews," he wrote Lyell apropos of the *Origin*, "and I am really quite sick of myself."[37] Some reviewers, even when they evoked Darwin's praise for their cogency, irritated him by their unfairness. Of one such review that appeared in the *Athenaeum* almost immediately after the *Origin* came off the press, he was swift to acclaim its skill. But the author's tactics, he complained to Hooker, were "base." "He would, on no account, burn me, but he will get the wood ready, and tell the black beasts how to catch me. . . ."[38] It was not long before he was able to take a more tranquil view. "I have got to take pleasure in thinking how I could best snub my reviewers," he confided to Lyell.[39] By 1872 he was as detached about the opinions expressed in reviews as it was possible for an author to be. Unless commentators had something crucial to contribute, he decided to "waste no more time" on the comments of critics.[40]

Yet none knew the weakness of evolutionary theory better than Darwin. Indeed, the best source for criticism of the *Origin of Species* available to hostile analysis was the *Origin* itself. Darwin correctly told Asa Gray that he could easily have written "a more damning review than has as yet appeared!"[41] He was continually surprised to find how little substance there was in the critical essays. Occasionally he despaired of the slow rate of intellectual change — a rate "almost as slow as the change of species." "I am getting wearied at the storm of hostile reviews," he complained somewhat petulantly, "and hardly any useful. . . ."[42]

But, if Darwin required approbation and encouragement, he was also generous in bestowing them upon others. Hooker, Lyell, Wallace, and Gray were the beneficiaries of his critical plaudits as he was of theirs.[43] Many unknown students, striving for recognition, were staggered by a note from the master telling them of the stimulation he had derived from their published work. Frequently, his aid, unsolicited and unheralded, took a more substantial form. Together with others, he gave Huxley a large sum to enable him to recapture his health. He once bought a ticket to India for a struggling naturalist and gave him other financial assistance that his promising research might continue.[44] These instances reveal Darwin's spirit — to give of himself, of his means, and to give unpretentiously that the goals of others might be achieved.

This was the Charles Darwin who became the symbol of an intellectual revolution. Darwinian evolution was unique in a highly important respect. Darwin demonstrated that individual species of plants and animals evolved by natural means from previously existing plants and animals. He demonstrated the idea of evolution historically; he defined the concept of natural selection hypothetically. By giving every living form a dimension in time and by relating each genetically, he implicated every variety of life in every other variety. By extending the notion of evolution to all living things, Darwin extended the logic of science to all forms of existence. Before Darwin, a rigid distinction between the world of matter and the world of life dominated the minds of scholars. The material world referred to one sphere of existence, but man, mind, and morals were held to refer to a spiritual order of being. After Darwin, the nature of man, of mind, and morals appeared in new and altered relations. The logic of science and the dynamics of evolution became applicable to all forms of human activity. Once man was swept into the evolutionary orbit, a revolution in Western thought was initiated. Man was seen to be a part of nature, and nature was seen to be a part of man. The Darwinian revolution was not a revolution in science alone; it was a revolution in man's conception of himself and in man's conception of all his works.

# The Darwins

# *Erasmus Darwin: Charles Darwin's Appraisal of his Grandfather*[45]

Erasmus Darwin was descended from a Lincolnshire family, and the first of his ancestors of whom we know anything was William Darwin, who possessed a small estate at Cleatham. He was also yeoman of the armoury of Greenwich to James I. and Charles I. This office was probably almost a sinecure, and certainly of very small value. He died in 1644, and we have reason to believe from gout. It is, therefore, probable that Erasmus, as well as many other members of the family, inherited from this William, or some of his predecessors, their strong tendency to gout; and it was an early attack of gout which made Erasmus a vehement advocate for temperance throughout his whole life.

The second William Darwin (born 1620) served as Captain-Lieutenant in Sir W. Pelham's troop of horse, and fought for the king. His estate was sequestrated by the Parliament, but he was afterwards pardoned on payment of a heavy fine. In a petition to Charles II. he speaks of his almost utter ruin from having adhered to the royal cause, and it appears that he had become a barrister. This circumstance probably led to his marrying the daughter of Erasmus Earle, Serjeant-at-law; and hence Erasmus Darwin derived his Christian name.

The eldest son from this marriage, William (born 1655), married the heiress of Robert Waring, of Wilsford, in the county of Nottingham. This lady also inherited the manor of Elston, which has remained ever since in the family.

This third William Darwin had two sons — William, and Robert who was educated as a barrister, and who was the father of Erasmus. I suppose that the Cleatham and the Waring properties were left to William, who seems to have followed no profession, and the Elston estate to Robert; for when the latter married, he gave up his profession and lived ever afterwards at Elston. There is a portrait of him at Elston Hall, and he looks, with his great wig and bands, like a dignified doctor of divinity. He seems to have had some taste for science, for he was an early member of the well-known Spalding Club; and the celebrated antiquary, Dr. Stukeley, in 'An Account of the almost entire Sceleton of a large animal,' &c., published in the 'Philosophical Transactions,' April and May 1719, begins his paper as follows: — "Having an account from my friend, Robert Darwin, Esq., of Lincoln's Inn, a Person of Curiosity, of a human Sceleton impressed in Stone, found lately by the Rector of Elston," &c. Stukeley then speaks of it as a great rarity, "the like whereof has not been observed before in this island, to my knowledge." Judging from a sort of litany written by Robert, and handed down in the family, he was a strong advocate of temperance, which his son ever afterwards so strongly advocated: —

*From a morning that doth shine,*
*From a boy that drinketh wine,*
*From a wife that talketh Latine,*
*Good Lord deliver me.*

It is suspected that the third line may be accounted for by his wife, the mother of Erasmus, having been a very learned lady.

The eldest son of Robert, christened Robert Waring, succeeded to the estate of Elston, and died there at the age of ninety-two, a bachelor. He had a strong taste for poetry, like his youngest brother Erasmus. Robert also cultivated botany, and when an oldish man, he published his 'Principia Botanica.' This book in MS. was beautifully written, and my father declared that he believed it was published because his old uncle could not endure that such fine calligraphy should be wasted. But this was hardly just, as the work contains many curious notes on biology — a subject wholly neglected in England in the last century. The public, moreover, appreciated the book, as the copy in my possession is the third edition.

Of the second son, William Alvey, I know nothing. A third son, John, became the rector of Elston, the living being in the gift of the family. The fourth son, and the youngest of the children, was Erasmus, the subject of the present memoir, who was born on the 12th Dec. 1731, at Elston Hall.

His elder brother, Robert, states, in a letter to my father (May 19, 1802), that Erasmus "was always fond of poetry. He was also always fond of mechanicks. I remember him when very young making an ingenious alarum for his watch (clock?); he used also to show little experiments in electricity with a rude apparatus he then invented with a bottle." The same tastes, therefore, appeared very early in life which prevailed to the day of his death. "He had always a dislike to much exercise and rural diversions, and it was with great difficulty that we could ever persuade him to accompany us."

When ten years old (1741), he was sent to Chesterfield School, where he remained for nine years. His sister, Susannah, wrote to him at school in 1748, and I give part of the letter as a curiosity. She was then a young lady between eighteen and nineteen years old. She died unmarried, and her nephew, Dr. Robert Darwin (my father), who was deeply attached to her, always spoke of her as the very pattern of an old lady, so nice looking, so gentle, kind, and charitable, and passionately fond of flowers. The first part of her letter consists of gossip and family news, and is not worth giving.

### Susannah Darwin *to* Erasmus

Dear Brother,

I come now to ye chief design of my Letter, and that is to acquaint you with my Abstinence this Lent, which you will find on ye other side, it being a strict account of ye first 5 days, and all ye rest has been conformable thereto; I shall be glad to hear from you wth an account of your temperance this lent, wch I expect far exceeds mine. As soon as we kill our hog I intend to take part thereof with ye Family, for I'm informed by a learned Divine yt Hogs Flesh is Fish, and has been so ever since ye Devil entered into ym and they ran into ye Sea; if you and the rest of the Casuists in your neighborhood are of ye same oppinion, it will be a greater satisfaction to me, in resolving so knotty a point of Conscience. This being all at present I conclude with all our dues to you and Bror.

Your affectionate sister,
S. Darwin

Judging from two letters . . . he seems to have felt a degree of respect, gratitude, and affection for the several masters unusual in a schoolboy. Both these letters were accompanied by an inevitable copy of verses, those addressed to the head-master being of considerable length, and in imitation of the 5th Satire of Persius. His two elder brothers accompanied him to St. John's College, Cambridge; and this seems to have been a severe strain on their father's income. They appear, in consequence, to have been thrifty and honourably economical; so much so that they mended their own clothes; and, many years afterwards, Erasmus boasted to his second wife that, if she cut the heel out of a stocking, he would put a new one in without missing a stitch. He won the Exeter Scholarship at St. John's, which was worth only £16 per annum. No doubt he studied the classics whilst at Cambridge, for he did so to the end of his life, as shown by the many quotations in his latest work, 'The Temple of Nature.' He must also have studied mathematics to a certain extent, for, when he took his Bachelor of Arts degree, in 1754, he was at the head of the Junior Optimes. Nor did he neglect medicine; and he left Cambridge during one term to attend Hunter's lectures in London. As a matter of course, he wrote poetry whilst at Cambridge, and a poem on 'The Death of Prince Frederick,' in 1751, was published many years afterwards in 1795, in the European Magazine.

In the autumn of 1754 he went to Edinburgh to study medicine, and while there, seems to have been as rigidly economical as at Cambridge. . . .

In November 1756, Erasmus settled in Lichfield, and now his life may be said to have begun in earnest; for it was here, and in or near Derby, to which place he removed in 1781, that he published all his works. Owing to two or three very successful cases, he soon got into some practice at Lichfield as a physician, when twenty-five years old. A year afterwards (Dec. 1757) he married Miss Mary Howard, aged 17–18 years, who, judging from all that I have heard of her, and from some of her letters, must have been a superior and charming woman. She died after a long and suffering illness in 1770. They seem to have lived together most happily during the thirteen years of their married life, and she was tenderly nursed by her husband during her last illness.

In 1781, eleven years after the death of his first wife, he married the widow of Colonel Chandos Pole, of Radburn Hall. He had become acquainted with her in the Spring of 1778, when she had come to Lichfield in order that he might attend her children professionally. It is evident from the many MS. verses addressed to her before their marriage, that Dr. Darwin was passionately attached to her, even during the lifetime of her husband, who died in 1780. These verses are somewhat less artificial than his published ones. On his second marriage he left Lichfield, and after living two years at Radburn Hall, he removed into the town of Derby, and ultimately to Breadsall Priory, a few miles from the town, where he died in 1802.

There is little to relate about his life at either Lichfield or Derby, and, as I am not attempting a connected narrative, I will here give such impressions as I have formed of his intellect and character, and a few of his letters which are either interesting in themselves, or which throw light upon what he thought and felt.

His correspondence with many distinguished men was large; but most of the letters which I possess or have seen are uninteresting, and not worth publication. Medicine and mechanics alone roused him to write with any interest. He occasionally corresponded with Rousseau, with whom he became acquainted in an odd manner, but none of their letters have been preserved. Rousseau was living in 1766 at Mr. Davenport's house, Wootton Hall, and used to spend much of his time "in the well-known cave upon the terrace in melancholy contemplation." He disliked being interrupted, so Dr. Darwin, who was then a stranger to him, sauntered by the cave, and minutely examined a plant growing in front of it. This drew forth Rousseau, who was interested in botany, and they conversed together, and afterwards corresponded during several years.

Amongst the old letters preserved, there is one without any date from Hutton, the founder of the modern science of geology, and I extract its commencement, as proceeding from so illustrious a scientific man. Dr. Darwin seems to have complained to him of having been cheated by some publisher; and Hutton answers: —

If you have no more money than you use, then be as sparing of it as you please, but if you have money to spend, then pray learn to let yourself be cheated, that is, learn to lay out money for which you have no other use. If this be not philosophy, at least it is good sense; for why the devil should a man have money to be a plague to him, when it is so easy to throw it away; and if thro' a spirit of general benevolence you are afraid of mankind suffering from this root of all evil, for God's sake send it to the bottom of the sea, it there can only poison fish and it will there make in time a noble fossil specimen.

My father spoke of Dr. Darwin as having great powers of conversation. Lady Charleville, who had been accustomed to the most brilliant society in London, told him that Dr. Darwin was one of the most agreeable men whom she had ever met. He himself used to say "there were two sorts of agreeable persons in conversation parties — agreeable talkers and agreeable listeners."

He stammered greatly, and it is surprising that this defect did not spoil his powers of conversation. A young man once asked him in, as he thought, an offensive manner, whether he did not find stammering very inconvenient. He answered, "No, Sir, it gives me time for reflection, and saves me from asking impertinent questions."

He possessed, according to my father, great facility in explaining any difficult subject; and he himself attributed this power to his habit of always talking about whatever he was studying, "turning and moulding the subject according to the capacity of his hearers." He compared himself to Gil Blas's uncle, who learned the grammar by teaching it to his nephew.

He published an ode on the folly of atheism, with the motto "I am fearfully and wonderfully made," of which the first verse is as follows:

1.

Dull atheist, could a giddy dance
  Of atoms lawless hurl'd
Construct so wonderful, so wise,
  So harmonised a world?

Judging from his published works, letters, and all that I have been able to gather about him, the vividness of his imagination seems to have been one of his pre-eminent characteristics. This led to his great originality of thought, his prophetic spirit both in science and in the mechanical arts, and to his overpowering tendency to theorise and generalise. Nevertheless, his remarks . . . on the value of experiments and the use of hypotheses show that he had the true spirit of a philosopher. That he possessed uncommon powers of observation must be admitted. The diversity of the subjects to which he attended is surprising. But of all his characteristics, the incessant activity or energy of his mind was, perhaps, the most remarkable.

My father seems to have urged him, about the year 1793, to leave off professional work; he answered, "it is a dangerous experiment, and generally ends either in drunkenness or hypochondriacism. Thus I reason, one must do something (so country squires fox-hunt), otherwise one grows weary of life, and becomes a prey of ennui. Therefore one may as well do something advantageous to oneself and friends or to mankind, as employ oneself in cards or other things equally insignificant." During his frequent and long journeys, he read and wrote much in his carriage, which was fitted up for the purpose. Nor was travelling an easy affair in those days, for owing to the state of the roads, a carriage could hardly reach some of the houses which he had to visit; and I hear from one of his granddaughters that an old horse named the "Doctor," with a saddle on, used to follow behind the carriage, without being in any way fastened to it; and when the road was too bad, he got out and rode upon Doctor. This horse lived to a great age, and was buried at the Priory.

When at home he was an early riser; and he had his papers so arranged (as I have heard from my father) that if he awoke in the night he was able to get up and continue his work for a time, until he felt sleepy. Considering his indomitable activity, it is a singular fact that he suffered much from a sense of fatigue.

On my once remarking to my father, how greatly fatigued he seemed to be after his day's work, he answered, "I inherit it from my father."

It is remarkable that in so large a town as Derby, and at so late a period as 1784, there was no public institution for the relief of the poor in sickness. Dr. Darwin therefore at this time drew up a circular, the MS. of which is in my possession, stating that "as the small-pox has already made great ravages in Derby, showing much malignity even at its commencement; and as it is now three years since it was last epidemic in this town, there is great reason to fear that it will become very fatal in the approaching spring, particularly amongst the poor, who want both the knowledge and the assistance necessary for the preservation of their children." He accordingly proposed that a society should be formed — the members to subscribe a guinea each, and that a room should be hired as a dispensary, where the medical men of the town might give their attendance gratuitously. The poor were to be directed to take their prescriptions in due order to all the druggists in the town, apparently to disarm opposition. The circular then expresses the hope that the dispensary "may prove the foundation-stone of a future infirmary."

In this same year of 1784 he seems to have taken the chief part in founding a Philosophical Society in Derby. The members met for the first time at his house, and he delivered to them a short but striking address, from which the following passages may be given: "I come now to the second source of our accurate ideas. As we are fashioned and constituted by the niggard hand of Nature with such imperfect and contracted faculties, with so few and such imperfect senses; while the bodies, which surround us, are indued with infinite variety of properties; with attractions, repulsions, gravitations, exhalations, polarities, minuteness, irresistance, &c., which are not cognizable by our dull organs of sense, or not adapted to them; what are we to do? shall we sit down contented with ignorance, and after we have procured our food, sleep away our time like the inhabitants of the woods and pastures? No, certainly! — since there is another way by which we may indirectly become acquainted with those properties of bodies, which escape our senses; and that is by *observing and registering their effects upon each other*. This is the tree of knowledge, whose fruit forbidden to the brute creation has been plucked by the daring hand of *experimental philosophy*."

He concludes the address with the words: "I hope at some distant time, perhaps not very distant, by our own publications we may add something to the common heap of knowledge; which I prophecy will never cease to accumulate, so long as the human footstep is seen upon the earth."

As it is interesting to see how far Erasmus Darwin transmitted his characteristic qualities of mind to his descendants, I will give a short account of his children. He had three sons by his first wife (besides two who died in infancy), and four sons and three daughters by his second wife. His eldest son, Charles (born September 3, 1758), was a young man of extraordinary promise, but died (May 15, 1778) before he was twenty-one years old from the effects of a wound received whilst dissecting the brain of a child. He inherited from his father a strong taste for various branches of science, for writing verses, and for mechanics. "Tools were his playthings," and making "machines was one of the first efforts of his ingenuity, and one of the first sources of his amusement."

He also inherited stammering. With the hope of curing him, his father sent him to France when about eight years old (1766–1767), with a private tutor, thinking that if he was not allowed to speak English for a time, the habit of stammering might be lost; and it is a curious fact that in after years when speaking French he never stammered. At a very early age he collected specimens of all kinds. When sixteen years old he was sent for a year to Oxford, but he did not like the place, and "thought (in the words of his father) that the vigour of the mind languished in the pursuit of classical elegance, like Hercules at the distaff, and sighed to be removed to the robuster exercise of the medical school of Edinburgh." He stayed three years at Edinburgh, working hard at his medical studies, and attending "with diligence all the sick poor of the parish of Waterleith, and supplying them with the necessary medicines." The Aesculapian Society awarded him its first gold medal for an experimental enquiry on pus and mucus. Notices of him appeared in various journals; and all the writers agree about his uncommon energy and abilities. He seems, like his father, to have excited the warm affection of his friends. Professor Andrew Duncan, in whose family vault Charles was buried, cut a lock of hair from the corpse, and took it to a jeweller, whose apprentice, afterwards the famous Sir H. Raeburn, set it in a locket for a memorial. The venerable professor spoke to me about him with the warmest affection forty-seven years after his death, when I was a young medical student in Edinburgh. The inscription on his tomb, written by his father, says, with more truth than is usual on such occasions: "Possessed of uncommon abilities and activity, he had acquired knowledge in every department of medical and philosophical science, much beyond his years."

About the character of his second son, Erasmus (born 1759), I have little to say, for, though he wrote poetry, he seems to have had none of the other tastes of his father. He had, however, his own peculiar tastes, viz. genealogy, the collecting of coins, and statistics. When a boy he counted all the houses in the city of Lichfield, and found out the number of inhabitants in as many as he could; he thus made a census, and when a real one was first made, his estimate was found to be nearly accurate. His disposition was quiet and retiring. My father had a very high opinion of his abilities, and this was probably just. . . .

The third son, Robert Waring Darwin (my father, born 1766), did not inherit any aptitude for poetry or mechanics, nor did he possess, as I think, a scientific mind. He published, in

Vol. lxxvi. of the 'Philosophical Transactions,' a paper on Ocular Spectra, which Wheatstone told me was a remarkable production for the period; but I believe that he was largely aided in writing it by his father. He was elected a Fellow of the Royal Society in 1788. I cannot tell why my father's mind did not appear to me fitted for advancing science; for he was fond of theorising, and was incomparably the most acute observer whom I ever knew. But his powers in this direction were exercised almost wholly in the practice of medicine, and in the observation of human character. He intuitively recognised the disposition or character, and even read the thoughts, of those with whom he came into contact with extraordinary acuteness. This skill partly accounts for his great success as a physician, for it impressed his patients with belief in him; and my father used to say that the art of gaining confidence was the chief element in a doctor's worldly success.

Erasmus brought him to Shrewsbury before he was twenty-one years old, and left him £20, saying, "Let me know when you want more, and I will send it to you." His uncle, the rector of Elston, afterwards also sent him £20, and this was the sole pecuniary aid which he ever received. I have heard him say that his practice during the first year allowed him to keep two horses and a man-servant. By the second year he was in considerable, and ever afterwards in very large, practice. His success was the more remarkable, as he for some time detested the profession, and declared that if he had been sure of gaining £100 a year in any other way he would never have practised as a doctor.

Of all his characteristic qualities, his sympathy was pre-eminent, and I believe it was this which made him for a time hate his profession, as it constantly brought suffering before his eyes. Sympathy with the joy of others is a much rarer endowment than sympathy with their pains, and it is no exaggeration to say that to give pleasure to others was to my father an intense pleasure. He died November 13th, 1849 [*sic*]. . . .[1]

Of the children of Erasmus by his second marriage, one son became a cavalry officer, a second rector of Elston, and a third, Francis (born 1786, died 1859), a physician, who travelled far in countries rarely visited in those days. He showed his taste of Natural History by being fond of keeping a number of wild and curious animals. I may add that one of his sons, Captain Darwin, is a great sportsman, and has published a little book, the 'Gamekeeper's Manual' (4th ed. 1863), which shows keen observation and knowledge of the habits of various animals. The eldest daughter of Erasmus, Violetta, married S. Tertius Galton, and I feel sure that their son, Francis, will be willing to attribute the remarkable originality of his mind in large part to inheritance from his maternal grandfather.

[1] 1848.

# *Robert Waring Darwin: Charles Darwin's Recollections of his Father*[46]

I may here add a few pages about my father, who was in many ways a remarkable man.

He was about 6 feet 2 inches in height, with broad shoulders, and very corpulent, so that he was the largest man whom I ever saw. When he last weighed himself, he was 24 stone, but afterwards increased much in weight. His chief mental characteristics were his powers of observation and his sympathy, neither of which have I ever seen exceeded or even equalled. His sympathy was not only with the distresses of others, but in a greater degree with the pleasures of all around him. This led him to be always scheming to give pleasure to others, and, though hating extravagance, to perform many generous actions. For instance, . . . a small manufacturer in Shrewsbury came to him one day, and said he should be bankrupt unless he could at once borrow £10,000, but that he was unable to give any legal security. My father heard his reasons for believing that he could ultimately repay the money, and from [his] intuitive perception of character felt sure that he was to be trusted. So he advanced this sum, which was a very large one for him while young, and was after a time repaid.

I suppose that it was his sympathy which gave him unbounded power of winning confidence, and as a consequence made him highly successful as a physician. He began to practise before he was twenty-one years old, and his fees during the first year paid for the keep of two horses and a servant. On the following year his practice was large, and so continued for about sixty years, when he ceased to attend on any one. His great success as a doctor was the more remarkable, as he told me that he at first hated his profession so much that if he had been sure of the smallest pittance, or if his father had given him any choice, nothing should have induced him to follow it. To the end of his life, the thought of an operation almost sickened him, and he could scarcely endure to see a person bled — a horror which he has transmitted to me — and I remember the horror which I felt as a schoolboy in reading about Pliny (I think) bleeding to death in a warm bath. . . .

Owing to my father's power of winning confidence, many patients, especially ladies, consulted him when suffering from any misery, as a sort of Father-Confessor. He told me that they always began by complaining in a vague manner about their health, and by practice he soon guessed what was really the matter. He then suggested that they had been suffering in their minds, and now they would pour out their troubles, and he heard nothing more about the body. . . . Owing to my father's skill in winning confidence he received many strange confessions of misery and guilt. He often remarked how many miserable wives he had known. In several instances husbands and wives had gone on pretty well together for between twenty and thirty years, and then hated each other bitterly; this he attributed to their having lost a common bond in their young children having grown up.

But the most remarkable power which my father possessed was that of reading the characters, and even the thoughts of those whom he saw even for a short time. We had many instances of the power, some of which seemed almost supernatural. It saved my father from ever making (with one exception, and the character of this man was soon discovered) an unworthy friend. A strange clergyman came to Shrewsbury, and seemed to be a rich man; everybody called on him, and he was invited to many houses. My father called, and on his return home told my sisters on no account to invite him or his family to our house; for he felt sure that the man was not to be trusted. After a few months he suddenly bolted, being heavily in debt, and was found out to be little better than an habitual swindler. Here is a case of trustfulness which not many men would have ventured on. An Irish gentleman, a complete stranger, called on my father one day, and said that he had lost his purse, and that it would be a serious inconvenience to him to wait in Shrewsbury until he could receive a remittance from Ireland. He then asked my father to lend him £20, which was immediately done, as my father felt certain that the story was a true one. As soon as a letter could arrive from Ireland, one came with the most profuse thanks, and enclosing, as he said, a £20 Bank of England note, but no note was enclosed. I asked my father whether this did not stagger him, but he answered 'not in the least.' On the next day another letter came with many apologies for having forgotten (like a true Irishman) to put the note into his letter of the day before. . . . [A gentleman] brought his nephew, who was insane but quite gentle, to my father; and the young man's insanity led him to accuse himself of all the crimes under heaven. When my father afterwards talked over the matter with the uncle, he said, 'I am sure that your nephew is really guilty of . . . a heinous crime.' Whereupon [the gentleman] said, 'Good God, Dr. Darwin, who told you; we thought that no human being knew the fact except ourselves!' My father told me the story many years after the event, and I asked him how he distinguished the true from the false self-accusations; and it was very characteristic of my father that he said he could not explain how it was.

The sharpness of his observation led him to predict with remarkable skill the course of any illness, and he suggested endless small details of relief. I was told that a young doctor in Shrewsbury, who disliked my father, used to say that he was wholly unscientific, but owned that his power of predicting the end of an illness was unparalleled. Formerly when he thought that I should be a doctor, he talked much to me about his patients. In the old days the practice of bleeding largely was universal, but my father maintained that far more evil was thus caused than good done; and he advised me if ever I was myself ill not to allow any doctor to take more than an extremely small quantity of blood. Long before typhoid fever was recognized as distinct, my father told me that two utterly distinct kinds of illness were confounded under the name of typhus fever. He was vehement against drinking, and was convinced of both the direct and inherited evil effects of alcohol when habitually taken even in moderate quantity in a very large majority of cases. But he admitted and advanced instances of certain persons who could drink largely during their whole lives without apparently suffering any evil effects, and he believed that he could often beforehand tell who would thus not suffer. He himself never drank a drop of any alcoholic fluid. This remark reminds me of a case showing how a witness under the most favourable circumstances may be utterly mistaken. A gentleman-farmer was strongly urged by my father not to drink, and was encouraged by being told that he himself never touched any spirituous liquor. Whereupon the gentleman said, 'Come, come, Doctor, this won't do — though it is very kind of you to say so for my sake — for I know that you take a very large glass of hot gin and water every evening after your dinner.' So my father asked him how he knew this. The man answered, 'My cook was your kitchen-maid for two or three years, and she saw the butler every day prepare and take to you the gin and water.' The explanation was that my father had the odd habit of drinking hot water in a very tall and large glass after his dinner; and the butler used first to put some cold water in the glass, which the girl mistook for gin, and then filled it up with boiling water from the kitchen boiler.

My father used to tell me many little things which he had found useful in his medical practice. Thus ladies often cried much while telling him their troubles, and thus caused much loss of his precious time. He soon found that begging them to command and restrain themselves, always made them weep the more, so that afterwards he always encouraged them to go on crying, saying that this would relieve them more than anything else, and with the invariable result that they soon ceased to cry, and he could hear what they had to say and give his advice. When patients who were very ill craved for some strange and unnatural food, my father asked them what had put such an idea into their heads: if they answered that they did not know, he would allow them to try the food, and often with success, as he trusted to their having a kind of instinctive desire; but if they answered that they had heard that the food in question had done good to some one else, he firmly refused his assent.

He gave one day an odd little specimen of human nature. When a very young man he was called in to consult with the family physician in the case of a gentleman of much distinction in Shropshire. The old doctor told the wife that the illness was of such a nature that it must end fatally. My father took a different view and maintained that the gentleman would recover: he was proved quite wrong in all respects (I think by autopsy) and he owned his error. He was then convinced that he should never again be consulted by this family; but after a few months the widow sent for him, having dismissed the old family doctor. My father was so much surprised at this, that he asked a friend of the widow to find out why he was again consulted. The widow answered her friend, that 'she would never again see the odious old doctor who said from the first that her husband would die, while Dr. Darwin always maintained that he would recover!'

In another case my father told a lady that her husband would certainly die. Some months afterward he saw the widow who was a very sensible woman, and she said, 'You are a very young man, and allow me to advise you always to give as long as you possibly can, hope to any near relative nursing a patient. You made me despair, and from that moment I lost strength.' My father said that he had often since seen the paramount importance, for the sake of the patient, of keeping up the hope and with it the strength of the nurse in charge. This he sometimes found difficult to do compatibly with truth. One old gentleman, however, caused him no such perplexity. He was sent for by Mr. P——, who said, 'From all that I have seen and heard of you I believe that you are the sort of man who will speak the truth, and if I ask, you will tell me when I am dying. Now I much desire that you should attend me if you will promise, whatever I may say, always to declare that I am not going to die.' My father acquiesced on the understanding that his words should in fact have no meaning.

My father possessed an extraordinary memory, especially for dates, so that he knew, when he was very old, the day of the birth, marriage, and death of a multitude of persons in Shropshire; and he once told me that this power annoyed him; for if he once heard a date, he could not forget it; and thus the deaths of many friends were often recalled to his mind. Owing to his strong memory he knew an extraordinary number of curious stories, which he liked to tell, as he was a great talker. He was generally in high spirits, and laughed and joked with every one — often with his servants — with the utmost freedom; yet he had the art of making every one obey him to the letter. Many persons were much afraid of him. I remember my father telling us one day, with a laugh, that several persons had asked him whether Miss ——, a grand old lady in Shropshire, had called on him, so that at last he enquired why they asked him; and was told that Miss ——, whom my father had somehow mortally offended, was telling everybody that she would call and tell 'that fat old doctor very plainly what she thought of him.' She had already called, but her courage had failed, and no one could have been more courteous and friendly. As a boy, I went to stay at the house of ——, whose wife was insane; and the poor creature, as soon as she saw me, was in the most abject state of terror that I ever saw, weeping bitterly and asking me over and over again, 'Is your father coming?' but was soon pacified. On my return home, I asked my father why she was so frightened, and he answered he was very glad to hear it, as he had frightened her on purpose, feeling sure that she would be kept in safety and much happier without any restraint, if her husband could influence her, whenever she became at all violent by proposing to send for Dr. Darwin; and these words succeeded perfectly during the rest of her long life.

My father was very sensitive, so that many small events annoyed him or pained him much. I once asked him, when he was old and could not walk, why he did not drive out for exercise; and he answered, 'Every road out of Shrewsbury is associated in my mind with some painful event.' Yet he was generally in high spirits. He was easily made very angry, but his kindness was unbounded. He was widely and deeply loved.

He was a cautious and good man of business, so that he hardly ever lost money by any investment, and left to his children a very large property. I remember a story showing how easily utterly false beliefs originate and spread. Mr. E——, a squire of one of the oldest families in Shropshire, and head partner in a bank, committed suicide. My father was sent for as a matter of form, and found him dead. I may mention, by the way, to show how matters were managed in those old days, that because Mr. E—— was a rather great man, and universally respected, no inquest was held over his body. My father, in returning home, thought it proper to call at the bank (where he had an account) to tell the managing partners of the event, as it was not improbable that it would cause a run on the bank. Well, the story was spread far and wide, that my father went into the bank, drew out all his money, left the bank, came back again, and said, 'I may just tell you that Mr. E—— has killed himself,' and then departed. It seems that it was then a common belief that money withdrawn from a bank was not safe until the person had passed out through the door of the bank. My father did not hear this story till some little time afterwards, when the managing partner said that he had departed from his invariable rule of never allowing anyone to see the account of another man, by having shown the ledger with my father's account to several persons, as this proved that my father had not drawn out a penny on that day. It would have been dishonourable in my father to have used his professional knowledge for his private advantage. Nevertheless, the supposed act was greatly admired by some persons; and many years afterwards, a gentleman remarked, 'Ah, Doctor, what a splendid man of business you were in so cleverly getting all your money safe out of that bank!'

My father's mind was not scientific, and he did not try to generalise his knowledge under general laws; yet he formed a theory for almost everything which occurred. I do not think I gained much from him intellectually; but his example ought to have been of much moral service to all his children. One of his golden rules (a hard one to follow) was, 'Never become the friend of any one whom you cannot respect.'

# *Charles Darwin: Autobiography*[47]

A German editor having written to me for an account of the development of my mind and character with some sketch of my autobiography, I have thought that the attempt would amuse me, and might possibly interest my children or their children. I know that it would have interested me greatly to have read even so short and dull a sketch of the mind of my grandfather, written by himself, and what he thought and did, and how he worked. I have attempted to write the following account of myself, as if I were a dead man in another world looking back at my own life. Nor have I found this difficult, for life is nearly over with me. I have taken no pains about my style of writing.

I was born at Shrewsbury on February 12th, 1809, and my earliest recollection goes back only to when I was a few months over four years old, when we went . . . sea-bathing, and I recollect some events and places there with some little distinctness.

My mother died in July 1817, when I was a little over eight years old, and it is odd that I can remember hardly anything about her except her death-bed, her black velvet gown, and her curiously constructed work-table. In the spring of this same year I was sent to a day-school in Shrewsbury, where I stayed a year. I have been told that I was much slower in learning than my younger sister Catherine, and I believe that I was in many ways a naughty boy.

By the time I went to this day-school my taste for natural history, and more especially for collecting, was well developed. I tried to make out the names of plants, and collected all sorts of things, shells, seals, franks, coins, and minerals. The passion for collecting which leads a man to be a systematic naturalist, a virtuoso, or a miser, was very strong in me, and was clearly innate, as none of my sisters or brother ever had this taste.

One little event during this year has fixed itself very firmly in my mind, and I hope that it has done so from my conscience having been afterwards sorely troubled by it; it is curious as showing that apparently I was interested at this early age in the variability of plants! I told another little boy . . . that I could produce variously coloured polyanthuses and primroses by watering them with certain coloured fluids, which was of course a monstrous fable, and had never been tried by me. I may here also confess that as a little boy I was much given to inventing deliberate falsehoods, and this was always done for the sake of causing excitement. For instance, I once gathered much valuable fruit from my father's trees and hid it in the shrubbery, and then ran in breathless haste to spread the news that I had discovered a hoard of stolen fruit.

I must have been a very simple little fellow when I first went to the school. A boy of the name of Garnett took me into a cake shop one day, and bought some cakes for which he did not pay, as the shopman trusted him. When we came out I asked him why he did not pay for them, and he instantly answered, "Why, do you not know that my uncle left a great sum of money to the town on condition that every tradesman should give whatever was wanted without payment to any one who

Charles and Catherine Darwin

wore his old hat and moved [it] in a particular manner?" and then went into another shop where he was trusted, and asked for some small article, moving his hat in the proper manner, and of course obtained it without payment. When we came out he said, "Now if you like to go by yourself into that cake-shop (how well I remember its exact position) I will lend you my hat, and you can get whatever you like if you move the hat on your head properly." I gladly accepted the generous offer, and went in and asked for some cakes, moved the old hat and was walking out of the shop, when the shopman made a rush at me, so I dropped the cakes and ran for dear life, and was astonished by being greeted with shouts of laughter by my false friend Garnett.

I can say in my own favour that I was as a boy humane, but I owed this entirely to the instruction and example of my sisters. I doubt indeed whether humanity is a natural or innate quality. I was very fond of collecting eggs, but I never took more than a single egg out of a bird's nest, except on one single occasion, when I took all, not for their value, but from a sort of bravado.

I had a strong taste for angling, and would sit for any number of hours on the bank of a river or pond watching the float; when at Maer I was told that I could kill the worms with salt and water, and from that day I never spitted a living worm, though at the expense probably of some loss of success.

Once as a very little boy whilst at the day school, or before that time, I acted cruelly, for I beat a puppy, I believe, simply from enjoying the sense of power; but the beating could not have been severe, for the puppy did not howl, of which I feel sure, as the spot was near the house. This act lay heavily on my conscience, as is shown by my remembering the exact spot where the crime was committed. It probably lay all the heavier from my love of dogs being then, and for a long time afterwards, a passion. Dogs seemed to know this, for I was an adept in robbing their love from their masters.

I remember clearly only one other incident during this year whilst at Mr. Case's daily school, — namely, the burial of a dragoon soldier; and it is surprising how clearly I can still see the horse with the man's empty boots and carbine suspended to the saddle, and the firing over the grave. This scene deeply stirred whatever poetic fancy there was in me.

In the summer of 1818 I went to Dr. Butler's great school in Shrewsbury, and remained there for seven years till Midsummer 1825, when I was sixteen years old. I boarded at this school, so that I had the great advantage of living the life of a true schoolboy; but as the distance was hardly more than a mile to my home, I very often ran there in the longer intervals between the callings over and before locking up at night. This, I think, was in many ways advantageous to me by keeping up home affections and interests. I remember in the early part of my school life that I often had to run very quickly to be in time, and from being a fleet runner was generally successful; but when in doubt I prayed earnestly to God to help me, and I well remember that I attributed my success to the prayers and not to my quick running, and marvelled how generally I was aided.

I have heard my father and elder sister say that I had, as a very young boy, a strong taste for long solitary walks; but what I thought about I know not. I often became quite absorbed, and once, whilst returning to school on the summit of the old fortifications round Shrewsbury, which had been converted into a public foot-path with no parapet on one side, I walked off and fell to the ground, but the height was only seven or eight feet. Nevertheless the number of thoughts which passed through my mind during this very short, but sudden and wholly unexpected fall, was astonishing, and seem hardly compatible with what physiologists have, I believe, proved about each thought requiring quite an appreciable amount of time.

Nothing could have been worse for the development of my mind than Dr. Butler's school, as it was strictly classical, nothing else being taught, except a little ancient geography and history. The school as a means of education to me was simply a blank. During my whole life I have been singularly incapable of mastering any language. Especial attention was paid to verse-making, and this I could never do well. I had many friends, and got together a good collection of old verses, which by patching together, sometimes aided by other boys, I could work into any subject. Much attention was paid to learning by heart the lessons of the previous day; this I could effect with great facility, learning forty or fifty lines of Virgil or Homer, whilst I was in morning chapel; but this exercise was utterly useless, for every verse was forgotten in forty-eight hours. I was not idle, and with the exception of versification, generally worked conscientiously at my classics, not using cribs. The sole pleasure I ever received from such studies, was from some of the odes of Horace, which I admired greatly.

When I left the school I was for my age neither high nor low in it; and I believe that I was considered by all my masters and by my father as a very ordinary boy, rather below the common standard in intellect. To my deep mortification my father once said to me, "You care for nothing but shooting, dogs, and rat-catching, and you will be a disgrace to yourself and all your family." But my father, who was the kindest man I ever knew and whose memory I love with all my heart, must have been angry and somewhat unjust when he used such words.

Looking back as well as I can at my character during my school life, the only qualities which at this period promised well for the future, were, that I had strong and diversified tastes, much zeal for whatever interested me, and a keen pleasure in understanding any complex subject or thing. I was taught Euclid by a private tutor, and I distinctly remember the intense satisfaction which the clear geometrical proofs gave me. I remember with equal distinctness the delight which my uncle gave me (the father of Francis Galton) by explaining the principle of the vernier of a barometer. With respect to diversified tastes, independently of science, I was fond of reading various books, and I used to sit for hours reading the historical plays of Shakespeare, generally in an old window in the thick walls of the school. I read also other poetry, such as Thomson's 'Seasons,' and the recently published poems of Byron and Scott. I mention this because later in life I wholly lost, to my great regret, all pleasure from poetry of any kind, including Shakespeare. In connection with pleasure from poetry, I may add that in 1822 a vivid delight in scenery was first awakened in my mind, during a riding tour on the borders of Wales, and this has lasted longer than any other aesthetic pleasure.

Early in my school days a boy had a copy of the 'Wonders of the World,' which I often read, and disputed with other boys about the veracity of some of the statements; and I believe that this book first gave me a wish to travel in remote countries, which was ultimately fulfilled by the voyage of the *Beagle*. In the latter part of my school life I became passionately fond of shooting; I do not believe that any one could have shown more zeal for the most holy cause than I did for shooting birds. How well I remember killing my first snipe, and my excitement was so great that I had much difficulty in reloading my gun from the trembling of my hands. This taste long continued, and I became a very good shot. When at Cambridge I used to practise throwing up my gun to my shoulder before a looking-glass to see that I threw it up straight. Another and better plan was to get a friend to wave about a lighted candle, and then to fire at it with a cap on the nipple, and if the aim was accurate the little puff of air would blow out the candle. The explosion of the cap caused a sharp crack, and I was told that the tutor of the college remarked, "What an extraordinary thing it is, Mr. Darwin seems to spend hours in cracking a horse-whip in his room, for I often hear the crack when I pass under his windows."

I had many friends amongst the schoolboys, whom I loved dearly, and I think that my disposition was then very affectionate.

With respect to science, I continued collecting minerals with much zeal, but quite unscientifically — all that I cared about was a new-*named* mineral, and I hardly attempted to classify them. I must have observed insects with some little care, for when ten years old (1819) I went for three weeks to Plas Edwards on the sea-coast in Wales, I was very much interested and surprised at seeing a large black and scarlet Hemipterous insect, many moths (Zygaena), and a Cicindela which are not found in Shropshire. I almost made up my mind to begin collecting all the insects which I could find dead, for on consulting my sister I concluded that it was not right to kill insects for the sake of making a collection. From reading White's 'Selborne,' I took much pleasure in watching the habits of birds, and even made notes on the subject. In my simplicity I remember wondering why every gentleman did not become an ornithologist.

Towards the close of my school life, my brother worked hard at chemistry, and made a fair laboratory with proper apparatus in the tool-house in the garden, and I was allowed to aid him as a servant in most of his experiments. He made all the gases and many compounds, and I read with care several books on chemistry, such as Henry and Parkes' 'Chemical Catechism.' The subject interested me greatly, and we often used to go on working till rather late at night. This was the best part of my education at school, for it showed me practically the meaning of experimental science. The fact that we worked at chemistry somehow got known at school, and as it was an unprecendented fact, I was nicknamed "Gas." I was also once publicly rebuked by the head-master, Dr. Butler, for thus wasting my time on such useless subjects; and he called me very unjustly a "poco curante," and as I did not understand what he meant, it seemed to me a fearful reproach.

As I was doing no good at school, my father wisely took me away at a rather earlier age than usual, and sent me (Oct. 1825) to Edinburgh University with my brother, where I stayed for two years or sessions. My brother was completing his medical studies, though I do not believe he ever really intended to practise, and I was sent there to commence them. But soon after this period I became convinced from various small circumstances that my father would leave me property enough to subsist on with some comfort, though I never imagined that I should be so rich a man as I am; but my belief was sufficient to check any strenuous effort to learn medicine.

The instruction at Edinburgh was altogether by lectures, and these were intolerably dull, with the exception of those on chemistry by Hope; but to my mind there are no advantages and many disadvantages in lectures compared with reading. Dr. Duncan's lectures on Materia Medica at 8 o'clock on a winter's morning are something fearful to remember. Dr. —— made his lectures on human anatomy as dull as he was himself, and the subject disgusted me. It has proved one of the greatest evils in my life that I was not urged to practise dissection, for I should soon have got over my disgust; and the practice would have been invaluable for all my future work. This has been an irremediable evil, as well as my incapacity to draw. I also attended regularly the clinical wards in the hospital. Some of the cases distressed me a good deal, and I still have vivid pictures before me of some of them; but I was not so foolish as to allow this to lessen my attendance. I cannot understand why this part of my medical course did not interest me in a greater degree; for during the summer before coming to Edinburgh I began attending some of the poor people, chiefly children and women in Shrewsbury: I wrote down as full an account as I could of the case with all the symptoms, and read them [*sic*] aloud to my father, who suggested further inquiries and advised me what medicine to give, which I made up myself. At one time I had at least a dozen patients, and I felt a keen interest in the work. My father, who was by far the best judge of character whom I ever knew, declared that I should make a successful physician, — meaning by this one who would get many patients. He maintained that the chief element of success was exciting confidence; but what he saw in me which convinced him that I should create confidence I know not. I also attended on two occasions the operating theatre in the hospital at Edinburgh, and saw two very bad operations, one on a child, but I rushed away before they were completed. Nor did I ever attend again, for hardly any inducement would have been strong enough to make me do so; this being long before the blessed days of chloroform. The two cases fairly haunted me for many a long year.

My brother stayed only one year at the University, so that during the second year I was left to my own resources; and this was an advantage, for I became well acquainted with several young men fond of natural science. One of them was Ainsworth, who afterwards published his travels in Assyria; he was a Wernerian geologist, and knew a little about many subjects. Dr. Coldstream was a very different young man, prim, formal, highly religious, and most kind-hearted; he afterwards published some good zoological articles. A third young man was Hardie, who would, I think, have made a good botanist, but died early in India. Lastly, Dr. Grant, my senior by several years, but how I became acquainted with him I cannot remember; he published some first-rate zoological papers, but after coming to London as Professor in University College, he did nothing more in science, a fact which has always been inexplicable to me. I knew him well; he was dry and formal in manner, with much enthusiasm beneath his outer crust. He one day, when we were walking together, burst forth in high admiration of Lamarck and his views on evolution. I listened in silent astonishment, and as far as I can judge without any effect on my mind. I had previously read the 'Zoonomia' of my grandfather, in which similar views are maintained, but without producing any effect on me. Nevertheless it is probable that . . . hearing rather early in life such views maintained and praised may have favoured my upholding them under a different form in my 'Origin of Species.' At this time I admired greatly the 'Zoonomia;' but on reading it a second time after an interval of ten or fifteen years, I was much disappointed; the proportion of speculation being so large to the facts given.

Drs. Grant and Coldstream attended much to marine Zoology, and I often accompanied the former to collect animals in the tidal pools, which I dissected as well as I could. I also became friends with some of the Newhaven fishermen, and sometimes accompanied them when they trawled for oysters, and thus got many specimens. But from not having had any regular practice in dissection, and from possessing only a wretched microscope, my attempts were very poor. Nevertheless I made one interesting little discovery, and read, about the beginning of the year 1826, a short paper on the subject before the Plinian Society. This was that the so-called ova of Flustra had the power of independent movement by means of cilia, and were in fact larvae. In another short paper I showed that the little globular bodies which had been supposed to be the young state of *Fucus loreus* were the egg-cases of the worm-like *Pontobdella muricata.*

The Plinian Society was encouraged and, I believe, founded by Professor Jameson: it consisted of students and met in an underground room in the University for the sake of reading papers on natural science and discussing them. I used regularly to attend, and the meetings had a good effect on me in stimulating my zeal and giving me new congenial acquaintances. . . . The papers which were read to our little society were not printed, so that I had not the satisfaction of seeing my paper in print; but I believe Dr. Grant noticed my small discovery in his excellent memoir on Flustra.

I was also a member of the Royal Medical Society, and attended pretty regularly; but as the subjects were exclusively medical, I did not much care about them. Much rubbish was talked there, but there were some good speakers, of whom the best was the present Sir J. Kay-Shuttleworth. Dr. Grant took me occasionally to the meetings of the Wernerian Society, where various papers on natural history were read, discussed, and afterwards published in the 'Transactions.' I heard Audubon deliver there some interesting discourses on the habits of N. American birds, sneering somewhat unjustly at Waterton. By the way, a negro lived in Edinburgh, who had travelled with Waterton, and gained his livelihood by stuffing birds, which he did excellently: he gave me lessons for payment, and I used often to sit with him, for he was a very pleasant and intelligent man.

Mr. Leonard Horner also took me once to a meeting of the Royal Society of Edinburgh, where I saw Sir Walter Scott in the chair as President, and he apologised to the meeting as not feeling fitted for such a position. I looked at him and at the whole scene with some awe and reverence, and I think it was owing to this visit during my youth, and to my having attended the Royal Medical Society, that I felt the honour of being elected a few years ago an honorary member of both these Societies, more than any other similar honour. If I had been told at that time that I should one day have been thus honoured, I declare that I should have thought it as ridiculous and improbable, as if I had been told that I should be elected King of England.

During my second year at Edinburgh I attended ——'s lectures on Geology and Zoology, but they were incredibly dull. The sole effect they produced on me was the determination never as long as I lived to read a book on Geology, or in any way to study the science. Yet I feel sure that I was prepared for a philosophical treatment of the subject; for an old Mr. Cotton in Shropshire, who knew a good deal about rocks, had pointed out to me two or three years previously a well-known large erratic boulder in the town of Shrewsbury, called the "bell-stone"; he told me that there was no rock of the same kind nearer than Cumberland or Scotland, and he solemnly assured me that the world would come to an end before any one would be able to explain how this stone came where it now lay. This produced a deep impression on me, and I meditated over this wonderful stone. So that I felt the keenest delight when I first read of the action of icebergs in transporting boulders, and I gloried in the progress of Geology. Equally striking is the fact that I, though now only sixty-seven years old, heard the Professor, in a field lecture at Salisbury Craigs, discoursing on a trap-dyke, with amygdaloidal margins and the strata indurated on each side, with volcanic rocks all around us, say that it was a fissure filled with sediment from above, adding with a sneer that there were men who maintained that it had been injected from beneath in a molten condition. When I think of this lecture, I do not wonder that I determined never to attend to Geology.

From attending ——'s lectures, I became acquainted with the curator of the museum, Mr. Macgillivray, who afterwards published a large and excellent book on the birds of Scotland. I had much interesting natural-history talk with him, and he was very kind to me. He gave me some rare shells, for I at that time collected marine mollusca, but with no great zeal.

My summer vacations during these two years were wholly given up to amusements, though I always had some book in hand, which I read with interest. During the summer of 1826 I took a long walking tour with two friends with knapsacks on our backs through North Wales. We walked thirty miles most days, including one day the ascent of Snowdon. I also went with my sister [on] a riding tour in North Wales, a servant with saddle-bags carrying our clothes. The autumns were devoted to shooting chiefly at Mr. Owen's, at Woodhouse, and at my Uncle Jos's, at Maer. My zeal was so great that I used to place my shooting-boots open by my bed-side when I went to bed, so as not to lose half a minute in putting them on in the morning; and on one occasion I reached a distant part of the Maer estate, on the 20th of August for black-game shooting, before I could see: I then toiled on with the gamekeeper the whole day through thick heath and young Scotch firs.

How I did enjoy shooting! but I think that I must have been half-consciously ashamed of my zeal, for I tried to persuade myself that shooting was almost an intellectual employment; it required so much skill to judge where to find most game and to hunt the dogs well.

One of my autumnal visits to Maer in 1827 was memorable from meeting there Sir J. Mackintosh, who was the best converser I ever listened to. I heard afterwards with a glow of pride that he had said, "There is something in that young man that interests me." This must have been chiefly due to his perceiving that I listened with much interest to everything which he said, for I was as ignorant as a pig about his subjects of history, politics, and moral philosophy. To hear of praise from an eminent person, though no doubt apt or certain to excite vanity, is, I think, good for a young man, as it helps to keep him in the right course.

My visits to Maer during these two or three succeeding years were quite delightful, independently of the autumnal shooting. Life there was perfectly free; the country was very pleasant for walking or riding; and in the evening there was much very agreeable conversation, not so personal as it generally is in large family parties, together with music. In the summer the whole family used often to sit on the steps of the old portico, with the flower-garden in front, and with the steep wooded bank opposite the house reflected in the lake, with here and there a fish rising or a water-bird paddling about. Nothing has left a more vivid picture on my mind than these evenings at Maer. I was also attached to and greatly revered my Uncle Jos; he was silent and reserved, so as to be a rather awful man; but he sometimes talked openly with me. He was the very type of an upright man, with the clearest judgment. I do not believe that any power on earth could have made him swerve an inch from what he considered the right course.

*Cambridge* 1828–1831. — After having spent two sessions in Edinburgh, my father perceived, or he heard from my sisters, that I did not like the thought of being a physician, so he proposed that I should become a clergyman. He was very properly vehement against my turning into an idle sporting man, which then seemed my probable destination. I asked for some time to consider, as from what little I had heard or thought on the subject I had scruples about declaring my belief in all the dogmas of the Church of England; though otherwise I liked the thought of being a country clergyman. Accordingly I read with care

'Pearson on the Creeds,' and a few other books on divinity; and as I did not then in the least doubt the strict and literal truth of every word in the Bible, I soon persuaded myself that our Creed must be fully accepted.

Considering how fiercely I have been attacked by the orthodox, it seems ludicrous that I once intended to be a clergyman. Nor was this intention and my father's wish ever formally given up, but died a natural death when, on leaving Cambridge, I joined the *Beagle* as naturalist. If the phrenologists are to be trusted, I was well fitted in one respect to be a clergyman. A few years ago the secretaries of a German psychological society asked me earnestly by letter for a photograph of myself; and some time afterwards I received the proceedings of one of the meetings, in which it seemed that the shape of my head had been the subject of a public discussion, and one of the speakers declared that I had the bump of reverence developed enough for ten priests.

As it was decided that I should be a clergyman, it was necessary that I should go to one of the English universities and take a degree; but as I had never opened a classical book since leaving school, I found to my dismay, that in the two intervening years I had actually forgotten, incredible as it may appear, almost everything which I had learnt, even to some few of the Greek letters. I did not therefore proceed to Cambridge at the usual time in October, but worked with a private tutor in Shrewsbury, and went to Cambridge after the Christmas vacation, early in 1828. I soon recovered my school standard of knowledge, and could translate easy Greek books, such as Homer and the Greek Testament, with moderate facility.

During the three years which I spent at Cambridge my time was wasted, as far as the academical studies were concerned, as completely as at Edinburgh and at school. I attempted mathematics, and even went during the summer of 1828 with a private tutor to Barmouth, but I got on very slowly. The work was repugnant to me, chiefly from my not being able to see any meaning in the early steps in algebra. This impatience was very foolish, and in after years I have deeply regretted that I did not proceed far enough at least to understand something of the great leading principles of mathematics, for men thus endowed seem to have an extra sense. But I do not believe that I should ever have succeeded beyond a very low grade. With respect to Classics I did nothing except attend a few compulsory college lectures, and the attendance was almost nominal. In my second year I had to work for a month or two to pass the Little-Go, which I did easily. Again, in my last year I worked with some earnestness for my final degree of B.A., and brushed up my Classics, together with a little Algebra and Euclid, which latter gave me much pleasure, as it did at school. In order to pass the B.A. examination, it was also necessary to get up Paley's 'Evidences of Christianity,' and his 'Moral Philosophy.' This was done in a thorough manner, and I am convinced that I could have written out the whole of the 'Evidences' with perfect correctness, but not of course in the clear language of Paley. The logic of this book and, as I may add, of his 'Natural Theology,' gave me as much delight as did Euclid. The careful study of these works, without attempting to learn any part by rote, was the only part of the academical course which, as I then felt and as I still believe, was of the least use to me in the education of my mind. I did not at that time trouble myself about Paley's premises; and taking these on trust, I was charmed and convinced by the long line of argumentation. By answering well the examination questions in Paley, by doing Euclid well, and by not failing miserably in Classics, I gained a good place among the . . . men who do not go in for honours. Oddly enough, I cannot remember how high I stood, and my memory fluctuates between the fifth, tenth, or twelfth, name on the list.

Public lectures on several branches were given in the University, attendance being quite voluntary; but I was so sickened with lectures at Edinburgh that I did not even attend Sedgwick's eloquent and interesting lectures. Had I done so I should probably have become a geologist earlier than I did. I attended, however, Henslow's lectures on Botany, and liked them much for their extreme clearness, and the admirable illustrations; but I did not study botany. Henslow used to take his pupils, including several of the older members of the University, [on] field excursions, on foot or in coaches, to distant places, or in a barge down the river, and lectured on the rarer plants and animals which were observed. These excursions were delightful.

Although . . . there were some redeeming features in my life at Cambridge, my time was sadly wasted there, and worse than wasted. From my passion for shooting and for hunting, and, when this failed, for riding across country, I got into a sporting set, including some dissipated low-minded young men. We used often to dine together in the evening, though these dinners often included men of a higher stamp, and we sometimes drank too much, with jolly singing and playing at cards afterwards. I know that I ought to feel ashamed of days and evenings thus spent, but as some of my friends were very pleasant, and we were all in the highest spirits, I cannot help looking back to these times with much pleasure.

But I am glad to think that I had many other friends of a widely different nature. I was very intimate with Whitley, who was afterwards Senior Wrangler, and we used continually to take long walks together. He inoculated me with a taste for pictures and good engravings, of which I bought some. I frequently went to the Fitzwilliam Gallery, and my taste must have been fairly good, for I certainly admired the best pictures, which I discussed with the old curator. I read also with much interest Sir Joshua Reynolds' book. This taste, though not natural to me, lasted for several years, and many of the pictures in the National Gallery in London gave me much pleasure; that of Sebastian del Piombo exciting in me a sense of sublimity.

I also got into a musical set, I believe by means of my warm-hearted friend, Herbert, who took a high wrangler's degree. From associating with these men, and hearing them play, I acquired a strong taste for music, and used very often to time my walks so as to hear on week days the anthem in King's College Chapel. This gave me intense pleasure, so that my backbone would sometimes shiver. I am sure that there was no affectation or mere imitation in this taste, for I used generally to go by myself to King's College, and I sometimes hired the chorister boys to sing in my rooms. Nevertheless I am so utterly destitute of an ear, that I cannot perceive a discord, or keep time and hum a tune correctly; and it is a mystery how I could possibly have derived pleasure from music.

My musical friends soon perceived my state, and sometimes amused themselves by making me pass an examination, which consisted in ascertaining how many tunes I could recognize, when they were played rather more quickly or slowly than usual. 'God save the King,' when thus played, was a sore puzzle. There was another man with almost as bad an ear as I had, and strange to say he played a little on the flute. Once I had the triumph of beating him in one of our musical examinations.

But no pursuit at Cambridge was followed with nearly so much eagerness or gave me so much pleasure as collecting beetles. It was the mere passion for collecting, for I did not dissect them, and rarely compared their external characters with published descriptions, but got them named anyhow. I will give a proof of my zeal: one day, on tearing off some old bark, I saw two rare beetles, and seized one in each hand; then I saw a third and new kind, which I could not bear to lose, so that I popped the one which I held in my right hand into my mouth. Alas! it ejected some intensely acrid fluid, which burnt my tongue so that I was forced to spit the beetle out, which was lost, as was the third one.

I was very successful in collecting, and invented two new methods; I employed a labourer to scrape during the winter, moss off old trees and place it in a large bag, and likewise to collect the rubbish at the bottom of the barges in which reeds are brought from the fens, and thus I got some very rare species.

No poet ever felt more delighted at seeing his first poem published than I did at seeing in Stephens' 'Illustrations of British Insects,' the magic words, "captured by C. Darwin, Esq." I was introduced to entomology by my second cousin, W. Darwin Fox, a clever and most pleasant man, who was then at Christ's College, and with whom I became well acquainted, and went out collecting, with Albert Way of Trinity, who in after years became a well-known archaeologist; also with H. Thompson of the same College, afterwards a leading agriculturist, chairman of a great railway, and Member of Parliament. It seems therefore that a taste for collecting beetles is some indication of future success in life!

I am surprised what an indelible impression many of the beetles which I caught at Cambridge have left on my mind. I can remember the exact appearance of certain posts, old trees and banks where I made a good capture. The pretty *Panagaeus crux-major* was a treasure in those days, and here at Down I saw a beetle running across a walk, and on picking it up instantly perceived that it differed slightly from *P. crux-major,* and it turned out to be *P. quadripunctatus,* which is only a variety or closely allied species, differing from it very slightly in outline. I had never seen in those old days Licinus alive, which to an uneducated eye hardly differs from many of the black Carabidous beetles; but my sons found here a specimen, and I instantly recognised that it was new to me; yet I had not looked at a British beetle for the last twenty years.

I have not as yet mentioned a circumstance which influenced my whole career more than any other. This was my friendship with Professor Henslow. Before coming up to Cambridge, I had heard of him from my brother as a man who knew every branch of science, and I was accordingly prepared to reverence him. He kept open house once every week when all undergraduates and some older members of the University, who were attached to Science, used to meet in the evening. I soon got, through Fox, an invitation, and went there regularly. Before long I became well acquainted with Henslow, and during the latter half of my time at Cambridge took long walks with him on most days; so that I was called by some of the dons "the man who walks with Henslow;" and in the evening I was very often asked to join his family dinner. His knowledge was great in botany, entomology, chemistry, mineralogy, and geology. His strongest taste was to draw conclusions from long-continued minute observations. His judgment was excellent, and his whole mind well balanced; but I do not suppose that any one would say that he possessed much original genius.

He was deeply religious, and so orthodox, that he told me one day he should be grieved if a single word of the Thirty-nine Articles were altered. His moral qualities were in every way admirable. He was free from every tinge of vanity or other petty feeling; and I never saw a man who thought so little about himself or his own concerns. His temper was imperturbably good, with the most winning and courteous manners; yet, as I have seen, he could be roused by any bad action to the warmest indignation and prompt action.

I once saw in his company in the streets of Cambridge almost as horrid a scene as could have been witnessed during the French Revolution. Two body-snatchers had been arrested, and whilst being taken to prison had been torn from the constable by a crowd of the roughest men, who dragged them by their legs along the muddy and stony road. They were covered from head to foot with mud, and their faces were bleeding either from having been kicked or from the stones; they looked like corpses, but the crowd was so dense that I got only a few momentary glimpses of the wretched creatures. Never in my life have I seen such wrath painted on a man's face as was shown by Henslow at this horrid scene. He tried repeatedly to penetrate the mob; but it was simply impossible. He then rushed away to the mayor, telling me not to follow him, but to get more policemen. I forget the issue, except that the two men were got into the prison without being killed.

Henslow's benevolence was unbounded, as he proved by his many excellent schemes for his poor parishioners, when in after years he held the living of Hitcham. My intimacy with such a man ought to have been, and I hope was, an inestimable benefit. I cannot resist mentioning a trifling incident, which showed his kind consideration. Whilst examining some pollen-grains on a damp surface, I saw the tubes exserted, and instantly rushed off to communicate my surprising discovery to him. Now I do not suppose any other professor of botany could have helped laughing at my coming in such a hurry to make such a communication. But he agreed how interesting the phenomenon was, and explained its meaning, but made me clearly understand how well it was known; so I left him not in the least mortified, but well pleased at having discovered for myself so remarkable a fact, but determined not to be in such a hurry again to communicate my discoveries.

Dr. Whewell was one of the older and distinguished men who sometimes visited Henslow, and on several occasions I walked home with him at night. Next to Sir J. Mackintosh he was the best converser on grave subjects to whom I ever listened. Leonard Jenyns, who afterwards published some good essays in Natural History, often stayed with Henslow, who was his brother-in-law. I visited him at his parsonage . . . and had many a good walk and talk with him about Natural History. I became also acquainted with several other men older than me, who did not care much about science, but were friends of Henslow. One was a Scotchman, brother of Sir Alexander Ramsay, and tutor of Jesus College; he was a delightful man, but did not live for many years. Another was Mr. Dawes, afterwards Dean of Hereford, and famous for his success in the education of the poor. These men and others of the same standing, together with Henslow, used sometimes to take distant excursions into the country, which I was allowed to join, and they were most agreeable.

Looking back, I infer that there must have been something in me a little superior to the common run of youths, otherwise the above-mentioned men, so much older than me and higher in academical position, would never have allowed me to associate with them. Certainly I was not aware of any such superiority, and I remember one of my sporting friends, Turner, who saw me at work with my beetles, saying that I should some day be a Fellow of the Royal Society, and the notion seemed to me preposterous.

During my last year at Cambridge, I read with care and profound interest Humboldt's 'Personal Narrative.' This work, and Sir J. Herschel's 'Introduction to the Study of Natural Philosophy,' stirred up in me a burning zeal to add even the most humble contribution to the noble structure of Natural Science. No one or a dozen other books influenced me nearly so much as these two. I copied out from Humboldt long passages about Teneriffe, and read them aloud on one of the above-mentioned excursions, to (I think) Henslow, Ramsay, and Dawes, for on a previous occasion I had talked about the glories of Teneriffe, and some of the party declared they would endeavour to go there; but I think that they were only half in earnest. I was, however, quite in earnest, and got an introduction to a merchant in London to enquire about ships; but the scheme was, of course, knocked on the head by the voyage of the *Beagle*.

My summer vacations were given up to collecting beetles, to some reading, and short tours. In the autumn my whole time was devoted to shooting. . . . Upon the whole the three years which I spent at Cambridge were the most joyful in my happy life; for I was then in excellent health, and almost always in high spirits.

As I had at first come up to Cambridge at Christmas, I was forced to keep two terms after passing my final examination, at the commencement of 1831; and Henslow then persuaded me to begin the study of geology. Therefore on my return to Shropshire I examined sections, and coloured a map of parts round Shrewsbury. Professor Sedgwick intended to visit North Wales in the beginning of August to pursue his famous geological investigations amongst the older rocks, and Henslow asked him to allow me to accompany him. Accordingly he came and slept at my father's house.

A short conversation with him during this evening produced a strong impression on my mind. Whilst examining an old gravel-pit near Shrewsbury, a labourer told me that he had found in it a large worn tropical Volute shell, such as may be seen on the chimney-pieces of cottages; and as he would not sell the shell, I was convinced that he had really found it in the pit. I told Sedgwick of the fact, and he at once said (no doubt truly) that it must have been thrown away by some one into the pit; but then added, if really embedded there it would be the greatest misfortune to geology, as it would overthrow all that we know about the superficial deposits of the Midland Counties. These gravel-beds belong in fact to the glacial period, and in after years I found in them broken arctic shells. But I was then utterly astonished at Sedgwick not being delighted at so wonderful a fact as a tropical shell being found near the surface in the middle of England. Nothing before had ever made me thoroughly realise, though I had read various scientific books, that science consists in grouping facts so that general laws or conclusions may be drawn from them.

Next morning we started for Llangollen, Conway, Bangor, and Capel Curig. This tour was of decided use in teaching me a little how to make out the geology of a country. Sedgwick often sent me on a line parallel to his, telling me to bring back specimens of the rocks and to mark the stratification on a map. I have little doubt that he did this for my good, as I was too ignorant to have aided him. On this tour I had a striking instance how easy it is to overlook phenomena, however conspicuous, before they have been observed by any one. We spent many hours in Cwm Idwal, examining all the rocks with extreme care, as Sedgwick was anxious to find fossils in them; but neither of us saw a trace of the wonderful glacial phenomena all around us; we did not notice the plainly scored rocks, the perched boulders, the lateral and terminal moraines. Yet these phenomena are so conspicuous that, as I declared in a paper published many years afterwards in the 'Philosophical Magazine,' a house burnt down by fire did not tell its story more plainly than did this valley. If it had still been filled by a glacier, the phenomena would have been less distinct than they now are.

At Capel Curig I left Sedgwick and went in a straight line by compass and map across the mountains to Barmouth, never following any track unless it coincided with my course. I thus came on some strange wild places, and enjoyed much this manner of travelling. I visited Barmouth to see some Cambridge friends who were reading there, and thence returned to Shrewsbury and to Maer for shooting; for at that time I should have thought myself mad to give up the first days of partridge-shooting for geology or any other science.

## *Voyage of the 'Beagle' from December* 27, 1831, *to October* 2, 1836.

On returning home from my short geological tour in North Wales, I found a letter from Henslow, informing me that Captain Fitz-Roy was willing to give up part of his own cabin to any young man who would volunteer to go with him without pay as naturalist to the Voyage of the *Beagle.* I have given, as I believe, in my MS. Journal an account of all the circumstances which then occurred; I will here only say that I was instantly eager to accept the offer, but my father strongly objected, adding the words, fortunate for me, "If you can find any man of common sense who advises you to go I will give my consent." So I wrote that evening and refused the offer. On the next morning I went to Maer to be ready for September 1st, and, whilst out shooting, my uncle sent for me, offering to drive me over to Shrewsbury and talk with my father, as my uncle thought it would be wise in me to accept the offer. My father always maintained that he was one of the most sensible men in the world, and he at once consented in the kindest manner. I had been rather extravagant at Cambridge, and to console my father, said "that I should be deuced clever to spend more than my allowance whilst on board the *Beagle;*" but he answered with a smile, "But they tell me you are very clever."

Next day I started for Cambridge to see Henslow, and thence to London to see Fitz-Roy, and all was soon arranged. Afterwards, on becoming very intimate with Fitz-Roy, I heard that I had run a very narrow risk of being rejected, on account of the shape of my nose! He was an ardent disciple of Lavater, and was convinced that he could judge of a man's character by the outline of his features; and he doubted whether any one with my nose could possess sufficient energy and determination for the voyage. But I think he was afterwards well satisfied that my nose had spoken falsely.

Fitz-Roy's character was a singular one, with very many noble features: he was devoted to his duty, generous to a fault, bold, determined, and indomitably energetic, and an ardent friend to all under his sway. He would undertake any sort of trouble to assist those whom he thought deserved assistance. He was a handsome man, strikingly like a gentleman, with highly courteous manners, which resembled those of his maternal uncle, the famous Lord Castlereagh, as I was told by the Minister at Rio.

Fitz-Roy's temper was a most unfortunate one. It was usually worst in the early morning, and with his eagle eye he could generally detect something amiss about the ship, and was then unsparing in his blame. He was very kind to me, but was a man very difficult to live with on the intimate terms which necessarily followed from our messing by ourselves in the same cabin. We had several quarrels; for instance, early in the voyage at Bahia, in Brazil, he defended and praised slavery, which I abominated, and told me that he had just visited a great slave-owner, who had called up many of his slaves and asked them whether they were happy, and whether they wished to be free, and all answered "No." I then asked him, perhaps with a sneer, whether he thought that the answer of slaves in the presence of their master was worth anything? This made him excessively angry, and he said that as I doubted his word we could not live any longer together. I thought that I should have been compelled to leave the ship; but as soon as the news spread, which it did quickly, as the captain sent for the first lieutenant to assuage his anger by abusing me, I was deeply gratified by receiving an invitation from all the gun-room officers to mess with them. But after a few hours Fitz-Roy showed his usual magnanimity by sending an officer to me with an apology and a request that I would continue to live with him.

His character was in several respects one of the most noble which I have ever known.

The voyage of the *Beagle* has been by far the most important event in my life, and has determined my whole career; yet it depended on so small a circumstance as my uncle offering to drive me thirty miles to Shrewsbury, which few uncles would have done, and on such a trifle as the shape of my nose. I have always felt that I owe to the voyage the first real training or education of my mind; I was led to attend closely to several branches of natural history, and thus my powers of observation were improved, though they were always fairly developed.

The investigation of the geology of all the places visited was far more important, as reasoning here comes into play. On first examining a new district nothing can appear more hopeless than the chaos of rocks; but by recording the stratification and nature of the rocks and fossils at many points, always reasoning and predicting what will be found elsewhere, light soon begins to dawn on the district, and the structure of the whole becomes more or less intelligible. I had brought with me the first volume of Lyell's 'Principles of Geology,' which I studied attentively; and the book was of the highest service to me in many ways. The very first place which I examined, namely St. Jago in the Cape de Verde islands, showed me clearly the wonderful superiority of Lyell's manner of treating geology, compared with that of any other author, whose works I had with me or ever afterwards read.

Another of my occupations was collecting animals of all classes, briefly describing and roughly dissecting many of the marine ones; but from not being able to draw, and from not having sufficient anatomical knowledge, a great pile of MS. which I made during the voyage has proved almost useless. I thus lost much time, with the exception of that spent in acquiring some knowledge of the Crustaceans, as this was of service when in after years I undertook a monograph of the Cirripedia.

During some part of the day I wrote my Journal and took much pains in describing carefully and vividly all that I had seen; and this was good practice. My Journal served also, in part, as letters to my home, and portions were sent to England whenever there was an opportunity.

The above various special studies were, however, of no importance compared with the habit of energetic industry and of concentrated attention to whatever I was engaged in, which I then acquired. Everything about which I thought or read was made to bear directly on what I had seen or was likely to see; and this habit of mind was continued during the five years of the voyage. I feel sure that it was this training which has enabled me to do whatever I have done in science.

Looking backwards, I can now perceive how my love for science gradually preponderated over every other taste. During the first two years my old passion for shooting survived in nearly full force, and I shot myself all the birds and animals for my collection; but gradually I gave up my gun more and more, and finally altogether, to my servant, as shooting interfered with my work, more especially with making out the geological structure of a country. I discovered, though unconsciously and insensibly, that the pleasure of observing and reasoning was a much higher one than that of skill and sport. That my mind became developed through my pursuits during the voyage is rendered probable by a remark made by my father, who was the most acute observer whom I ever saw, of a sceptical disposition, and far from being a believer in phrenology; for on first seeing me after the voyage, he turned round to my sisters, and exclaimed, "Why, the shape of his head is quite altered."

To return to the voyage. On Septembter 11th (1831), I paid a flying visit with Fitz-Roy to the *Beagle* at Plymouth. Thence to Shrewsbury to wish my father and sisters a long farewell. On October 24th I took up my residence at Plymouth, and remained there until December 27th, when the *Beagle* finally left the shores of England for her circumnavigation of the world. We made two earlier attempts to sail, but were driven back each time by heavy gales. These two months at Plymouth were the most miserable which I ever spent, though I exerted myself in various ways. I was out of spirits at the thought of leaving all my family and friends for so long a time, and the weather seemed to me inexpressibly gloomy. I was also troubled with palpitation and pain about the heart, and like many a young ignorant man, especially one with a smattering of medical knowledge, was convinced that I had heart disease. I did not consult any doctor, as I fully expected to hear the verdict that I was not fit for the voyage, and I was resolved to go at all hazards.

I need not here refer to the events of the voyage as I have given a sufficiently full account in my published Journal. The glories of the vegetation of the Tropics rise before my mind at the present time more vividly than anything else; though the sense of sublimity, which the great deserts of Patagonia and the forest-clad mountains of Tierra del Fuego excited in me, has left an indelible impression on my mind. The sight of a naked savage in his native land is an event which can never be forgotten. Many of my excursions on horseback through wild countries, or in the boats, some of which lasted several weeks, were deeply interesting: their discomfort and some degree of danger were at that time hardly a drawback, and none at all afterwards. I also reflect with high satisfaction on some of my scientific work, such as solving the problem of coral islands, and making out the geological structure of certain islands, for instance, St. Helena. Nor must I pass over the discovery of the singular relations of the animals and plants inhabiting the several islands of the Galapagos archipelago, and of all of them to the inhabitants of South America.

As far as I can judge of myself, I worked to the utmost during the voyage from the mere pleasure of investigation, and from my strong desire to add a few facts to the great mass of facts in Natural Science. But I was also ambitious to take a fair place among scientific men, — whether more ambitious or less so than most of my fellow-workers, I can form no opinion.

The geology of St. Jago is very striking, yet simple: a stream of lava formerly flowed over the bed of the sea, formed of triturated recent shells and corals, which it has baked into a hard white rock. Since then the whole island has been upheaved. But the line of white rock revealed to me a new and important fact, namely, that there had been afterwards subsidence round the craters, which had since been in action, and had poured forth lava. It then first dawned on me that I might perhaps write a book on the geology of the various countries visited, and this made me thrill with delight. That was a memorable hour to me, and how distinctly I can call to mind the low cliff of lava beneath which I rested, with the sun glaring hot, a few strange desert plants growing near, and with living corals in the tidal pools at my feet. Later in the voyage, Fitz-Roy asked me to read some of my Journal, and declared it would be worth publishing; so here was a second book in prospect!

Towards the close of our voyage I received a letter whilst at Ascension, in which my sisters told me that Sedgwick had called on my father, and said that I should take a place among the leading scientific men. I could not at the time understand how he could have learnt anything of my proceedings, but I heard (I believe afterwards) that Henslow had read some of the letters which I wrote to him before the Philosophical Society of Cambridge, and had printed them for private distribution. My collection of fossil bones, which had been sent to Henslow, also excited considerable attention amongst palaeontologists. After reading this letter, I clambered over the mountains of Ascension with a bounding step, and made the volcanic rocks resound under my geological hammer. All this shows how ambitious I was; but I think that I can say with truth that in after years, though I cared in the highest degree for the approbation of such men as Lyell and Hooker, who were my friends, I did not care much about the general public. I do not mean to say that a favourable review or a large sale of my books did not please me greatly, but the pleasure was a fleeting one, and I am sure that I have never turned one inch out of my course to gain fame.

# The Making of a Scientist: The *Beagle* Voyage

# *An Opportunity Almost Missed*[48]

*J. S. Henslow to Charles Darwin.*

*Cambridge, August 24, 1831.*

MY DEAR DARWIN,

. . . I have been asked by Peacock, who will read and forward this to you from London, to recommend him a Naturalist as a companion to Captain Fitz-Roy, employed by Government to survey the southern extremity of America. I have stated that I consider you to be the best qualified person I know of who is likely to undertake such a situation. I state this not in the supposition of your being a *finished* naturalist, but as amply qualified for collecting, observing, and noting anything worthy to be noted in Natural History. Peacock has the appointment at his disposal, and if he cannot find a man willing to take the office, the opportunity will probably be lost. Captain Fitz-Roy wants a man (I understand) more as a companion than a mere collector, and would not take anyone, however good a naturalist, who was not recommended to him likewise as a *gentleman.* Particulars of salary, &c., I know nothing. The voyage is to last two years, and if you take plenty of books with you, anything you please may be done. You will have ample opportunities at command. In short, I suppose there never was a finer chance for a man of your zeal and spirit; Captain Fitz-Roy is a young man. . . . Don't put on any modest doubts or fears about your disqualifications, for I assure you I think you are the very man they are in search of; so conceive yourself to be tapped on the shoulder by your bum-bailiff and affectionate friend,

J. S. Henslow.

The expedition is to sail on the 25th of September (at earliest), so there is no time to be lost.

*George Peacock to Charles Darwin.*

[1831.]

My Dear Sir,

I received Henslow's letter last night too late to forward it to you by the post; a circumstance which I do not regret, as it has given me an opportunity of seeing Captain Beaufort at the Admiralty (the Hydrographer), and of stating to him the offer which I have made to you. He entirely approves of it, and you may consider the situation at your absolute disposal. I trust that you will accept it, as it is an opportunity which should not be lost, and I look forward with great interest to the benefit which our collections of Natural History may receive from your labours.

The circumstances are these: —

Captain Fitz-Roy (a nephew of the Duke of Grafton) sails at the end of September, in a ship to survey . . . the South Coast of Tierra del Fuego, afterwards to visit the South Sea Islands, and to return by the Indian Archipelago to England. The expedition is entirely for scientific purposes, and the ship will generally wait your leisure for researches in Natural History. . . . Captain Fitz-Roy is a public-spirited and zealous officer, of delightful manners, and greatly beloved by all his brother officers. . . . You may be sure . . . of having a very pleasant companion, who will enter heartily into all your views. . . .

The Admiralty are not disposed to give a salary, though they will furnish you with an official appointment, and every accommodation. If a salary should be required . . . I am inclined to think that it would be granted.

Believe me, my dear Sir,

Very truly yours,

George Peacock.

*Charles Darwin to J. S. Henslow.*

*Shrewsbury, Tuesday* [August 30, 1831.]

My Dear Sir,

Mr. Peacock's letter arrived on Saturday, and I received it late yesterday evening. As far as my own mind is concerned, I should, I think *certainly*, most gladly have accepted the opportunity which you so kindly have offered me. But my father, although he does not decidedly refuse me, gives such strong advice against going, that I should not be comfortable if I did not follow it.

My father's objections are these: the unfitting me to settle down as a Clergyman, my little habit of seafaring, *the shortness of the time,* and the chance of my not suiting Captain Fitz-Roy. It is certainly a very serious objection, the very short time for all my preparations, as not only body but mind wants making up for such an undertaking. But if it had not been for my father I would have taken all risks. What was the reason that a Naturalist was not long ago fixed upon? I am very much obliged for the trouble you have had about it; there certainly could not have been a better opportunity. . . .

Yours most sincerely,

My dear Sir,

Ch. Darwin.

I have written to Mr. Peacock, and I mentioned that I have asked you to send one line in the chance of his not getting my letter. I have also asked him to communicate with Captain Fitz-Roy. Even if I was to go, my father disliking would take away all energy, and I should want a good stock of that. Again I must thank you, it adds a little to the heavy but pleasant load of gratitude which I owe to you.

*Charles Darwin to Robert Waring Darwin.*

[Maer] *August 31* [1831].

My Dear Father,

I am afraid I am going to make you again very uncomfortable. But, upon consideration, I think you will excuse me once again, stating my opinions on the offer of the voyage. My excuse and reason is the different way all the Wedgwoods view the subject from what you and my sisters do.

I have given Uncle Jos what I fervently trust is an accurate and full list of your objections, and he is kind enough to give his opinions on all. The list and his answers will be enclosed. But may I beg of you one favour, it will be doing me the greatest kindness, if you will send me a decided answer, yes or no? If the latter, I should be most ungrateful if I did not implicitly yield to your better judgment, and to the kindest indulgence you have shown me all through my life; and you may rely upon it I will never mention the subject again. If your answer should be yes; I will go directly to Henslow and consult deliberately with him, and then come to Shrewsbury.

The danger appears to me and all the Wedgwoods not great. The expense can not be serious, and the time I do not think, anyhow, would be more thrown away than if I stayed at home. But pray do not consider that I am so bent on going that I would for one *single moment* hesitate, if you thought that after a short period you should continue uncomfortable.

I must again state I cannot think it would unfit me hereafter for a steady life. I do hope this letter will not give you much uneasiness. I send it by the car to-morrow morning; if you make up your mind directly will you send me an answer on the following day by the same means? If this letter should find you not at home, I hope you will answer as soon as you conveniently can.

I do not know what to say about Uncle Jos' kindness; I never can forget how he interests himself about me.

Believe me, my dear father,

Your affectionate son,

CHARLES DARWIN.

*Dr. Darwin's Objections to the* Beagle *Project*:

1. Disreputable to my character as a Clergyman hereafter.
2. A wild scheme.
3. That they must have offered to many others before me the place of Naturalist.
4. And from its not being accepted there must be some serious objection to the vessel or expedition.
5. That I should never settle down to a steady life hereafter.
6. That the accommodations would be most uncomfortable.
7. That you [*i.e.*, Dr. Darwin] should consider it as again changing my profession.
8. That it would be a useless undertaking.

*Josiah Wedgwood to Robert Waring Darwin.*

*Maer, August 31, 1831.*

MY DEAR DOCTOR,

I feel the responsibility of your application to me on the offer that has been made to Charles as being weighty, but as you have desired Charles to consult me, I cannot refuse to give the result of such consideration. . . .

Charles has put down what he conceives to be your principal objections, and I think the best course I can take will be to state what occurs to me upon each of them.

1. I should not think that it would be in any degree disreputable to his character as a Clergyman. I should on the contrary think the offer honourable to him; and the pursuit of Natural History, though certainly not professional, is very suitable to a clergyman.

2. I hardly know how to meet this objection, but he would have definite objects upon which to employ himself, and might acquire and strengthen habits of application, and I should think would be as likely to do so as in any way in which he is likely to pass the next two years at home.

3. The notion did not occur to me in reading the letters; and on reading them again with that object in my mind I see no ground for it.

4. I cannot conceive that the Admiralty would send out a bad vessel on such a service. As to objections to the expedition, they will differ in each man's case, and nothing would, I think, be inferred in Charles's case, if it were known that others had objected.

5. You are a much better judge of Charles's character than I can be. If on comparing this mode of spending the next two years with the way in which he will probably spend them, if he does not accept this offer, you think him more likely to be rendered unsteady and unable to settle, it is undoubtedly a weighty objection. Is it not the case that sailors are prone to settle in domestic and quiet habits?

6. I can form no opinion on this further than that if appointed by the Admiralty he will have a claim to be as well accommodated as the vessel will allow.

7. If I saw Charles now absorbed in professional studies I should probably think it would not be advisable to interrupt them; but this is not, and I think, will not be the case with him. His present pursuit of knowledge is in the same track as he would have to follow in the expedition.

8. The undertaking would be useless as regards his profession, but looking upon him as a man of enlarged curiosity, it affords him such an opportunity of seeing men and things as happens to few.

You will bear in mind that I have had very little time for consideration, and that you and Charles are the persons who must decide.

I am,

My dear Doctor,

Affectionately yours,

Josiah Wedgwood.

*Charles Darwin to J. S. Henslow.*

*Cambridge, Red Lion* [Sept 2], *1831.*

My Dear Sir,

I am just arrived; you will guess the reason. My father has changed his mind. I trust the place is not given away.

I am very much fatigued, and am going to bed.

I dare say you have not yet got my second letter.

How soon shall I come to you in the morning? Send a verbal answer.

Good night,

Yours,

C. Darwin.

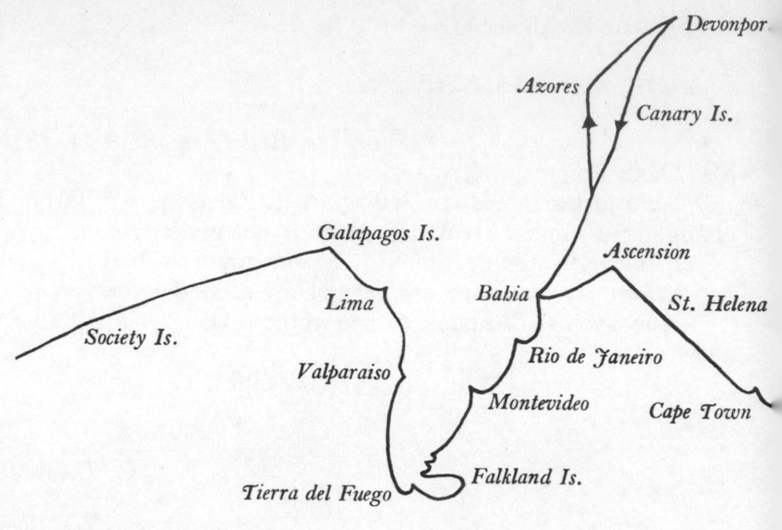


# *The Voyage*[49]

*Charles Darwin to Caroline Darwin.*

*March 30, 1833.*
(—April 12th)

FALKLAND ISLAND,
BERKLEY SOUND.

MY DEAR CAROLINE,

The *Beagle* will sail in a few days for Monte Video, and as this sheet of paper is very large I have taken good time to begin my letter. It is now four months since my last letter, so I will write a sort of Journal of everything which has since happened. That we might not lose the long days we made a straight course for the South: my first introduction to the notorious Terra del F. was at Good Success Bay, and the master of ceremonies was a gale of wind. This place was visited by Capt. Cook. When ascending the mountains, which caused so many disasters to Mr. Banks, I felt that I was treading on ground which to me was classic. We here saw the native Fuegian: an untamed savage is I really think one of the most extraordinary spectacles in the world: — the difference between a domesticated and wild animal is far more strikingly marked in Man: in the naked barbarian,

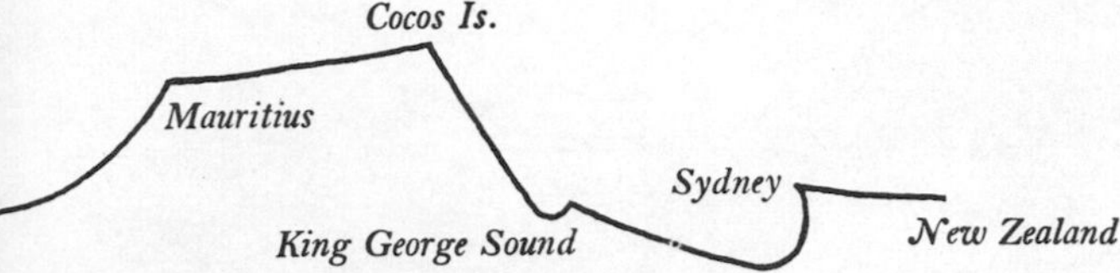


Route of the *Beagle* voyage, 1831-1836

with his body coated with paint, whose very gestures, whether they may be peacable [*sic*] or hostile are unintelligible, with difficulty we see a fellow creature. No drawing or description will at all explain the extreme interest which is created by the first sight of savages. It is an interest which almost repays one for a cruize [*sic*] in these latitudes: and this I assure you is saying a good deal.

We doubled Cape Horn on a beautiful afternoon: it was however the last we were doomed to have for some time. After trying to make head against the westerly Gales, we put into a cove near the Cape. Here we experienced some tremendous weather: the gusts of wind fairly tear up the water and carry clouds of spray. We again put to sea, with no better success, gales succeeded gales, with such short intervals, that a ship can do nothing. . . . The Captain told me to wait till we shipped a sea: it was prophetic: for at noon we shipped a great one, and it is a sight for landsmen to remember. One of our boats was knocked to pieces and was immediately cut away: the water being deep on the deck, it did me an infinity of harm, as it wetted a great deal of paper and dried plants. I suffered also much from sea-sickness, and yet with all this I am becoming

quite hardened: it makes me however, think with greater ecstasy of the warm serene air and the beautiful forms of the Tropics. No disciple of Mahomet ever looked to his seventh heaven with greater zeal, than I do to those regions. . . . These Fuegians are Cannibals: but we have good reason to suppose it carried on to an extent which hitherto has been unheard of in the world. . . . In winter they sometimes eat the women: — certain it is the women are in a very small proportion. Yet we could not believe it. But the other day a Sealing Captain said that a Fuegian boy whom he had, said the same thing. Upon being asked "Why no eat dogs"? the boy answered "Dog catch otter: — women good for nothing: man very hungry." He said they smothered them: it is difficult to disbelieve two such distinct explicit accounts and given by boys. Was ever anything so atrocious heard of, to work them like slaves to procure food in the summer, and occasionally in winter to eat them. I feel quite a disgust at the very sound of the voices of these miserable savages. . . .

Believe me my dear Caroline,

Yours very sincerely,

CHAS. DARWIN.

# *Observations at the Galapagos*[50]

*September 15th.* — This archipelago consists of ten principal islands, of which five exceed the others in size. They are situated under the Equator, and between five and six hundred miles westward of the coast of America. They are all formed of volcanic rocks; a few fragments of granite curiously glazed and altered by the heat, can hardly be considered as an exception. Some of the craters, surmounting the larger islands, are of immense size, and they rise to a height of between three and four thousand feet. Their flanks are studded by innumerable smaller orifices. I scarcely hesitate to affirm, that there must be in the whole archipelago at least two thousand craters. These consist either of lava and scoriæ, or of finely-stratified, sandstone-like tuff. Most of the latter are beautifully symmetrical; they owe their origin to eruptions of volcanic mud without any lava: it is a remarkable circumstance that every one of the twenty-eight tuff-craters which were examined, had their southern sides either much lower than the other sides, or quite broken down and removed. As all

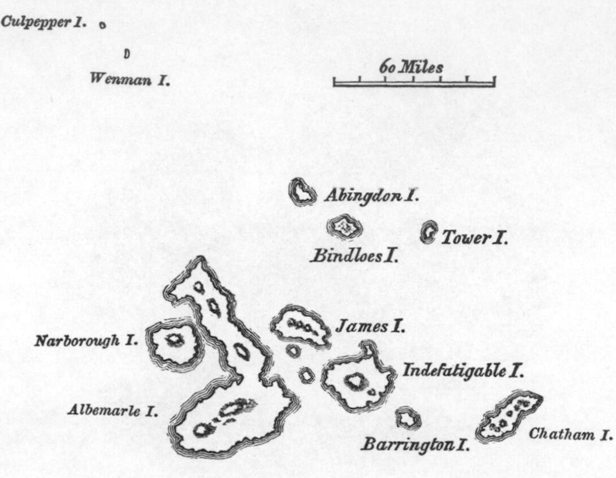


Galapagos Archipelago

these craters have apparently been formed when standing in the sea, and as the waves from the trade-wind and the swell from the open Pacific here unite their forces on the southern coasts of all the islands, this singular uniformity in the broken state of the craters, composed of the soft and yielding tuff, is easily explained.

Considering that these islands are placed directly under the equator, the climate is far from being excessively hot; this seems chiefly caused by the singularly low temperature of the surrounding water, brought here by the great southern Polar current. Excepting during one short season, very little rain falls, and even then it is irregular; but the clouds generally hang low. Hence, whilst the lower parts of the island are very sterile, the upper parts, at a height of a thousand feet and upwards, possess a damp climate and a tolerably luxuriant vegetation. This is especially the case on the windward sides of the islands, which first receive and condense the moisture from the atmosphere.

In the morning (17th) we landed on Chatham Island, which, like the others, rises with a tame and rounded outline, broken here and there by scattered hillocks, the remains of former craters. Nothing could be less inviting than the first appearance. A broken field of black basaltic lava, thrown into the most rugged waves, and crossed by great fissures, is every where covered by stunted, sun-burnt brushwood, which shows little signs of life. The dry and parched surface, being heated by the noonday sun, gave to the air a close and sultry feeling, like that from a stove: we fancied even that the bushes smelt unpleasantly. Although I diligently tried to collect as many plants as possible, I succeeded in getting very few; and such wretched-looking little weeds would have better become an arctic than an equatorial Flora. The brushwood appears, from a short distance, as leafless as our trees during winter; and it was some time before I discovered that not only almost every plant was now in full leaf, but that the greater number were in flower. The commonest bush is one of the Euphorbiaceæ: an acacia and a great odd-looking cactus are the only trees which afford any shade. After the season of heavy rains, the islands are said to appear for a short time partially green. The volcanic island of Fernando Noronha, placed in many respects under nearly similar conditions, is the only other country where I have seen a vegetation at all like this of the Galapagos islands.

The *Beagle* sailed round Chatham Island, and anchored in several bays. One night I slept on shore on a part of the island, where black truncated cones were extraordinarily numerous: from one small eminence I counted sixty of them, all surmounted by craters more or less perfect. The greater number consisted merely of a ring of red scoriæ or slags, cemented together: and their height above the plain of lava was not more than from fifty to a hundred feet: none had been very lately active. The entire surface of this part of the island seems to have been permeated, like a sieve, by the subterranean vapours: here and there the lava, whilst soft, has been blown into great bubbles; and in other parts, the tops of caverns similarly formed have fallen in, leaving circular pits with steep sides. From the regular form of the many craters, they gave to the country an artificial appearance, which vividly reminded me of those parts of Staffordshire, where the great iron-foundries are most numerous. The day was glowing hot, and the scrambling over the rough surface and through the intricate thickets, was very fatiguing; but I was well repaid by the strange Cyclopean scene. As I was walking along I met two large tortoises, each of which must have weighed at least two hundred pounds: one was eating a piece of cactus, and as I approached, it stared at me and slowly stalked away; the other gave a deep hiss, and drew in its head. These huge reptiles, surrounded by the black lava, the leafless shrubs, and large cacti, seemed to my fancy like some antediluvian animals. The few dull-coloured birds cared no more for me, than they did for the great tortoises.

*23rd.* — The *Beagle* proceeded to Charles Island. This archipelago has long been frequented, first by the Bucaniers, and latterly by whalers, but it is only within the last six years, that a small colony has been established here. The inhabitants are between two and three hundred in number: they are nearly all people of colour, who have been banished for political crimes from the Republic of the Equator, of which Quito is the capital. The settlement is placed about four and a half miles inland, and at a height probably of a thousand feet. In the first part of the road we passed through leafless thickets, as in Chatham Island. Higher up, the woods gradually became greener: and as soon as we crossed the ridge of the island, we were cooled by a fine southerly breeze, and our sight refreshed by a green and thriving vegetation. In this upper region coarse grasses and ferns abound; but there are no tree-ferns: I saw nowhere any member of the Palm family, which is the more singular, as 360 miles northward, Cocos Island takes its name from the number of cocoa-nuts. The houses are irregularly scattered over a flat space of ground, which is cultivated with sweet potatoes and bananas. It will not easily be imagined how pleasant the sight of black mud was to us, after having been so long accustomed to the parched soil of Peru and northern Chile. The inhabitants, although complaining of poverty, obtain, without much trouble, the means of subsistence. In the woods there are many wild pigs and goats; but the staple article of animal food is supplied by the tortoises. Their numbers have of course been greatly reduced in this island, but the people yet count on two days' hunting giving them food for the rest of the week. It is said that formerly single vessels have taken away as many as seven hundred, and that the ship's company of a frigate some years since brought down in one day two hundred tortoises to the beach.

*September 29th.* — We doubled the south-west extremity of Albemarle Island, and the next day were nearly becalmed between it and Narborough Island. Both are covered with immense deluges of black naked lava, which have flowed either over the rims of the great caldrons, like pitch over the rim of a pot in which it has been boiled, or have burst forth from smaller orifices on the flanks; in their descent they have spread over miles of the sea-coast. On both of these islands, eruptions are known to have taken place; and in Albemarle, we saw a small jet of smoke curling from the summit of one of the great craters. In the evening we anchored in Bank's Cove, in Albemarle Island. The next morning I went out walking. To the south of the broken tuff-crater, in which the *Beagle* was anchored, there was another beautifully symmetrical one of an elliptic form; its longer axis was a little less than a mile, and its depth about 500 feet. At its bottom there was a shallow lake, in the middle of which a tiny crater formed an islet. The day was overpoweringly hot, and the lake looked clear and blue: I hurried down the cindery slope, and choked with dust eagerly tasted the water — but, to my sorrow, I found it salt as brine.

The rocks on the coast abounded with great black lizards, between three and four feet long; and on the hills, an ugly yellowish-brown species was equally common. We saw many of this latter kind, some clumsily running out of our way, and others shuffling into their burrows. I shall presently describe in more detail the habits of both these reptiles. The whole of this northern part of Albemarle Island is miserably sterile.

*October 8th.*—We arrived at James Island; this island, as well as Charles Island, were long since thus named after our kings of the Stuart line. Mr. Bynoe, myself, and our servants were left here for a week, with provisions and a tent, whilst the *Beagle* went for water. We found here a party of Spaniards, who had been sent from Charles Island to dry fish, and to salt tortoise-meat. About six miles inland, and at the height of nearly 2000 feet, a hovel had been built in which two men lived, who were employed in catching tortoises, whilst the others were fishing on the coast. I paid this party two visits, and slept there one night. As in the other islands, the lower region was covered by nearly leafless bushes, but the trees were here of a larger growth than elsewhere, several being two feet and some even two feet nine inches in diameter. The upper region being kept damp by the clouds, supports a green and flourishing vegetation. So damp was the ground, that there were large beds of a coarse cyperus, in which great numbers of a very small water-rail lived and bred. While staying in this upper region, we lived entirely upon tortoise-meat: the breast-plate roasted (as the Gauchos do *carne con cuero*), with the flesh on it, is very good; and the young tortoises make excellent soup; but otherwise the meat to my taste is indifferent.

One day we accompanied a party of the Spaniards in their whale-boat to a salina, or lake from which salt is procured. After landing, we had a very rough walk over a rugged field of recent lava, which has almost surrounded a tuff-crater, at the bottom of which the salt-lake lies. The water is only three or four inches deep, and rests on a layer of beautifully crystallized, white salt. The lake is quite circular, and is fringed with a border of bright green succulent plants; the almost precipitous walls of the crater are clothed with wood, so that the scene was altogether both picturesque and curious. A few years since, the sailors belonging to a sealing-vessel murdered their captain in this quiet spot; and we saw his skull lying among the bushes.

During the greater part of our stay of a week, the sky was cloudless, and if the trade-wind failed for an hour, the heat became very oppressive. On two days, the thermometer within the tent stood for some hours at 93°; but in the open air, in the wind and sun, at only 85°. The sand was extremely hot; the thermometer placed in some of a brown colour immediately rose to 137°, and how much above that it would have risen, I do not know, for it was not graduated any higher. The black sand felt much hotter, so that even in thick boots it was quite disagreeable to walk over it.

The natural history of these islands is eminently curious, and well deserves attention. Most of the organic productions are aboriginal creations, found nowhere else; there is even a difference between the inhabitants of the different islands; yet all show a marked relationship with those of America, though separated from that continent by an open space of ocean, between 500 and 600 miles in width. The archipelago is a little world within itself, or rather a satellite attached to America, whence it has derived a few stray colonists, and has received the general character of its indigenous productions. Considering the small size of these islands, we feel the more astonished at the number of their aboriginal beings, and at their confined range. Seeing every height crowned with its crater, and the boundaries of most of the lava-streams still distinct, we are led to believe that within a period, geologically recent, the unbroken ocean was here spread out. Hence, both in space and time, we seem to be brought somewhat near to that great fact — that mystery of mysteries — the first appearance of new beings on this earth.

Of terrestrial mammals, there is only one which must be considered as indigenous, namely, a mouse (Mus Galapagoensis), and this is confined, as far as I could ascertain, to Chatham island, the most easterly island of the group. It belongs, as I am informed by Mr. Waterhouse, to a division of the family of mice characteristic of America. At James Island, there is a rat sufficiently distinct from the common kind to have been named and described by Mr. Waterhouse; but as it belongs to the old-world division of the family, and as this island has been frequented by ships for the last hundred and fifty years, I can hardly doubt that this rat is merely a variety, produced by the new and peculiar climate, food, and soil, to which it has been subjected. Although no one has a right to speculate without distinct facts, yet even with respect to the Chatham island mouse, it should be borne in mind, that it may possibly be an American species imported here; for I have seen, in a most unfrequented part of the Pampas, a native mouse living in the roof of a newly-built hovel, and therefore its transportation in a vessel is not improbable: analogous facts have been observed by Dr. Richardson in North America.

Of land-birds I obtained twenty-six kinds, all peculiar to the group and found nowhere else, with the exception of one lark-like finch from North America (Dolichonyx oryzivorus), which ranges on that continent as far north as 54°, and generally frequents marshes. The other twenty-five birds consist, firstly, of a hawk, curiously intermediate in structure between a Buzzard and the American group of carrion-feeding Polybori; and with these latter birds it agrees most closely in every habit and even tone of voice. Secondly, there are two owls, representing the short-eared and white barn-owls of Europe. Thirdly, a wren, three tyrant fly-catchers (two of them species of Pyrocephalus, one or both of which would be ranked by some ornithologists as only varieties), and a dove — all analogous to, but distinct from, American species. Fourthly, a swallow, which though differing from the Progne purpurea of both Americas, only in being rather duller coloured, smaller, and slenderer, is considered by Mr. Gould as specifically distinct. Fifthly, there are three species of mocking-thrush — a form highly characteristic of America. The remaining land-birds form a most singular group of finches, re-

1. Geospiza magnirostris
2. Geospiza fortis
3. Geospiza parvula
4. Certhidea olivacea

lated to each other in the structure of their beaks, short tails, form of body, and plumage; there are thirteen species, which Mr. Gould has divided into four sub-groups. All these species are peculiar to this archipelago; and so is the whole group, with the exception of one species of the sub-group Cactornis, lately brought from Bow island, in the Low Archipelago. Of Cactornis, the two species may be often seen climbing about the flowers of the great cactus-trees; but all the other species of this group of finches, mingled together in flocks, feed on the dry and sterile ground of the lower districts. The males of all, or certainly of the greater number, are jet black; and the females (with perhaps one or two exceptions) are brown. The most curious fact is the perfect gradation in the size of the beaks in the different species of Geospiza, from one as large as that of a hawfinch to that of a chaffinch, and (if Mr. Gould is right in including his sub-group, Certhidea, in the main group), even to that of a warbler. The largest beak in the genus Geospiza is shown in Fig. 1, and the smallest in Fig. 3; but instead of there being only one intermediate species, with a beak of the size shown in Fig. 2, there are no less than six species with insensibly graduated beaks. The beak of the sub-group Certhidea, is shown in Fig. 4. The beak of Cactornis is somewhat like that of a starling; and that of the fourth sub-group, Camarhynchus, is slightly parrot-shaped. Seeing this gradation and diversity of structure in one small, intimately related group of birds, one might really fancy that from an original paucity of birds in this archipelago, one species had been taken and modified for different ends. In a like manner it might be fancied that a bird originally a buzzard, had been induced here to undertake the office of the carrion-feeding Polybori of the American continent.

Of waders and water-birds I was able to get only eleven kinds, and of these only three (including a rail confined to the damp summits of the islands) are new species. Considering the wandering habits of the gulls, I was surprised to find that the species inhabiting these islands is peculiar, but allied to one from the southern parts of South America. The far greater peculiarity of the land-birds, namely, twenty-five out of twenty-six being new species or at least new races, compared with the waders and web-footed birds, is in accordance with the greater range which these latter orders have in all parts of the world. We shall hereafter see this law of aquatic forms, whether marine or fresh-water, being less peculiar at any given point of the earth's surface than the terrestrial forms of the same classes, strikingly illustrated in the shells, and in a lesser degree in the insects of this archipelago.

Two of the waders are rather smaller than the same species brought from other places: the swallow is also smaller, though it is doubtful whether or not it is distinct from its analogue. The two owls, the two tyrant flycatchers (Pyrocephalus) and the dove, are also smaller than the analogous but distinct species, to which they are most nearly related; on the other hand, the gull is rather larger. The two owls, the swallow, all three species of mocking-thrush, the dove in its separate colours though not in its whole plumage, the Totanus, and the gull, are likewise duskier coloured than their analogous species; and in the case of the mocking-thrush and Totanus, than any other species of the two genera. With the exception of a wren with a fine yellow breast, and of a tyrant fly-catcher with a scarlet tuft and breast, none of the birds are brilliantly coloured, as might have been expected in an equatorial district. Hence it would appear probable, that the same causes which here make the immigrants of some species smaller, make most of the peculiar Galapageian species also smaller, as well as very generally more dusky coloured. All the plants have a wretched, weedy appearance, and I did not see one beautiful flower. The insects, again, are small sized and dull coloured, and, as Mr. Waterhouse informs me, there is nothing in their general appearance which would have led him to imagine that they had come from under the equator. The birds, plants, and insects have a desert character, and are not more brilliantly coloured than those from southern Patagonia; we may, therefore, conclude that the usual gaudy colouring of the inter-tropical productions, is not related either to the heat or light of those zones, but to some other cause, perhaps to the conditions of existence being generally favourable to life.

We will now turn to the order of reptiles, which gives the most striking character to the zoology of these islands. The species are not numerous, but the numbers of individuals of each species are extraordinarily great. There is one small lizard belonging to a South American genus, and two species (and probably more) of the Amblyrhynchus — a genus confined to the Galapagos islands. There is one snake which is numerous; it is identical, as I am informed by M. Bibron, with the Psammophis Temminckii from Chile. Of sea-turtle I believe there is more than one species; and of tortoises there are, as we shall presently show, two or three species or races. Of toads and frogs there are none: I was surprised at this, considering how well suited for them the temperate and damp upper woods appeared to be. It recalled to my mind the remark made by Bory St. Vincent,[1] namely, that none of this family are found on any of the volcanic islands in the great oceans. As far as I can ascertain from various works, this seems to hold good throughout the Pacific, and even in the large islands of the Sandwich archipelago. Mauritius offers an apparent exception, where I saw the Rana Mascariensis in abundance: this frog is said now to inhabit the Seychelles, Madagascar, and Bourbon; but on the other hand, Du Bois, in his voyage of 1669, states that there were no reptiles in Bourbon except tortoises; and the Officier du Roi asserts that before 1768 it had been attempted, without success, to introduce frogs into Mauritius —I presume, for the purpose of eating: hence it may be well doubted whether this frog is an aboriginal of these islands. The absence of the frog family in the oceanic islands is the more remarkable, when contrasted with the case of lizards, which swarm on most of the smallest islands. May this difference not be caused, by the greater facility with which the eggs of lizards, protected by calcareous shells, might be transported through salt-water, than could the slimy spawn of frogs?

I will first describe the habits of the tortoise (Testudo nigra, formerly called Indica), which has been so frequently alluded to. These animals are found, I believe, on all the islands of the Archipelago; certainly on the greater number. They frequent in preference the high damp parts, but they likewise live in the lower and arid districts. I have already shown, from the numbers which have been caught in a single day, how very numerous they must be. Some grow to an immense size: Mr. Lawson, an Englishman, and vice-governor of the colony, told us that he had seen several so large, that it required six or eight men to lift them from the ground; and that some had afforded as much as two hundred pounds of meat. The old males are the largest, the

[1] Voyage aux Quatre Iles d'Afrique. With respect to the Sandwich Islands, see Tyerman and Bennett's Journal, vol. i, p. 434. For Mauritius, see Voyage par un Officier, &c., Part i, p. 170. There are no frogs in the Canary Islands (Webb et Berthelot, Hist. Nat. des Iles Canaries). I saw none at St. Jago in the Cape de Verde. There are none at St. Helena.

females rarely growing to so great a size: the male can readily be distinguished from the female by the greater length of its tail. The tortoises which live on those islands where there is no water, or in the lower and arid parts of the others, feed chiefly on the succulent cactus. Those which frequent the higher and damp regions, eat the leaves of various trees, a kind of berry (called guayavita) which is acid and austere, and likewise a pale green filamentous lichen (Usnera plicata), that hangs in tresses from the boughs of the trees.

The tortoise is very fond of water, drinking large quantities, and wallowing in the mud. The larger islands alone possess springs, and these are always situated towards the central parts, and at a considerable height. The tortoises, therefore, which frequent the lower districts, when thirsty, are obliged to travel from a long distance. Hence broad and well-beaten paths branch off in every direction from the wells down to the sea-coast; and the Spaniards by following them up, first discovered the watering-places. When I landed at Chatham Island, I could not imagine what animal travelled so methodically along well-chosen tracks. Near the springs it was a curious spectacle to behold many of these huge creatures, one set eagerly travelling onwards with outstretched necks, and another set returning, after having drunk their fill. When the tortoise arrives at the spring, quite regardless of any spectator, he buries his head in the water above his eyes, and greedily swallows great mouthfuls, at the rate of about ten in a minute. The inhabitants say each animal stays three or four days in the neighbourhood of the water, and then returns to the lower country; but they differed respecting the frequency of these visits. The animal probably regulates them according to the nature of the food on which it has lived. It is, however, certain, that tortoises can subsist even on those islands, where there is no other water than what falls during a few rainy days in the year.

I believe it is well ascertained, that the bladder of the frog acts as a reservoir for the moisture necessary to its existence: such seems to be the case with the tortoise. For some time after a visit to the springs, their urinary bladders are distended with fluid, which is said gradually to decrease in volume, and to become less pure. The inhabitants, when walking in the lower district, and overcome with thirst, often take advantage of this circumstance, and drink the contents of the bladder if full: in one I saw killed, the fluid was quite limpid, and had only a very slightly bitter taste. The inhabitants, however, always first drink the water in the pericardium, which is described as being best.

The tortoises, when purposely moving towards any point, travel by night and day, and arrive at their journey's end much sooner than would be expected. The inhabitants, from observing marked individuals, consider that they travel a distance of about eight miles in two or three days. One large tortoise, which I watched, walked at the rate of sixty yards in ten minutes, that is 360 yards in the hour, or four miles a day, — allowing a little time for it to eat on the road. During the breeding season, when the male and female are together, the male utters a hoarse roar or bellowing, which, it is said, can be heard at the distance of more than a hundred yards. The female never uses her voice, and the male only at these times; so that when the people hear this noise, they know that the two are together. They were at this time (October) laying their eggs. The female, where the soil is sandy, deposits them together, and covers them up with sand; but where the ground is rocky she drops them indiscriminately in any hole: Mr. Bynoe found seven placed in a fissure. The egg is white and spherical; one which I measured was seven inches and three-eighths in circumference, and therefore larger than a hen's egg. The young tortoises, as soon as they are hatched, fall a prey in great numbers to the carrion-feeding buzzard. The old ones seem generally to die from accidents, as from falling down precipices: at least, several of the inhabitants told me, that they had never found one dead without some evident cause.

The inhabitants believe that these animals are absolutely deaf; certainly they do not overhear a person walking close behind them. I was always amused when overtaking one of these great monsters, as it was quietly pacing along, to see how suddenly, the instant I passed, it would draw in its head and legs, and uttering a deep hiss fall to the ground with a heavy sound, as if struck dead. I frequently got on their backs, and then giving a few raps on the hinder part of their shells, they would rise up and walk away; — but I found it very difficult to keep my balance. The flesh of this animal is largely employed, both fresh and salted; and a beautifully clear oil is prepared from the fat. When a tortoise is caught, the man makes a slit in the skin near its tail, so as to see inside its body, whether the fat under the dorsal plate is thick. If it is not, the animal is liberated; and it is said to recover soon from this strange operation. In order to secure the tortoises, it is not sufficient to turn them like turtle, for they are often able to get on their legs again.

There can be little doubt that this tortoise is an aboriginal inhabitant of the Galapagos; for it is found on all, or nearly all, the islands, even on some of the smaller ones where there is no water; had it been an imported species, this would hardly have been the case in a group which has been so little frequented. Moreover, the old Bucaniers found this tortoise in greater numbers even than at present: Wood and Rogers also, in 1708, say that it is the opinion of the Spaniards, that it is found nowhere else in this quarter of the world. It is now widely distributed; but it may be questioned whether it is in any other place an aboriginal. The bones of a tortoise at Mauritius, associated with those of the extinct Dodo, have generally been considered as belonging to this tortoise: if this had been so, undoubtedly it must have been there indigenous; but M. Bibron informs me that he believes that it was distinct, as the species now living there certainly is.

The Amblyrhynchus, a remarkable genus of lizards, is confined to this archipelago: there are two species, resembling each other in general form, one being terrestrial and the other aquatic. This latter species (A. cristatus) was first characterized by Mr. Bell, who well foresaw, from its short, broad head, and strong claws of equal length, that its habits of life would turn out very peculiar, and different from those of its nearest ally, the Iguana. It is extremely common on all the islands throughout the group, and lives exclusively on the rocky sea-beaches, being never found, at least I never saw one, even ten yards in-shore. It is a hideous-looking creature, of a dirty black colour, stupid, and sluggish in its movements. The usual length of a full-grown one is about a yard, but there are some even four feet long; a large one weighed twenty pounds: on the island of Albemarle they seem to grow to a greater size than elsewhere. Their tails are flattened sideways, and all four feet partially webbed. They are occasionally seen some hundred yards from the shore, swimming about; and Captain Collnett, in his Voyage, says, "They go to sea in herds a-fishing, and sun themselves on the rocks; and may be called alligators in miniature." It must not, however, be supposed that

H.M.S. *Beagle*

they live on fish. When in the water this lizard swims with perfect ease and quickness, by a serpentine movement of its body and flattened tail — the legs being motionless and closely collapsed on its sides. A seaman on board sank one, with a heavy weight attached to it, thinking thus to kill it directly; but when, an hour afterwards, he drew up the line, it was quite active. Their limbs and strong claws are admirably adapted for crawling over the rugged and fissured masses of lava, which everywhere form the coast. In such situations, a group of six or seven of these hideous reptiles may oftentimes be seen on the black rocks, a few feet above the surf, basking in the sun with outstretched legs.

I opened the stomachs of several, and found them largely distended with minced sea-weed (Ulvæ), which grows in thin foliaceous expansions of a bright green or a dull red colour. I do not recollect having observed this sea-weed in any quantity on the tidal rocks; and I have reason to believe it grows at the bottom of the sea, at some little distance from the coast. If such be the case, the object of these animals occasionally going out to sea is explained. The stomach contained nothing but the sea-weed. Mr. Bynoe, however, found a piece of a crab in one; but this might have got in accidentally, in the same manner as I have seen a caterpillar, in the midst of some lichen, in the paunch of a tortoise. The intestines were large, as in other herbivorous animals. The nature of this lizard's food, as well as the structure of its tail and feet, and the fact of its having been seen voluntarily swimming out at sea, absolutely prove its aquatic habits; yet there is in this respect one strange anomaly, namely, that when frightened it will not enter the water. Hence it is easy to drive these lizards down to any little point overhanging the sea, where they will sooner allow a person to catch hold of their tails than jump into the water. They do not seem to have any notion of biting; but when much frightened they squirt a drop of fluid from each nostril. I threw one several times as far as I could, into a deep pool left by the retiring tide; but it invariably returned in a direct line to the spot where I stood. It swam near the bottom, with a very graceful and rapid movement, and occasionally aided itself over the uneven ground with its feet. As soon as it arrived near the edge, but still being under water, it tried to conceal itself in the tufts of sea-weed, or it entered some crevice. As soon as it thought the danger was past, it crawled out on the dry rocks, and shuffled away as quickly as it could. I several times caught this same lizard, by driving it down to a point, and though possessed of such perfect powers of diving and swimming, nothing would induce it to enter the water; and as often as I threw it in, it returned in the manner above described. Perhaps this singular piece of apparent stupidity may be accounted for by the circumstance, that this reptile has no enemy whatever on shore, whereas at sea it must often fall a prey to the numerous sharks. Hence, probably, urged by a fixed and hereditary instinct that the shore is its place of safety, whatever the emergency may be, it there takes refuge.

During our visit (in October), I saw extremely few small individuals of this species, and none I should think under a year old. From this circumstance it seems probable that the breeding season had not then commenced. I asked several of the inhabitants if they knew where it laid its eggs: they said that they knew nothing of its propagation, although well acquainted with the eggs of the land kind — a fact, considering how very common this lizard is, not a little extraordinary.

We will now turn to the terrestrial species (A. Demarlii), with a round tail, and toes without webs. This lizard, instead of being found like the other on all the islands, is confined to the central part of the archipelago, namely to Albemarle, James, Barrington, and Indefatigable islands. To the southward, in Charles, Hood, and Chatham islands, and to the northward, in Towers, Bindloes, and Abingdon, I neither saw nor heard of any. It would appear as if it had been created in the centre of the archipelago, and thence had been dispersed only to a certain distance. Some of these lizards inhabit the high and damp parts of the islands, but they are much more numerous in the lower and sterile districts near the coast. I cannot give a more forcible proof of their numbers, than by stating that when we were left at James Island, we could not for some time find a spot free from their burrows on which to pitch our single tent. Like their brothers the sea-kind, they are ugly animals, of a yellowish orange beneath, and of a brownish red colour above: from their low facial angle they have a singularly stupid appearance. They are, perhaps, of a rather less size than the marine species; but several of them weighed between ten and fifteen pounds. In their movements they are lazy and half torpid. When not frightened, they slowly crawl along with their tails and bellies dragging on the ground. They often stop, and doze for a minute or two, with closed eyes and hind legs spread out on the parched soil.

They inhabit burrows, which they sometimes make between fragments of lava, but more generally on level patches of the soft sandstone-like tuff. The holes do not appear to be very deep, and

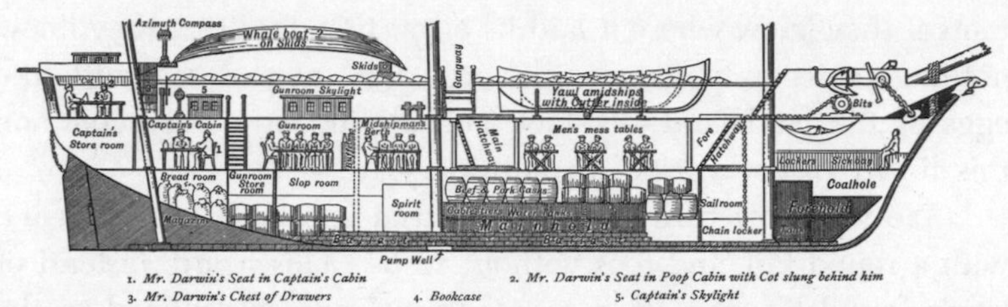


Sectional view of H.M.S. *Beagle*

they enter the ground at a small angle; so that when walking over these lizard-warrens, the soil is constantly giving way, much to the annoyance of the tired walker. This animal, when making its burrow, works alternately the opposite sides of its body. One front leg for a short time scratches up the soil, and throws it towards the hind foot, which is well placed so as to heave it beyond the mouth of the hole. That side of the body being tired, the other takes up the task, and so on alternately. I watched one for a long time, till half its body was buried; I then walked up and pulled it by the tail; at this it was greatly astonished, and soon shuffled up to see what was the matter; and then stared me in the face, as much as to say, "What made you pull my tail?"

They feed by day, and do not wander far from their burrows; if frightened, they rush to them with a most awkward gait. Except when running down hill, they cannot move very fast, apparently from the lateral position of their legs. They are not at all timorous: when attentively watching any one, they curl their tails, and, raising themselves on their front legs, nod their heads vertically, with a quick movement, and try to look very fierce: but in reality they are not at all so; if one just stamps on the ground, down go their tails, and off they shuffle as quickly as they can. I have frequently observed small fly-eating lizards, when watching anything, nod their heads in precisely the same manner; but I do not at all know for what purpose. If this Amblyrhynchus is held and plagued with a stick, it will bite it very severely; but I caught many by the tail, and they never tried to bite me. If two are placed on the ground and held together, they will fight, and bite each other till blood is drawn.

The individuals, and they are the greater number, which inhabit the lower country, can scarcely taste a drop of water throughout the year; but they consume much of the succulent cactus, the branches of which are occasionally broken off by the wind. I several times threw a piece to two or three of them when together; and it was amusing enough to see them trying to seize and carry it away in their mouths, like so many hungry dogs with a bone. They eat very deliberately, but do not chew their food. The little birds are aware how harmless these creatures are: I have seen one of the thick-billed finches picking at one end of a piece of cactus (which is much relished by all the animals of the lower region), whilst a lizard was eating at the other end; and afterwards the little bird with the utmost indifference hopped on the back of the reptile.

I opened the stomachs of several, and found them full of vegetable fibres and leaves of different trees, especially of an acacia. In the upper region they live chiefly on the acid and astringent berries of the guayavita, under which trees I have seen these lizards and huge tortoises feeding together. To obtain the acacia-leaves they crawl up the low stunted trees; and it is not uncommon to see a pair quietly browsing, whilst seated on a branch several feet above the ground. These lizards, when cooked, yield a white meat, which is liked by those whose stomachs soar above all prejudices. Humboldt has remarked that in intertropical South America, all lizards which inhabit dry regions are esteemed delicacies for the table. The inhabitants state that those which inhabit the upper damp parts drink water, but that the others do not, like the tortoises, travel up for it from the lower sterile country. At the time of our visit, the females had within their bodies numerous large, elongated eggs, which they lay in their burrows: the inhabitants seek them for food.

These two species of Amblyrhynchus agree, as I have already stated, in their general structure, and in many of their habits. Neither have that rapid movement, so characteristic of the genera Lacerta and Iguana. They are both herbivorous, although the kind of vegetation on which they feed is so very different. Mr. Bell has given the name to the genus from the shortness of the snout; indeed, the form of the mouth may almost be compared to that of the tortoise: one is led to suppose that this is an adaptation to their herbivorous appetites. It is very interesting thus to find a well-characterized genus, having its marine and terrestrial species, belonging to so confined a portion of the world. The aquatic species is by far the most remarkable, because it is the only existing lizard which lives on marine vegetable productions. As I at first observed, these islands are not so remarkable for the number of the species of reptiles, as for that of the individuals; when we remember the well-beaten paths made by the thousands of huge tortoises — the many turtles — the great warrens of the terrestrial Amblyrhynchus — and the groups of the marine species basking on the coast-rocks of every island — we must admit that there is no other quarter of the world where this Order replaces the herbivorous mammalia in so extraordinary a manner. The geologist on hearing this will probably refer back in his mind to the Secondary epochs, when lizards, some herbivorous, some carnivorous, and of dimensions comparable only with our existing whales, swarmed on the land and in the sea. It is, therefore, worthy of his observation, that this archipelago, instead of possessing a humid climate and rank vegetation, cannot be considered otherwise than extremely arid, and, for an equatorial region, remarkably temperate.

To finish with the zoology: the fifteen kinds of sea-fish which I procured here are all new species; they belong to twelve genera, all widely distributed, with the exception of Prionotus, of which the four previously known species live on the eastern side of America. Of land-shells I collected sixteen kinds (and two marked varieties), of which, with the exception of one Helix found at Tahiti, all are peculiar to this archipelago: a single fresh-water shell (Paludina) is common to Tahiti and Van Diemen's Land. Mr. Cuming, before our voyage, procured here ninety species of sea-shells, and this does not include several species not yet specifically examined, of Trochus, Turbo, Monodonta, and Nassa. He has been kind enough to give me the following interesting results: of the ninety shells, no less than forty-seven are unknown elsewhere — a wonderful fact, considering how widely distributed sea-shells generally are. Of the forty-three shells found in other parts of the world, twenty-five inhabit the western coast of America, and of these eight are distinguishable as varieties; the remaining eighteen (including one variety) were found by Mr. Cuming in the Low archipelago, and some of them also at the Philippines. This fact of shells from islands in the central part of the Pacific occurring here, deserves notice, for not one single sea-shell is known to be common to the islands of that ocean and to the west coast of America. The space of open sea running north and south off the west coast, separates two quite distinct conchological provinces; but at the Galapagos Archipelago we have a halting-place, where many new forms have been created, and whither these two great conchological provinces have each sent several colonists. The American province has also sent here representative species; for there is a Galapageian species of Monoceros, a genus only found on the west coast of America; and there are Galapageian species of Fissurella and Cancellaria, genera common on the west coast, but not found (as I am informed by Mr. Cuming) in the central islands of the Pacific. On the other hand, there are Galapageian species of Oniscia and Stylifer, genera common to the West Indies and to the Chinese and Indian seas, but not found either on the west coast of America or in the central Pacific. I may here add, that after the comparison by Messrs. Cuming and Hinds of about 2000 shells from the eastern and western coasts of America, only one single shell was found in common, namely, the Purpura patula, which inhabits the West Indies, the coast of Panama, and the Galapagos. We have, therefore, in this quarter of the world, three great conchological sea-provinces, quite distinct, though surprisingly near each other, being separated by long north and south spaces either of land or of open sea.

I took great pains in collecting the insects, but, excepting Tierra del Fuego, I never saw in this respect so poor a country. Even in the upper and damp region I procured very few, excepting some minute Diptera and Hymenoptera, mostly of common mundane forms. As before remarked, the insects, for a tropical region, are of very small size and dull colours. Of beetles I collected twenty-five species (excluding a Dermestes and Corynetes imported, wherever a ship touches); of these, two belong to the Harpalidæ, two to the Hydrophilidæ, nine to three families of the Heteromera, and the remaining twelve to as many different families. This circumstance of insects (and I may add plants), where few in number, belonging to many different families, is, I believe, very general. Mr. Waterhouse, who has published[2] an account of the insects of this archipelago, and to whom I am indebted for the above details, informs me that there are several new genera; and that of the genera not new, one or two are American, and the rest of mundane distribution. With the exception of a wood-feeding Apate, and of one or probably two water-beetles from the American continent, all the species appear to be new.

The botany of this group is fully as interesting as the zoology. Dr. J. Hooker will soon publish in the "Linnean Transactions" a

[2] Ann. and Mag. of Nat. Hist., vol. xvi, p. 19.

full account of the Flora, and I am much indebted to him for the following details. Of flowering plants there are, as far as at present is known, 185 species, and 40 cryptogamic species, making together 225; of this number I was fortunate enough to bring home 193. Of the flowering plants, 100 are new species, and are probably confined to this archipelago. Dr. Hooker conceives that, of the plants not so confined, at least 10 species found near the cultivated ground at Charles Island, have been imported. It is, I think, surprising that more American species have not been introduced naturally, considering that the distance is only between 500 and 600 miles from the continent; and that (according to Collnett, p. 58) drift-wood, bamboos, canes, and the nuts of a palm, are often washed on the south-eastern shores. The proportion of 100 flowering plants out of 185 (or 175 excluding the imported weeds) being new, is sufficient, I conceive, to make the Galapagos Archipelago a distinct botanical province; but this Flora is not nearly so peculiar as that of St. Helena, nor, as I am informed by Dr. Hooker, of Juan Fernandez. The peculiarity of the Galapageian Flora is best shown in certain families; — thus there are 21 species of Compositæ, of which 20 are peculiar to this archipelago; these belong to twelve genera, and of these genera no less than ten are confined to the archipelago! Dr. Hooker informs me that the Flora has an undoubted Western American character; nor can he detect in it any affinity with that of the Pacific. If, therefore, we except the eighteen marine, the one fresh-water, and one land-shell, which have apparently come here as colonists from the central islands of the Pacific, and likewise the one distinct Pacific species of the Galapageian group of finches, we see that this archipelago, though standing in the Pacific Ocean, is zoologically part of America.

If this character were owing merely to immigrants from America, there would be little remarkable in it; but we see that a vast majority of all the land animals, and that more than half of the flowering plants, are aboriginal productions. It was most striking to be surrounded by new birds, new reptiles, new shells, new insects, new plants, and yet by innumerable trifling details of structure, and even by the tones of voice and plumage of the birds, to have the temperate plains of Patagonia, or the hot dry deserts of Northern Chile, vividly brought before my eyes. Why, on these small points of land, which within a late geological period must have been covered by the ocean, which are formed of basaltic lava, and therefore differ in geological character from the American continent, and which are placed under a peculiar climate, — why were their aboriginal inhabitants, associated, I may add, in different proportions both in kind and number from those on the continent, and therefore acting on each other in a different manner — why were they created on American types of organization? It is probable that the islands of the Cape de Verd group resemble, in all their physical conditions, far more closely the Galapagos Islands than these latter physically resemble the coast of America; yet the aboriginal inhabitants of the two groups are totally unlike; those of the Cape de Verd Islands bearing the impress of Africa, as the inhabitants of the Galapagos Archipelago are stamped with that of America.

I have not as yet noticed by far the most remarkable feature in the natural history of this archipelago; it is, that the different islands to a considerable extent are inhabited by a different set of beings. My attention was first called to this fact by the Vice-Governor, Mr. Lawson, declaring that the tortoises differed from the different islands, and that he could with certainty tell from which island any one was brought. I did not for some time pay sufficient attention to this statement, and I had already partially mingled together the collections from two of the islands. I never dreamed that islands, about fifty or sixty miles apart, and most of them in sight of each other, formed of precisely the same rocks, placed under a quite similar climate, rising to a nearly equal height, would have been differently tenanted; but we shall soon see that this is the case. It is the fate of most voyagers, no sooner to discover what is most interesting in any locality, than they are hurried from it; but I ought, perhaps, to be thankful that I obtained sufficient material to establish this most remarkable fact in the distribution of organic beings.

The inhabitants, as I have said, state that they can distinguish the tortoises from the different islands; and that they differ not only in size, but in other characters. Captain Porter has described[3] those from Charles and from the nearest island to it, namely, Hood Island, as having their shells in front thick and turned up like a Spanish saddle, whilst the tortoises from James Island are rounder, blacker, and have a better taste when cooked. M. Bibron, moreover, informs me that he has seen what he considers two distinct species of tortoise from the Galapagos, but he does not know from which islands. The specimens that I brought from three islands were young ones; and probably owing to this cause, neither Mr. Gray nor myself could find in them any specific differences. I have remarked that the marine Amblyrhynchus was larger at Albemarle Island than elsewhere; and M. Bibron informs me that he has seen two distinct aquatic species of this genus; so that the different islands probably have their representative species or races of the Amblyrhynchus, as well as of the tortoise. My attention was first thoroughly aroused, by comparing together the numerous specimens, shot by myself and several other parties on board, of the mocking-thrushes, when, to my astonishment, I discovered that all those from Charles Island belonged to one species (Mimus trifasciatus); all from Albemarle Island to M. parvulus; and all from James and Chatham Islands (between which two other islands are situated, as connecting links) belonged to M. melanotis. These two latter species are closely allied, and would by some ornithologists be considered as only well-marked races or varieties; but the Mimus trifasciatus is very distinct. Unfortunately most of the specimens of the finch tribe were mingled together; but I have strong reasons to suspect that some of the species of the sub-group Geospiza are confined to separate islands. If the different islands have their representatives of Geospiza, it may help to explain the

[3] Voyage in the U. S. ship *Essex*, vol. i, p. 215.

singularly large number of the species of this sub-group in this one small archipelago, and as a probable consequence of their numbers, the perfectly graduated series in the size of their beaks. Two species of the sub-group Cactornis, and two of Camarhynchus, were procured in the archipelago; and of the numerous specimens of these two sub-groups shot by four collectors at James Island, all were found to belong to one species of each; whereas the numerous specimens shot either on Chatham or Charles Island (for the two sets were mingled together) all belonged to the two other species: hence we may feel almost sure that these islands possess their representative species of these two sub-groups. In land-shells this law of distribution does not appear to hold good. In my very small collection of insects, Mr. Waterhouse remarks, that of those which were ticketed with their locality, not one was common to any two of the islands.

If we now turn to the Flora, we shall find the aboriginal plants of the different islands wonderfully different. I give all the following results on the high authority of my friend Dr. J. Hooker. I may premise that I indiscriminately collected everything in flower on the different islands, and fortunately kept my collections separate. Too much confidence, however, must not be placed in the proportional results, as the small collections brought home by some other naturalists, though in some respects confirming the results, plainly show that much remains to be done in the botany of this group: the Leguminosæ, moreover, have as yet been only approximately worked out: —

| Name of Island. | Total No. of Species. | No. of Species found in other parts of the world. | No. of Species confined to the Galapagos Archipelago. | No. confined to the one Island. | No. of Species confined to the Galapagos Archipelago, but found on more than the one Island. |
|---|---|---|---|---|---|
| James Island | 71 | 33 | 38 | 30 | 8 |
| Albemarle Island | 46 | 18 | 26 | 22 | 4 |
| Chatham Island | 32 | 16 | 16 | 12 | 4 |
| Charles Island | 68 | 39 (or 29, if the probably imported plants be subtracted) | 29 | 21 | 8 |

Hence we have the truly wonderful fact, that in James Island, of the thirty-eight Galapageian plants, or those found in no other part of the world, thirty are exclusively confined to this one island; and in Albemarle Island, of the twenty-six aboriginal Galapageian plants, twenty-two are confined to this one island, that is, only four are at present known to grow in the other islands of the archipelago; and so on, as shown in the above table, with the plants from Chatham and Charles Islands. This fact will, perhaps, be rendered even more striking, by giving a few illustrations: — thus, Scalesia, a remarkable arborescent genus of the Compositæ, is confined to the archipelago: it has six species; one from Chatham, one from Albemarle, one from Charles Island, two from James Island, and the sixth from one of the three latter islands, but it is not known from which: not one of these six species grows on any two islands. Again, Euphorbia, a mundane or widely distributed genus, has here eight species, of which seven are confined to the archipelago, and not one found on any two islands: Acalyphia and Borreria, both mundane genera, have respectively six and seven species, none of which have the same species on two islands, with the exception of one Borreria, which does occur on two islands. The species of the Compositæ are particularly local; and Dr. Hooker has furnished me with several other most striking illustrations of the difference of the species on the different islands. He remarks that this law of distribution holds good both with those genera confined to the archipelago, and those distributed in other quarters of the world: in like manner we have seen that the different islands have their proper species of the mundane genus of tortoise, and of the widely distributed American genus of the mocking-thrush, as well as of two of the Galapageian sub-groups of finches, and almost certainly of the Galapageian genus Amblyrhynchus.

The distribution of the tenants of this archipelago would not be nearly so wonderful, if, for instance, one island had a mocking-thrush, and a second island some other quite distinct genus; — if one island had its genus of lizard, and a second island another distinct genus, or none whatever; — or if the different islands were inhabited, not by representative species of the same genera of plants, but by totally different genera, as does to a certain extent hold good; for, to give one instance, a large berry-bearing tree at James Island has no representative species in Charles Island. But it is the circumstance, that several of the islands possess their own species of the tortoise, mocking-thrush, finches, and numerous plants, these species having the same general habits, occupying analogous situations, and obviously filling the same place in the natural economy of this archipelago, that strikes me with wonder. It may be suspected that some of these representative species, at least in the case of the tortoise and of some of the birds, may hereafter prove to be only well-marked races; but this would be of equally great interest to the philosophical naturalist. I have said that most of the islands are in sight of each other: I may specify that Charles Island is fifty miles from the nearest part of Chatham Island, and thirty-three miles from the nearest part of Albemarle Island. Chatham Island is sixty miles from the nearest part of James Island, but there are two intermediate islands between them which were not visited by me. James Island is only ten miles from the nearest part of Albemarle Island, but the two points where the collections were made are thirty-two miles apart. I must repeat, that neither the nature of the soil, nor height of the land, nor the climate, nor the general character of the associated beings, and therefore their action one on another, can differ much in the different islands. If there be any sensible difference in their climates, it must be between the windward group (namely Charles and Chatham Islands), and that to leeward; but there seems to be no corresponding difference in the productions of these two halves of the archipelago.

The only light which I can throw on this remarkable difference in the inhabitants of the different islands, is, that very strong currents of the sea running in a westerly and W.N.W. direction must separate, as far as transportal by the sea is concerned, the southern islands from the northern ones; and between these northern islands a strong N.W. current was observed, which must effectually separate James and Albemarle Islands. As the archipelago is free to a most remarkable degree from gales of wind, neither the birds, insects, nor lighter seeds, would be blown from island to island. And lastly, the profound depth of the ocean between the islands, and their apparently recent (in a geological sense) volcanic origin, render it highly unlikely that they were ever united; and this, probably, is a far more important consideration than any other, with respect to the geographical distribution of their inhabitants. Reviewing the facts here given, one is astonished at the amount of creative force, if such an expression may be used, displayed on these small, barren, and rocky islands; and still more so, at its diverse yet analogous action on points so near each other. I have said that the Galapagos Archipelago might be called a satellite attached to America, but it should rather be called a group of satellites, physically similar, organically distinct, yet intimately related to each other, and all related in a marked, though much lesser degree, to the great American continent.

I will conclude my description of the natural history of these islands, by giving an account of the extreme tameness of the birds.

This disposition is common to all the terrestrial species; namely, to the mocking-thrushes, the finches, wrens, tyrant-flycatchers, the dove, and carrion-buzzard. All of them often approached sufficiently near to be killed with a switch, and sometimes, as I myself tried, with a cap or hat. A gun is here almost superfluous; for with the muzzle I pushed a hawk off the branch of a tree. One day, whilst lying down, a mocking-thrush alighted on the edge of a pitcher, made of the shell of a tortoise, which I held in my hand, and began very quietly to sip the water; it allowed me to lift it from the ground whilst seated on the vessel: I often tried, and very nearly succeeded, in catching these birds by their legs. Formerly the birds appear to have been even tamer than at present. Cowley (in the year 1684) says that the "Turtle-doves were so tame, that they would often alight upon our hats and arms, so as that we could take them alive: they not fearing man, until such time as some of our company did fire at them, whereby they were rendered more shy." Dampier also, in the same year, says that a man in a morning's walk might kill six or seven dozen of these doves. At present, although certainly very tame, they do not alight on people's arms, nor do they suffer themselves to be killed in such large numbers. It is surprising that they have not become wilder; for these islands during the last hundred and fifty years have been frequently visited by bucaniers and whalers; and the sailors, wandering through the woods in search of tortoises, always take cruel delight in knocking down the little birds.

These birds, although now still more persecuted, do not readily become wild: in Charles Island, which had then been colonized about six years, I saw a boy sitting by a well with a switch in his hand, with which he killed the doves and finches as they came to drink. He had already procured a little heap of them for his dinner; and he said that he had constantly been in the habit of waiting by this well for the same purpose. It would appear that the birds of this archipelago, not having as yet learnt that man is a more dangerous animal than the tortoise or the Amblyrhynchus, disregard him, in the same manner as in England shy birds, such as magpies, disregard the cows and horses grazing in our fields.

The Falkland Islands offer a second instance of birds with a similar disposition. The extraordinary tameness of the little Opetiorhynchus has been remarked by Pernety, Lesson, and other voyagers. It is not, however, peculiar to that bird: the Polyborus, snipe, upland and lowland goose, thrush, bunting, and even some true hawks, are all more or less tame. As the birds are so tame there, where foxes, hawks, and owls, occur, we may infer that the absence of all rapacious animals at the Galapagos, is not the cause of their tameness here. The upland geese at the Falklands show, by the precaution they take in building on the islets, that they are aware of their danger from the foxes; but they are not by this rendered wild towards man. This tameness of the birds, especially of the waterfowl, is strongly contrasted with the habits of the same species in Tierra del Fuego, where for ages past they have been persecuted by the wild inhabitants. In the Falklands, the sportsman may sometimes kill more of the upland geese in one day than he can carry home; whereas in Tierra del Fuego, it is nearly as difficult to kill one, as it is in England to shoot the common wild goose.

In the time of Pernety (1763), all the birds there appear to have been much tamer than at present; he states that the Opetiorhynchus would almost perch on his finger; and that with a wand he killed ten in half an hour. At that period the birds must have been about as tame, as they now are at the Galapagos. They appear to have learnt caution more slowly at these latter islands than at the Falklands, where they have had proportionate means of experience; for besides frequent visits from vessels, those islands have been at intervals colonized during the entire period. Even formerly, when all the birds were so tame, it was impossible by Pernety's account to kill the black-necked swan — a bird of passage, which probably brought with it the wisdom learnt in foreign countries.

I may add that, according to Du Bois, all the birds at Bourbon in 1571–72, with the exception of the flamingoes and geese, were so extremely tame, that they could be caught by the hand, or killed in any number with a stick. Again, at Tristan d'Acunha in the Atlantic, Carmichael[4] states that the only two land-birds, a thrush and a bunting, were "so tame as to suffer themselves to be caught with a hand-net." From these several facts we may, I

[4] Linn. Trans., vol. xii, p. 496. The most anomalous fact on this subject which I have met with, is the wildness of the small birds in the Arctic parts of North America (as described by Richardson, Fauna Bor., vol. ii, p. 332), where they are said never to be persecuted. This case is the more strange, because it is asserted that some of the same species in their winter-quarters

think, conclude, first, that the wildness of birds with regard to man, is a particular instinct directed against *him,* and not dependent on any general degree of caution arising from other sources of danger; secondly, that it is not acquired by individual birds in a short time, even when much persecuted; but that in the course of successive generations it becomes hereditary. With domesticated animals we are accustomed to see new mental habits or instincts acquired and rendered hereditary; but with animals in a state of nature, it must always be most difficult to discover instances of acquired hereditary knowledge. In regard to the wildness of birds towards man, there is no way of accounting for it, except as an inherited habit: comparatively few young birds, in any one year, have been injured by man in England, yet almost all, even nestlings, are afraid of him; many individuals, on the other hand, both at the Galapagos and at the Falklands, have been pursued and injured by man, but yet have not learned a salutary dread of him. We may infer from these facts, what havoc the introduction of any new beast of prey must cause in a country, before the instincts of the indigenous inhabitants have become adapted to the stranger's craft or power.

---

in the United States are tame. There is much, as Dr. Richardson well remarks, utterly inexplicable connected with the different degrees of shyness and care with which birds conceal their nests. How strange it is that the English wood-pigeon, generally so wild a bird, should very frequently rear its young in shrubberies close to houses!

# An Intimate View of Charles Darwin

# *Return of a Nautical Zoologist*[51]

*Charles Darwin to Josiah Wedgwood.*

[Shrewsbury, October 5, 1836].

MY DEAR UNCLE,

The Beagle arrived on Sunday evening and I reached home late last night. My head is quite confused with so much delight, but I cannot allow my sisters to tell you first how happy I am to see all my dear friends again.

I am obliged to return in three or four days to London when the Beagle will be paid off, and then I shall pay Shrewsbury a longer visit. I am most anxious once again to see Maer and all its inhabitants, so that in the course of two or three weeks I hope in person to thank you, as being my First Lord of the Admiralty. I am so very happy I hardly know what I am writing.

Believe me,

Your most affectionate nephew,

CHAS. DARWIN.

Remember me most kindly to aunt Bessy and all at dear Maer.

*Caroline Darwin to Elizabeth Wedgwood.*

[October, 1836.]

MY DEAR ELIZABETH,

Charles is come home so little altered in looks from what he was five years ago and not a bit changed in his own dear self. He had landed at Falmouth on Sunday evening, and travelled night and day until he came to Shrewsbury late last night. We heard nothing of him until this morning when he walked in just before breakfast. We have had the very happiest morning — Charles so full of affection and delight at seeing my father looking so well and being with us all again.

He is looking very thin but well — he was so much pleased by finding your and Charlotte's kind notes ready to receive him. I shall indeed enjoy, my dear Eliz., going to Maer with him. How happy he will be to see you all again. When I began this letter I did not know he would feel tranquil enough to write himself, but he said he must be the first to tell uncle Jos of his arrival. He feels so very grateful to uncle Jos and you all, and has been asking about every one of you.

Now we have him really again at home I intend to begin to be glad he went this expedition, and now I can allow he has gained happiness and interest for the rest of his life. Good-bye dear Eliz. It is pleasant to write to those who sympathise so entirely with us.

*Emma Wedgwood to Fanny Hensleigh Wedgwood.*

*Maer, Monday,* [October 21, 1836].

. . . We are getting impatient for Charles [Darwin]'s arrival. . . . I hope he will come soon. We all ought to get up a little knowledge for him.

*Emma Wedgwood to Fanny Hensleigh Wedgwood.*

*Maer, Monday* [November 21, 1836].

. . . We enjoyed Charles's visit uncommonly. We had been very handsome in inviting all the outlyers of the family to meet him. . . . Charles talked away most pleasantly all the time; we plied him with questions without any mercy. . . . Caroline looks so happy and proud of him it is delightful to see her.

# *Darwin Takes a Wife*[52]

*Charles Darwin to Sir Charles Lyell.*

*Shrewsbury, Monday* [November 12, 1838].

My Dear Lyell,

. . . I write because I cannot avoid wishing to be the first person to tell Mrs. Lyell and yourself that I have the very good, and shortly since very unexpected fortune, of going to be married. The lady is my cousin, Miss Emma Wedgwood . . . we are connected by manifold ties, besides on my part by the most sincere love and hearty gratitude to her for accepting such a one as myself.

I determined when last at Maer to try my chance, but I hardly expected such good fortune would turn up for me. I shall be in town in the middle or the latter end of the ensuing week. I fear you will say I might very well have left my story untold till we met. But I deeply feel your kindness and friendship towards me, which, in truth, I may say, has been one chief source of happiness to me ever since my return to England: so you must excuse me. I am well sure, that Mrs. Lyell . . . will give me her hearty congratulations.

Believe me my dear Lyell,

Yours most truly obliged,

Chas. Darwin.

*Josiah Wedgwood to Robert Waring Darwin.*

*Maer, 15 Nov. 1838.*

My Dear Doctor,

A good, cheerful, and affectionate daughter is the greatest blessing a man can have, after a good wife — if I could have given such a wife to Charles without parting with a daughter there would be no drawback from my entire satisfaction in bestowing Emma upon him. You lately gave up a daughter — it is my turn now. At our time of life our happiness must be in a great measure reflected from our families, and I think there are few fathers who have on the whole more cause to be satisfied with the conduct and present circumstances and future prospects of our families. I could have parted with Emma to no one for whom I would so soon and so entirely feel as a father, and I am happy in believing that Charles entertains the kindest feeling for his uncle-father.

I propose to do for Emma what I did for Charlotte and for three of my sons, give a bond for £5000 and, to allow her £400 a year, as long as my income will supply it, which I have no reason for thinking will not be as long as I live.

Give my love to your fireside and believe me,

Affectionately yours,

Josiah Wedgwood.

My Dear Uncle,

I have begged a bit of Papa's letter to thank you from my heart for the delightful way in which you have received me into your family. . . . One of the things that gave me most happiness is Charles's affection and value for Papa. I am, my dear uncle, yours affectionately,

Emma W.

*Charles Darwin to Emma Wedgwood.*

*Shrewsbury, Wednesday Morning*
[November 14, 1838].

My Dear Emma,

Marianne and Susan will have told you what joy and happiness the news gave all here. We have had innumerable cogita-

Emma Darwin in 1840

tions; and the one conclusion I exult in is that there was never anyone so lucky as I have been, or so good as you. Indeed I can assure you, many times since leaving Maer, I have thought how little I expressed how much I owe to you; and as often as I think this, I vow to try to make myself good enough somewhat to deserve you. I hope you have taken deep thought about the sundry knotty points you will have to decide on. We must have a great deal of talk together when I come back on Saturday. Do have a fire in the Library — it is such a good place to have some quiet talk together. The question of houses, suburbs versus central London — rages violently around each fireplace in this house. Suburbs have rather the advantage at present; and this, of course, rather inclines one to seek out the arguments on the other side. The Governor gives much good advice to live, wherever it may be, the first year prudently and quietly. My chief fear is, that you will find, after living all your life with such large and agreeable parties as Maer only can boast of, our quiet evenings dull. You must bear in mind, as some young lady said, "all men are brutes," and that I take the line of being a solitary brute, so you must listen with much suspicion to all arguments in favour of retired places. I am so selfish, that I feel to have you to myself is having you so much more completely that I am not to be trusted. Like a child that has something it loves beyond measure, I long to dwell on the words my own dear Emma. As I am writing just as things come uppermost in my mind, I beg of you not to read my letters to anyone, for then I can fancy I am sitting by the side of my own dear future wife, and to her own self I do not care what nonsense I talk — so let me have my way, and scribble, without caring whether it be sense or nonsense. . . .

My father echoes and re-echoes uncle Jos's words, "You have drawn a prize!" . . . My own dear Emma, I kiss the hands with all humbleness and gratitude, which have so filled up for me the cup of happiness — It is my most earnest wish I may make myself worthy of you. Good-bye.

Most affectionately yours,

CHAS. DARWIN.

*Emma Wedgwood to Madame Sismondi.*

*Maer, Nov. 15th* [*1838*].

My Dear Aunt Jessie,

Nothing is pleasanter than writing good news, and I am sure you will be pleased with what I have to tell you. When you asked me about Charles Darwin, I did not tell you half the good I thought of him for fear you should suspect something, and though I knew how much I liked him, I was not the least sure of his feelings, as he is so affectionate, and so fond of Maer and all of us and demonstrative in his manners, that I did not think it meant anything, and the week I spent in London on my return from Paris, I felt sure he did not care about me. . . . He came to see us in the month of August, was in very high spirits and I was very happy in his company, and had the feeling that if he saw more of me, he would really like me. He came down again last Thursday . . ., and on Sunday he spoke to me, which was quite a surprise, as I thought we might go on in the sort of friendship we were in for years, and very likely nothing come of it after all. I was too much bewildered all day to feel my happiness and there was a large party in the house, so we did not tell anybody except Papa and Elizabeth and Catherine. Dear Papa, I wish you could have seen his tears of joy, for he has always had a great regard for Charles, and Charles looks up to him with the greatest reverence and affection. . . .

I must now tell you what I think of him, first premising that Eliz. thinks pretty nearly the same, as my opinion may not go for much with you. He is the most open, transparent man I ever saw, and every word expresses his real thoughts. He is particularly affectionate and very nice to his father and sisters, and perfectly sweet tempered, and possesses some minor qualities that add particularly to one's happiness, such as not being fastidious, and being humane to animals. We shall live in London, where he is fully occupied with being Secretary to the Geological Society and conducting a publication upon the animals of Australia. I am so glad he is a busy man. . . . I think I have egotized nearly enough, but I feel sure you and my dear uncle will enter entirely into my happiness.

. . . I don't think it of much consequence . . . that Charles drinks no wine, but I think it a pleasant thing. The real crook in my lot I have withheld from you, but I must own it to you sooner or later. It is that he has a great dislike to going to the play, so that I am afraid we shall have some domestic dissensions on that head. . . . On the other hand he stands concerts very well. He told me he should have spoken to me in August but was afraid, and I was pleased to find that he was not very sure of his answer this time. It was certainly a very unnecessary fear. . . . Your affectionate

Em. W.

I went strait into the Sunday School after the important interview, but found I was turning into an idiot and so came away.

*Charles Darwin to Emma Wedgwood.*

*Sunday Night, 12, Upper Gower Street*
[January 6, 1839].

My Dear Emma,

I have just returned from my little dinner at the Lyells' in which I did some geology and some *scrattle* about coal and coal-merchants. . . . So it is high time to order coal. I meant to have written you by yesterday's post, but I turned idle just at the right minute, but I hope you won't turn angry at the post-time minute. I am really ashamed of my letters of late, they have been so very egotistical, but what can be expected from a young householder who thinks of nothing but himself and *our* house all day long. By the way, this puts me in mind to give you a scolding for writing to me about "*your*" house: is it not *our* house? what is there, from me the geologist to the black sparrows in the garden, which is not your own property? and this puts me in mind to give you another *scolding* for sending me those *square* little sneers about my writing. Whoever read hieroglyphics without the context, and is not my hand more like hieroglyphics than common writing? Bad hand as it is, it serves me to tell you, you are my own dear Emma, and there is an end of my *scolding*.

. . . Good night and good-bye, my dearest, C.D.

*Sunday Night, Athanaeum* [January 20, 1839].

. . . I cannot tell you how much I enjoyed my Maer visit, I felt in anticipation my future tranquil life: how I do hope you may be as happy as I know I shall be: but it frightens me, as often as I think of what a family you have been one of. I was thinking this morning how it came that I, who am fond of talking and am scarcely ever out of spirits, should so entirely rest my notions of happiness on quietness and a good deal of solitude. But I believe the explanation is very simple, and I mention it because it will give you hopes that I shall gradually grow less of a *brute*. It is that during the five years of my voyage (and indeed I may add these two last), which from the active manner in which they have been passed may be said to be the commencement of my real life, the whole of my pleasure was derived from what passed in my mind while admiring views by myself, travelling across the wild deserts or glorious forests, or pacing the deck of the poor little *Beagle* at night. Excuse this much egotism, I give it you because I think you will humanize me, and soon teach me there is greater happiness than building theories and accumulating facts in silence and solitude. My own dearest Emma, I earnestly pray you may never regret the great, and I will add very good deed, you are to perform on *the* Tuesday. My own dear future wife, God bless you. . . .

The Lyells called on me to-day after church, as Lyell was so full of Geology he was obliged to disgorge; and I dine there on Tuesday for an especial conference. I was quite ashamed of myself to-day, for we talked for half-an-hour unsophisticated Geology, with poor Mrs. Lyell sitting by, a monument of patience. I want *practice* in ill-treating the female sex. I did not observe Lyell had any compunction; I hope to harden my conscience in time: few husbands seem to find it difficult to effect this.

Since my return I have taken several looks, as you will readily believe, into the drawing-room. I suppose my taste of harmonious colours is already deteriorated, for I declare the room begins to look less ugly. I take so much pleasure in the house, I declare I am just like a great overgrown child with a new toy; but then, not like a real child, I long to have a co-partner and possessor.

*Charles Darwin to Emma Wedgwood.*

*Saturday, Shrewsbury* [January 26, 1839].

My Dear Emma,

I have ten minutes to write in and I am determined to show you that I think myself of sufficient consequence for you to care to hear our plans. The house is in such a bustle, that I do not know what I write. I have got the ring, which is the most important piece of news I have to tell. My last two days in London, when I wanted to have most leisure, were rendered very uncomfortable by a bad headache, which continued two days and two nights, so that I doubted whether it ever meant to go and allow me to be married. The railroad yesterday, however, quite cured me. . . .

. . . The carriage is at the door all this time, so I cannot write any more. I had intended to have written you, my dear little wife, a long letter, but I do not know what I have said, but I know you are a very dear good soul, so good-bye.

Ever yours affectionately,

Chas. Darwin.

*Emma Darwin to Madame Sismondi.*

*12, Upper Gower Street, February 10* [1840].

My Dear Aunt Jessie,

. . . It is a pleasure in writing to you that one's letter is only seen by two, and one may say whatever comes uppermost, and so I will be as egotistical as ever I please. It is a great happiness to me when Charles is most unwell that he continues just as sociable as ever, and is not like the rest of the Darwins, who will not say how they really are; but he always tells me how he feels and never wants to be alone, but continues just as warmly affectionate as ever, so that I feel I am a comfort to him. And to you I may say that he is the most affectionate person possible. . . . It is a great advantage to have the power of expressing affection, and I am sure he will make his children very fond of him. I have been pretty well coaxed and spoilt all my life but I am more than ever now, so I hope it does one no harm, but I don't think it does.

# The Making of the *Origin of Species*

# *The Impact of Wallace*[53]

*London, June 30, 1858.*

My Dear Sir, — The accompanying papers, which we have the honour of communicating to the Linnean Society, and which all relate to the same subject, viz. the Laws which affect the Production of Varieties, Races, and Species, contain the results of the investigations of two indefatigable naturalists, Mr. Charles Darwin and Mr. Alfred Wallace.

These gentlemen having, independently and unknown to one another, conceived the same very ingenious theory to account for the appearance and perpetuation of varieties and of specific forms on our planet, may both fairly claim the merit of being original thinkers in this important line of inquiry; but neither of them having published his views, though Mr. Darwin has for many years past been repeatedly urged by us to do so, and both authors having now unreservedly placed their papers in our hands, we think it would best promote the interests of science that a selection from them should be laid before the Linnean Society.

Taken in the order of their dates, they consist of:—

1. Extracts from a MS. work on Species,[1] by Mr. Darwin, which was sketched in 1839, and copied in 1844, when the copy was read by Dr. Hooker, and its contents afterwards communicated to Sir Charles Lyell. The first Part is devoted to "The Variation of Organic Beings under Domestication and in their Natural State;" and the second chapter of that Part, from which we propose to read to the Society the extracts referred to, is headed, "On the Variation of Organic Beings in a state of Nature; on the Natural Means of Selection; on the Comparison of Domestic Races and true Species."

2. An abstract of a private letter addressed to Professor Asa Gray, of Boston, U.S., in October 1857, by Mr. Darwin, in which he repeats his views, and which shows that these remained unaltered from 1839 to 1857.

3. An Essay by Mr. Wallace, entitled "On the Tendency of Varieties to depart indefinitely from the Original Type." This was written at Ternate in February 1858, for the perusal of his friend and correspondent Mr. Darwin, and sent to him with the expressed wish that it should be forwarded to Sir Charles Lyell, if Mr. Darwin thought it sufficiently novel and interesting. So highly did Mr. Darwin appreciate the value of the views therein set forth, that he proposed, in a letter to Sir Charles Lyell, to obtain Mr. Wallace's consent to allow the Essay to be published as soon as possible. Of this step we highly approved, provided Mr. Darwin did not withhold from the public, as he was strongly inclined to do (in favour of Mr. Wallace), the memoir which he had himself written on the same subject, and which, as before stated, one of us had perused in 1844, and the contents of which we had both of us been privy to for many years. On representing this to Mr. Darwin, he gave us permission to make what use we thought proper of his memoir, &c.; and in adopting our present course, of presenting it to the Linnean Society, we have explained to him that we are not solely considering the relative claims to priority of himself and his friend, but the interests of science generally; for we feel it to be desirable that views founded on a wide deduction from facts, and matured by years of reflection, should constitute at once a goal from which others may start, and that, while the scientific world is waiting for the ap-

[1] This MS. work was never intended for publication, and therefore was not written with care — C.D. 1858.

Sir Joseph Dalton Hooker

pearance of Mr. Darwin's complete work, some of the leading results of his labours, as well as those of his able correspondent, should together be laid before the public.

We have the honour to be yours very obediently,

CHARLES LYELL
JOS. D. HOOKER

J. J. BENNETT, ESQ.,
*Secretary of the Linnean Society*

*I.*

*Extract from an unpublished Work on Species, by* C. DARWIN, *Esq., consisting of a portion of a Chapter entitled, "On the Variation of Organic Beings in a state of Nature; on the Natural Means of Selection; on the Comparison of Domestic Races and true Species."*

De Candolle, in an eloquent passage, has declared that all nature is at war, one organism with another, or with external

Sir Charles Lyell

nature. Seeing the contented face of nature, this may at first well be doubted; but reflection will inevitably prove it to be true. The war, however, is not constant, but recurrent in a slight degree at short periods, and more severely at occasional more distant periods; and hence its effects are easily overlooked. It is the doctrine of Malthus applied in most cases with tenfold force. As in every climate there are seasons, for each of its inhabitants, of greater and less abundance, so all annually breed; and the moral restraint which in some small degree checks the increase of mankind is entirely lost. Even slow-breeding mankind has doubled in twenty-five years; and if he could increase his food with greater ease, he would double in less time. But for animals without artificial means, the amount of food for each species must, *on an average,* be constant, whereas the increase of all organisms tends to be geometrical, and in a vast majority of cases at an enormous ratio. Suppose in a certain spot there are eight pairs of birds, and that *only* four pairs of them annually (including double hatches) rear only four young, and that these go on rearing their young at the same rate, then at the end of seven years (a short life, excluding violent deaths, for any bird) there will be 2048 birds, instead of the original sixteen. As this increase is quite impossible, we must conclude either that birds do not rear nearly half their young, or that the average life of a bird is, from accident, not nearly seven years. Both checks probably concur. The same kind of calculation applied to all plants and animals affords results more or less striking, but in very few instances more striking than in man.

Many practical illustrations of this rapid tendency to increase are on record, among which, during peculiar seasons, are the extraordinary numbers of certain animals; for instance, during the years 1826 to 1828, in La Plata, when from drought some millions of cattle perished, the whole country actually *swarmed* with mice. Now I think it cannot be doubted that during the breeding-season all the mice (with the exception of a few males or females in excess) ordinarily pair, and therefore that this astounding increase during three years must be attributed to a greater number than usual surviving the first year, and then breeding, and so on till the third year, when their numbers were brought down to their usual limits on the return of wet weather. Where man has introduced plants and animals into a new and favourable country, there are many accounts in how surprisingly few years the whole country has become stocked with them. This increase would necessarily stop as soon as the country was fully stocked; and yet we have every reason to believe, from what is known of wild animals, that *all* would pair in the spring. In the majority of cases it is most difficult to imagine where the checks fall — though generally, no doubt, on the seeds, eggs, and young; but when we remember how impossible, even in mankind (so much better known than any other animal), it is to infer from repeated casual observations what the average duration of life is, or to discover the different percentage of deaths to births in different countries, we ought to feel no surprise at our being unable to discover where the check falls in any animal or plant. It should always be remembered, that in most cases the checks are recurrent yearly in a small, regular degree, and in an extreme degree during unusually cold, hot, dry, or wet years, according to the constitution of the being in question. Lighten any check in the least degree, and the geometrical powers of increase in every organism will almost instantly increase the average number of the favoured species. Nature may be compared to a surface on which rest ten thousand sharp wedges touching each other and driven inwards by incessant blows. Fully to realize these views much reflection is requisite. Malthus on man should be studied; and all such cases as those of the mice in La Plata, of the cattle and horses when first turned out in South America, of the birds by our calculation, &c., should be well considered. Reflect on the enormous multiplying power *inherent and annually in action* in all animals; reflect on the countless seeds scattered by a hundred ingenious contrivances, year after year, over the whole face of the land; and yet we have every reason to suppose that the average percentage of each of the inhabitants of a country usually remains constant. Finally, let it be borne in mind that this average number of individuals (the external conditions remaining the same) in each country is kept up by recurrent struggles against other species or against external nature (as on the borders of the Arctic regions, where the cold checks life), and that ordinarily each individual of every species holds its place, either by its own struggle and capacity of acquiring nourishment in some period of its life, from the egg upwards; or by the struggle of its parents (in short-lived organisms, when the main check occurs at longer intervals) with other individuals of the *same* or *different* species.

But let the external conditions of a country alter. If in a small degree, the relative proportions of the inhabitants will in most cases simply be slightly changed; but let the number of inhabitants be small, as on an island, and free access to it from other countries be circumscribed, and let the change of conditions continue progressing (forming new stations), in such a case the original inhabitants must cease to be as perfectly adapted to the changed conditions as they were originally. It has been shown in a former part of this work, that such changes of external conditions would, from their acting on the reproductive system, probably cause the organization of those beings which were most affected to become, as under domestication, plastic. Now, can it be doubted, from the struggle each individual has to obtain subsistence, that any minute variation in structure, habits, or instincts, adapting that individual better to the new conditions, would tell upon its vigour and health? In the struggle it would have a better *chance* of surviving; and those of its offspring which inherited the variation, be it ever so slight, would also have a better *chance.* Yearly more are bred than can survive; the smallest grain in the balance, in the long run, must tell on which death shall fall, and which shall survive. Let this work of selection on the one hand, and death on the other, go on for a thousand generations, who will pretend to affirm that it would produce no effect, when we remember what, in a few years, Bakewell effected in cattle, and Western in sheep, by this identical principle of selection?

To give an imaginary example from changes in progress on an island: — let the organization of a canine animal which preyed chiefly on rabbits, but sometimes on hares, become slightly plastic; let these same changes cause the number of rabbits very slowly to decrease, and the number of hares to increase; the effect of this would be that the fox or dog would be driven to try to catch more hares: his organization, however, being slightly plastic, those individuals with the lightest forms, longest limbs, and best eyesight, let the difference be ever so small, would be slightly favoured, and would tend to live longer, and to survive during that time of the year when food was scarcest; they would also rear more young, which would tend to inherit these slight peculiarities. The less fleet ones would be rigidly destroyed. I can see no more reason to doubt that these causes in a thousand generations would produce a marked effect, and adapt the form of the fox or dog to the catching of hares instead of rabbits, than that greyhounds can be improved by selection and careful breeding. So would it be with plants under similar circumstances. If the number of individuals of a species with plumed seeds could be increased by greater powers of dissemination within its own area (that is, if the check to increase fell chiefly on the seeds), those seeds which were provided with ever so little more down, would in the long run be most disseminated; hence a greater number of seeds thus formed would germinate, and would tend to produce plants inheriting the slightly better-adapted down.[2]

Besides this natural means of selection, by which those individuals are preserved, whether in their egg, or larval, or mature state, which are best adapted to the place they fill in nature, there is a second agency at work in most unisexual animals, tending to produce the same effect, namely, the struggle of the males for the females. These struggles are generally decided by the law of battle, but in the case of birds, apparently, by the charms of their song, by their beauty or their power of courtship, as in the dancing rock-thrush of Guiana. The most vigorous and healthy males, implying perfect adaptation, must generally gain the victory in their contests. This kind of selection, however, is less rigorous than the other; it does not require the death of the less successful, but gives to them fewer descendants. The struggle falls, moreover, at a time of year when food is generally abundant, and perhaps the effect chiefly produced would be the modification of the secondary sexual characters, which are not related to the power of obtaining food, or to defence from enemies, but to fighting with or rivalling other males. The result of this struggle amongst the males may be compared in some respects to that produced by those agriculturists who pay less attention to the careful selection of all their young animals, and more to the occasional use of a choice mate.

[2] I can see no more difficulty in this, than in the planter improving his varieties of the cotton plant. — C.D. 1858.

## *II.*

### *Abstract of a Letter from* C. Darwin, *Esq., to Prof.* Asa Gray, *Boston, U.S., dated Down, September 5th, 1857.*

1. It is wonderful what the principle of selection by man, that is the picking out of individuals with any desired quality, and breeding from them, and again picking out, can do. Even breeders have been astounded at their own results. They can act on differences inappreciable to an uneducated eye. Selection has been *methodically* followed in *Europe* for only the last half century; but it was occasionally, and even in some degree methodically, followed in the most ancient times. There must have been also a kind of unconscious selection from a remote period, namely in the preservation of the individual animals (without any thought of their offspring) most useful to each race of man in his particular circumstances. The "roguing," as nurserymen call the destroying of varieties which depart from their type, is a kind of selection. I am convinced that intentional and occasional selection has been the main agent in the production of our domestic races; but however this may be, its great power of modification has been indisputably shown in later times. Selection acts only by the accumulation of slight or greater variations, caused by external conditions, or by the mere fact that in generation the child is not absolutely similar to its parent. Man, by this power of accumulating variations, adapts living beings to his wants — may be said to make the wool of one sheep good for carpets, of another for cloth, &c.

2. Now suppose there were a being who did not judge by mere external appearances, but who could study the whole internal organization, who was never capricious, and should go on selecting for one object during millions of generations; who will say what he might not effect? In nature we have some *slight* variation occasionally in all parts; and I think it can be shown that changed conditions of existence is the main cause of the child not exactly resembling its parents; and in nature geology shows us what changes have taken place, and are taking place. We have almost unlimited time; no one but a practical geologist can fully appreciate this. Think of the Glacial period, during the whole of which the same species at least of shells have

Alfred Russel Wallace

existed; there must have been during this period millions on millions of generations.

3. I think it can be shown that there is such an unerring power at work in *Natural Selection* (the title of my book), which selects exclusively for the good of each organic being. The elder de Candolle, W. Herbert, and Lyell have written excellently on the struggle for life; but even they have not written strongly enough. Reflect that every being (even the elephant) breeds at such a rate, that in a few years, or at most a few centuries, the surface of the earth would not hold the progeny of one pair. I have found it hard constantly to bear in mind that the increase of every single species is checked during some part of its life, or during some shortly recurrent generation. Only a few of those annually born can live to propagate their kind. What a trifling difference must often determine which shall survive, and which perish!

4. Now take the case of a country undergoing some change. This will tend to cause some of its inhabitants to vary slightly — not but that I believe most beings vary at all times enough for selection to act on them. Some of its inhabitants will be exterminated; and the remainder will be exposed to the mutual action

of a different set of inhabitants, which I believe to be far more important to the life of each being than mere climate. Considering the infinitely various methods which living beings follow to obtain food by struggling with other organisms, to escape danger at various times of life, to have their eggs or seeds disseminated, &c., &c., I cannot doubt that during millions of generations individuals of a species will be occasionally born with some slight variation, profitable to some part of their economy. Such individuals will have a better chance of surviving, and of propagating their new and slightly different structure; and the modification may be slowly increased by the accumulative action of natural selection to any profitable extent. The variety thus formed will either coexist with, or, more commonly, will exterminate its parent form. An organic being, like the woodpecker or misseltoe, may thus come to be adapted to a score of contingences—natural selection accumulating those slight variations in all parts of its structure, which are in any way useful to it during any part of its life.

5. Multiform difficulties will occur to every one, with respect to this theory. Many can, I think, be satisfactorily answered. *Natura non facit saltum* answers some of the most obvious. The slowness of the change, and only a very few individuals undergoing change at any one time, answers others. The extreme imperfection of our geological records answers others.

6. Another principle, which may be called the principle of divergence, plays, I believe, an important part in the origin of species. The same spot will support more life if occupied by very diverse forms. We see this in the many generic forms in a square yard of turf, and in the plants or insects on any little uniform islet, belonging almost invariably to as many genera and families as species. We can understand the meaning of this fact amongst the higher animals, whose habits we understand. We know that it has been experimentally shown that a plot of land will yield a greater weight if sown with several species and genera of grasses, than if sown with only two or three species. Now, every organic being, by propagating so rapidly, may be said to be striving its utmost to increase in numbers. So it will be with the offspring of any species after it has become diversified into varieties, or subspecies, or true species. And it follows, I think, from the foregoing facts, that the varying offspring of

each species will try (only few will succeed) to seize on as many and as diverse places in the economy of nature as possible. Each new variety or species, when formed, will generally take the place of, and thus exterminate its less well-fitted parent. This I believe to be the origin of the classification and affinities of organic beings at all times; for organic beings always *seem* to branch and sub-branch like the limbs of a tree from a common trunk, the flourishing and diverging twigs destroying the less vigorous — the dead and lost branches rudely representing extinct genera and families.

This sketch is *most* imperfect; but in so short a space I cannot make it better. Your imagination must fill up very wide blanks.

C. DARWIN.

## *III.*

### *On the Tendency of Varieties to depart indefinitely from the Original Type. By* ALFRED RUSSEL WALLACE.

One of the strongest arguments which have been adduced to prove the original and permanent distinctness of species is, that *varieties* produced in a state of domesticity are more or less unstable, and often have a tendency, if left to themselves, to return to the normal form of the parent species; and this instability is considered to be a distinctive peculiarity of all varieties, even of those occurring among wild animals in a state of nature, and to constitute a provision for preserving unchanged the originally created distinct species.

In the absence or scarcity of facts and observations as to *varieties* occurring among wild animals, this argument has had great weight with naturalists, and has led to a very general and somewhat prejudiced belief in the stability of species. Equally general, however, is the belief in what are called "permanent or true varieties," — races of animals which continually propagate their like, but which differ so slightly (although constantly) from some other race, that the one is considered to be a *variety* of the other. Which is the *variety* and which the original *species*, there is generally no means of determining, except in those rare cases in which the one race has been known to produce an offspring unlike itself and resembling the other. This, however, would seem quite incompatible with the "permanent invariability of species," but the difficulty is overcome by assuming that such varieties have strict limits, and can never again vary further from the original type, although they may return to it, which, from the analogy of the domesticated animals, is considered to be highly probable, if not certainly proved.

It will be observed that this argument rests entirely on the assumption, that *varieties* occurring in a state of nature are in all respects analogous to or even identical with those of domestic animals, and are governed by the same laws as regards their permanence or further variation. But it is the object of the present paper to show that this assumption is altogether false, that there is a general principle in nature which will cause many *varieties* to survive the parent species, and to give rise to successive variations departing further and further from the original type, and which also produces, in domesticated animals, the tendency of varieties to return to the parent form.

The life of wild animals is a struggle for existence. The full exertion of all their faculties and all their energies is required to preserve their own existence and provide for that of their infant offspring. The possibility of procuring food during the least favourable seasons, and of escaping the attacks of their most dangerous enemies, are the primary conditions which determine the existence both of individuals and of entire species. These conditions will also determine the population of a species; and by a careful consideration of all the circumstances we may be enabled to comprehend, and in some degree to explain, what at first sight appears so inexplicable — the excessive abundance of some species, while others closely allied to them are very rare.

The general proportion that must obtain between certain groups of animals is readily seen. Large animals cannot be so abundant as small ones; the carnivora must be less numerous than the herbivora; eagles and lions can never be so plentiful as pigeons and antelopes; the wild asses of the Tartarian deserts cannot equal in numbers the horses of the more luxuriant prairies and pampas of America. The greater or less fecundity of an animal is often considered to be one of the chief causes of its abundance or scarcity; but a consideration of the facts will show us that it really has little or nothing to do with the matter. Even the least prolific of animals would increase rapidly if unchecked, whereas it is evident that the animal population of the globe must be stationary, or perhaps, through the influence of man, decreasing. Fluctuations there may be; but permanent increase, except in restricted localities is almost impossible. For example, our own observation must convince us that birds do not go on increasing every year in a geometrical ratio, as they would do, were there not some powerful check to their natural increase. Very few birds produce less than two young ones each year, while many have six, eight, or ten; four will certainly be below the average; and if we suppose that each pair produce young only four times in their life, that will also be below the average, supposing them not to die either by violence or want of food. Yet at this rate how tremendous would be the increase in a few years from a single pair! A simple calculation will show that in fifteen years each pair of birds would have increased to nearly ten millions! whereas we have no reason to believe that the number of the birds of any country increases at all in fifteen or in one hundred and fifty years. With such powers of increase the population must have reached its limits, and have become stationary, in a very few years after the origin of each species. It is evident, therefore, that each year an immense number of birds must perish — as many in fact as are born; and as on the lowest calculation the progeny are each year twice as numerous as their parents, it follows that, whatever be the average number of individuals existing in any given country, *twice that number must perish annually,* — a striking result, but one which seems at least highly probable, and is perhaps under rather than over the truth. It would therefore appear that, as far as the continuance of the species and the keeping up of the average number of individuals are concerned, large broods are superfluous. On the average all above *one* become food for hawks and kites, wild cats and weasels, or perish of cold and hunger as winter comes on. This is strikingly proved by the case of particular species; for we find that their abundance in individuals bears no relation whatever to their fertility in producing offspring. Perhaps the most remarkable instance of an immense bird population is that of the passenger pigeon of the United States, which lays only one, or at most two eggs, and is said to rear generally but one young one. Why is this bird so extraordinarily abundant, while others producing two or three times as many young are much less plentiful? The explanation is not difficult. The food most congenial to this species, and on which it thrives best, is abundantly distributed over a very extensive region, offering such difference of soil and climate, that in one part or another of the area the supply never fails. The bird is capable of a very rapid and long-continued flight, so that it can pass without fatigue over the whole of the district it inhabits, and as soon as the supply of food begins to fail in one place is able to discover a fresh feeding-ground. This example strikingly shows us that the procuring of a constant supply of wholesome food is almost the sole condition requisite for ensuring the rapid increase of a given species, since neither the limited fecundity, nor the unrestrained attacks of birds of prey and of man are here sufficient to check it. In no other birds are these peculiar circumstances so strikingly combined. Either their food is more liable to failure, or they have not sufficient power of wing to search for it over an extensive area, or during some season of the year it becomes very scarce, and less wholesome substitutes have to be found; and thus, though more fertile in offspring, they can never increase beyond the supply of food in the least favourable seasons. Many birds can only exist by migrating, when their food becomes scarce, to regions possessing a milder, or at least a different climate, though, as these migrating birds are seldom excessively abundant, it is evident that the countries they visit are still deficient in a constant and abundant supply of wholesome food. Those whose organization does not permit them to migrate when their food becomes periodically scarce, can never attain a large population. This is probably the reason why woodpeckers are scarce with us, while in the tropics they are among the most abundant of solitary birds. Thus the house sparrow is more abundant than the redbreast, because its food is more constant and plentiful, — seeds of grasses being preserved during the winter, and our farm-yards and stubble-fields furnishing an almost inexhaustible supply. Why, as a general rule, are aquatic, and especially sea birds, very numerous in individuals? Not because they are more prolific than others, generally the contrary; but because their food never fails, the sea-shores and river-banks daily swarming with a fresh supply of small mollusca and crustacea. Exactly the same laws will apply to mammals. Wild cats are prolific and have few enemies; why then are they never as abundant as rabbits? The only intelligible answer is, that their supply of food is more precarious. It appears evident, therefore, that so long as a country remains physically unchanged, the numbers of its animal population cannot materially increase. If one species does so, some others requiring the same kind of food must diminish in proportion. The numbers that die annually must be immense; and as the individual existence of each animal depends upon itself, those that die must be the weakest — the very young, the aged, and the diseased, — while those that prolong their existence can only be the most perfect in health and vigour — those who are best able to obtain food regularly, and avoid their numerous enemies. It is, as we commenced by remarking, "a struggle for existence," in which the weakest and least perfectly organized must always succumb.

Now it is clear that what takes place among the individuals of a species must also occur among the several allied species of

The first 8 letters I
received from Darwin —
while in the Malay Archipelago)

N.B. The MSS. of my Paper sent to
Darwin and printed in the Journal
of the Linnean Society, was not
returned to me, and seems to be
lost. The proofs with the MSS. were
perhaps sent to Sir Charles Lyell,
or to the Secretary of the Linn. Soc.
& may some day be found. It
was written on thin foreign
note paper.

Alfred R. Wallace

Facsimile of Inscription by Alfred R. Wallace

a group, — viz. that those which are best adapted to obtain a regular supply of food, and to defend themselves against the attacks of their enemies and the vicissitudes of the seasons, must necessarily obtain and preserve a superiority in population; while those species which from some defect of power or organization are the least capable of counteracting the vicissitudes of food, supply, &c., must diminish in numbers, and, in extreme cases, become altogether extinct. Between these extremes the species will present various degrees of capacity for ensuring the means of preserving life; and it is thus we account for the abundance or rarity of species. Our ignorance will generally prevent us from accurately tracing the effects to their causes; but could we become perfectly acquainted with the organization and habits of the various species of animals, and could we measure the capacity of each for performing the different acts necessary to its safety and existence under all the varying circumstances by which it is surrounded, we might be able even to calculate the proportionate abundance of individuals which is the necessary result.

If now we have succeeded in establishing these two points — 1st, *that the animal population of a country is generally stationary, being kept down by a periodical deficiency of food, and other checks;* and, 2nd, *that the comparative abundance or scarcity of the individuals of the several species is entirely due to their organization and resulting habits, which, rendering it more difficult to procure a regular supply of food and to provide for their personal safety in some cases than in others, can only be balanced by a difference in the population which have to exist in a given area* — we shall be in a condition to proceed to the consideration of *varieties,* to which the preceding remarks have a direct and very important application.

Most or perhaps all the variations from the typical form of a species must have some definite effect, however slight, on the habits or capacities of the individuals. Even a change of colour might, by rendering them more or less distinguishable, affect their safety; a greater or less development of hair might modify their habits. More important changes, such as an increase in the power or dimensions of the limbs or any of the external organs, would more or less affect their mode of procuring food or the range of country which they inhabit. It is also evident that most changes would affect, either favourably or adversely, the powers of prolonging existence. An antelope with shorter or weaker legs must necessarily suffer more from the attacks of the feline carnivora; the passenger pigeon with less powerful wings would sooner or later be affected in its powers of procuring a regular supply of food; and in both cases the result must necessarily be a diminution of the population of the modified species. If, on the other hand, any species should produce a variety having slightly increased powers of preserving existence, that variety must inevitably in time acquire a superiority in numbers. These results must follow as surely as old age, intemperance, or scarcity of food produce an increased mortality. In both cases there may be many individual exceptions; but on the average the rule will invariably be found to hold good. All varieties will therefore fall into two classes — those which under the same conditions would never reach the population of the parent species, and those which would in time obtain and keep a numerical superiority. Now, let some alteration of physical conditions occur in the district — a long period of drought, a destruction of vegetation by locusts, the irruption of some new carnivorous animal seeking "pastures new" — any change in fact tending to render existence more difficult to the species in question, and tasking its utmost powers to avoid complete extermination; it is evident that, of all the individuals composing the species, those forming the least numerous and most feebly organized variety would suffer first, and, were the pressure severe, must soon become extinct. The same causes continuing in action, the parent species would next suffer, would gradually diminish in numbers, and with a recurrence of similar unfavourable conditions might also become extinct. The superior variety would then alone remain, and on a return to favourable circumstances would rapidly increase in numbers and occupy the place of the extinct species and variety.

The *variety* would now have replaced the *species*, of which it would be a more perfectly developed and more highly organized form. It would be in all respects better adapted to secure its safety, and to prolong its individual existence and that of the race. Such a variety *could not* return to the original form; for that form is an inferior one, and could never compete with it for existence. Granted, therefore, a "tendency" to reproduce the original type of the species, still the variety must ever remain preponderant in numbers, and under adverse physical conditions *again alone survive*. But this new, improved, and populous race might itself, in course of time, give rise to new varieties, exhibiting several diverging modifications of form, any of which, tending to increase the facilities for preserving existence, must, by the same general law, in their turn become predominant. Here, then, we have *progression and continued divergence* deduced from the general laws which regulate the existence of animals in a state of nature, and from the undisputed fact that varieties do frequently occur. It is not, however, contended that this result would be invariable; a change of physical conditions in the district might at times materially modify it, rendering the race which had been the most capable of supporting existence under the former conditions now the least so, and even causing the extinction of the newer and, for a time, superior race, while the old or parent species and its first inferior varieties continued to flourish. Variations in unimportant parts might also occur, having no perceptible effect on the life-preserving powers; and the varieties so furnished might run a course parallel with the parent species, either giving rise to further variations or returning to the former type. All we argue for is, that certain varieties have a tendency to maintain their existence longer than the original species, and this tendency must make itself felt; for though the doctrine of chances or averages can never be trusted to on a limited scale, yet, if applied to high numbers, the results come nearer to what theory demands, and, as we approach to an infinity of examples, become strictly accurate. Now the scale on which nature works is so vast — the numbers of individuals and periods of time with which she deals approach so near to infinity, that any cause, however slight, and however liable to be veiled and counteracted by accidental circumstances, must in the end produce its full legitimate results.

Let us now turn to domesticated animals, and inquire how varieties produced among them are affected by the principles here enunciated. The essential difference in the condition of wild and domestic animals is this, — that among the former, their well-being and very existence depend upon the full exercise and healthy condition of all their senses and physical powers, whereas, among the latter, these are only partially exercised, and in some cases are absolutely unused. A wild animal has to search, and often to labour, for every mouthful of food — to exercise sight, hearing, and smell in seeking it, and in avoiding dangers, in procuring shelter from the inclemency of the seasons, and in providing for the subsistence and safety of its offspring. There is no muscle of its body that is not called into daily and hourly activity; there is no sense or faculty that is not strengthened by continual exercise. The domestic animal, on the other hand, has food provided for it, is sheltered, and often confined, to guard it against the vicissitudes of the seasons, is carefully secured from the attacks of its natural enemies, and seldom even rears its young without human assistance. Half of its senses and faculties are quite useless; and the other half are but occasionally called into feeble exercise, while even its muscular system is only irregularly called into action.

Now when a variety of such an animal occurs, having increased power or capacity in any organ or sense, such increase is totally useless, is never called into action, and may even exist without the animal ever becoming aware of it. In the wild animal, on the contrary, all its faculties and powers being brought into full action for the necessities of existence, any increase becomes immediately available, is strengthened by exercise, and must even slightly modify the food, the habits, and the whole economy of the race. It creates as it were a new animal, one of superior powers, and which will necessarily increase in numbers and outlive those inferior to it.

Again, in the domesticated animal all variations have an equal chance of continuance; and those which would decidedly render a wild animal unable to compete with its fellows and continue its existence are no disadvantage whatever in a state of domesticity. Our quickly fattening pigs, short-legged sheep, pouter pigeons, and poodle dogs could never have come into existence in a state of nature, because the very first step towards such inferior forms would have led to the rapid extinction of the race; still less could they now exist in competition with their wild allies. The great speed but slight endurance of the race horse, the unwieldy strength of the ploughman's team, would both be useless in a state of nature. If turned wild on the pampas, such animals would probably soon become extinct, or under favourable circumstances might each lose those extreme qualities which would never be called into action, and in a few generations would revert to a common type, which must be that in which the various powers and faculties are so proportioned to each other as to be best adapted to procure food and secure safety, — that in which by the full exercise of every part of his organization the animal can alone continue to live. Domestic varieties, when turned wild, *must* return to something near the type of the original wild stock, *or become altogether extinct.*

We see, then, that no inferences as to varieties in a state of nature can be deduced from the observation of those occurring among domestic animals. The two are so much opposed to each other in every circumstance of their existence, that what applies to the one is almost sure not to apply to the other. Domestic animals are abnormal, irregular, artificial; they are subject to varieties which never occur and never can occur in a state of nature: their very existence depends altogether on human care; so far are many of them removed from that just proportion of faculties, that true balance of organization, by means of which alone an animal left to its own resources can preserve its existence and continue its race.

The hypothesis of Lamarck — that progressive changes in species have been produced by the attempts of animals to increase the development of their own organs, and thus modify their structure and habits — has been repeatedly and easily refuted by all writers on the subject of varieties and species, and it seems to have been considered that when this was done the whole question has been finally settled; but the view here developed renders such an hypothesis quite unnecessary, by showing that similar results must be produced by the action of principles constantly at work in nature. The powerful retractile talons of the falcon- and the cat-tribes have not been produced or increased by the volition of those animals; but among the different varieties which occurred in the earlier and less highly organized forms of these groups, *those always survived longest which had the greatest facilities for seizing their prey.* Neither did the giraffe acquire its long neck by desiring to reach the foliage of the more lofty shrubs, and constantly stretching its neck for the purpose, but because any varieties which occurred among its antitypes with a longer neck than usual *at once secured a fresh range of pasture over the same ground as their shorter-necked companions, and on the first scarcity of food were thereby enabled to outlive them.* Even the peculiar colours of many animals, especially insects, so closely resembling the soil or the leaves or the trunks on which they habitually reside, are explained on the same principle; for though in the course of ages varieties of many tints may have occurred, *yet those races having colours best adapted to concealment from their enemies would inevitably survive the longest.* We have also here an acting cause to account for that balance so often observed in nature, — a deficiency in one set of organs always being compensated by an increased development of some others — powerful wings accompanying weak feet, or great velocity making up for the absence of defensive weapons; for it has been shown that all varieties in which an unbalanced deficiency occurred could not long continue their existence. The action of this principle is exactly like that of the centrifugal governor of the steam engine, which checks and corrects any irregularities almost before they become evident; and in like manner no unbalanced deficiency in the animal kingdom can ever reach any conspicuous magnitude, because it would make itself felt at the very first step, by rendering existence difficult and extinction almost sure to follow. An origin such as is here advocated will also agree with the peculiar character of the modifications of form and structure which obtain in organized beings — the many lines of divergence from a central type, the increasing efficiency and power of a particular organ through a succession of allied species, and the remarkable persistence of unimportant parts such as colour, texture of plumage and hair, form of horns or crests, through a series of species differing considerably in more essential characters. It also furnishes us with a reason for that "more specialized structure" which Professor Owen states to be a characteristic of recent compared with extinct forms, and which would evidently be the result of the progressive modification of any organ applied to a special purpose in the animal economy.

We believe we have now shown that there is a tendency in nature to the continued progression of certain classes of *varieties* further and further from the original type — a progression to which there appears no reason to assign any definite limits — and that the same principle which produces this result in a state of nature will also explain why domestic varieties have a tendency to revert to the original type. This progression, by minute steps, in various directions, but always checked and balanced by the necessary conditions, subject to which alone existence can be preserved, may, it is believed, be followed out so as to agree with all the phenomena presented by organized beings, their extinction and succession in past ages, and all the extraordinary modifications of form, instinct, and habits which they exhibit.

*Ternate, February, 1858*

# The *Origin of Species*[54]

# *Natural Selection*

How will the struggle for existence, briefly discussed in the last chapter, act in regard to variation? Can the principle of selection, which we have seen is so potent in the hands of man, apply under nature? I think we shall see that it can act most efficiently. Let the endless number of slight variations and individual differences occurring in our domestic productions, and, in a lesser degree, in those under nature, be borne in mind; as well as the strength of the hereditary tendency. Under domestication, it may be truly said that the whole organisation becomes in some degree plastic. But the variability, which we almost universally meet with in our domestic productions, is not directly produced, as Hooker and Asa Gray have well remarked, by man; he can neither originate varieties, nor prevent their occurrence; he can preserve and accumulate such as do occur. Unintentionally he exposes organic beings to new and changing conditions of life, and variability ensues; but similar changes of conditions might and do occur under nature. Let it also be borne in mind how infinitely complex and close-fitting are the mutual relations of all organic beings to each other and to their physical conditions of life; and consequently what infinitely varied diversities of structure might be of use to each being under changing conditions of life. Can it, then, be thought improbable, seeing that variations useful to man have undoubtedly occurred, that other variations useful in some way to each being in the great and complex battle of life, should occur in the course of many successive generations. If such do occur, can we doubt (remembering that many more individuals are born than can possibly survive) that individuals having any advantage, however slight, over others, would have the best chance of surviving and of procreating their kind? On the other hand, we may feel sure that any variation in the least degree injurious would be rigidly destroyed. This preservation of favourable individual differences and variations, and the destruction of those which are injurious, I have called Natural Selection, or the Survival of the Fittest. Variations neither useful nor injurious would not be affected by natural selection, and would be left either a fluctuating element, as perhaps we see in certain polymorphic species, or would ultimately become fixed, owing to the nature of the organism and the nature of the conditions.

Several writers have misapprehended or objected to the term Natural Selection. Some have even imagined that natural selection induces variability, whereas it implies only the preservation of such variations as arise and are beneficial to the being under its conditions of life. No one objects to agriculturists speaking of the potent effects of man's selection; and in this case the individual differences given by nature, which man for some object selects, must of necessity first occur. Others have objected that the term selection implies conscious choice in the animals which become modified; and it has even been urged that, as plants have no volition, natural selection is not applicable to them! In the literal sense of the word, no doubt, natural selection is a false term; but who ever objected to chemists speaking of

An abstract of an Essay
on the
Origin
of
Species and Varieties
Through natural selection
by
Charles Darwin M.A.
Fellow of the Royal, Geological & Linn. Soc.

Darwin's original draft of the title page to the *Origin of Species*

the elective affinities of the various elements?—and yet an acid cannot strictly be said to elect the base with which it in preference combines. It has been said that I speak of natural selection as an active power or Deity; but who objects to an author speaking of the attraction of gravity as ruling the movements of the planets? Every one knows what is meant and is implied by such metaphorical expressions; and they are almost necessary for brevity. So again it is difficult to avoid personifying the word Nature; but I mean by Nature, only the aggregate action and product of many natural laws, and by laws the sequence of events as ascertained by us. With a little familiarity such superficial objections will be forgotten.

We shall best understand the probable course of natural selection by taking the case of a country undergoing some slight physical change, for instance, of climate. The proportional numbers of its inhabitants will almost immediately undergo a change, and some species will probably become extinct. We may conclude, from what we have seen of the intimate and complex manner in which the inhabitants of each country are bound together, that any change in the numerical proportions of the inhabitants, independently of the change of climate itself, would seriously affect the others. If the country were open on its borders, new forms would certainly immigrate, and this would likewise seriously disturb the relations of some of the former inhabitants. Let it be remembered how powerful the influence of a single introduced tree or mammal has been shown to be. But in the case of an island, or of a country partly surrounded by barriers, into which new and better adapted forms could not freely enter, we should then have places in the economy of nature which would assuredly be better filled up, if some of the original inhabitants were in some manner modified; for, had the area been open to immigration, these same places would have been seized on by intruders. In such cases, slight modifications, which in any way favoured the individuals of any species, by better adapting them to their altered conditions, would tend to be preserved; and natural selection would have free scope for the work of improvement.

We have good reason to believe, as shown in the first chapter, that changes in the conditions of life give a tendency to increased variability; and in the foregoing cases the conditions have changed, and this would manifestly be favourable to natural selection, by affording a better chance of the occurrence of profitable variations. Unless such occur, natural selection can do nothing. Under the term of "variations," it must never be forgotten that mere individual differences are included. As man can produce a great result with his domestic animals and plants by adding up in any given direction individual differences, so could natural selection, but far more easily from having incomparably longer time for action. Nor do I believe that any great physical change, as of climate, or any unusual degree of isolation to check immigration, is necessary in order that new and unoccupied places should be left, for natural selection to fill up by improving some of the varying inhabitants. For as all the inhabitants of each country are struggling together with nicely balanced forces, extremely slight modifications in the structure or habits of one species would often give it an advantage over others; and still further modifications of the same kind would often still further increase the advantage, as long as the species continued under the same conditions of life and profited by similar means of subsistence and defence. No country can be named in which all the native inhabitants are now so perfectly adapted to each other and to the physical conditions under which they live, that none of them could be still better adapted or improved; for in all countries, the natives have been so far conquered by naturalised productions, that they have allowed some foreigners to take firm possession of the land. And as foreigners have thus in every country beaten some of the natives, we may safely conclude that the natives might have been modified with advantage, so as to have better resisted the intruders.

As man can produce, and certainly has produced, a great result by his methodical and unconscious means of selection, what may not natural selection effect? Man can act only on external and visible characters: Nature, if I may be allowed to personify the natural preservation or survival of the fittest, cares nothing for appearances, except in so far as they are useful to any being. She can act on every internal organ, on every shade of constitutional difference, on the whole machinery of life. Man selects only for his own good: Nature only for that of the being which she tends. Every selected character is fully exercised by her, as is implied by the fact of their selection. Man keeps the natives of many climates in the same country; he seldom exercises each selected character in some peculiar and fitting manner; he feeds a long and a short beaked pigeon on the same food; he does not exercise a long-backed or long-legged quadruped in any peculiar manner; he exposes sheep with long and short wool to the same climate. He does not allow the most vigorous males to struggle for the females. He does not rigidly destroy all inferior animals, but protects during each varying season, as far as lies in his power, all his productions. He often begins his selection by some half-monstrous form; or at least by some modification prominent enough to catch the eye or to be plainly useful to him. Under nature, the slightest differences of structure or constitution may well turn the nicely balanced scale in the struggle for life, and so be preserved. How fleeting are the wishes and efforts of man! how short his time! and consequently how poor will be his results, compared with those accumulated by Nature during whole geological periods! Can we wonder, then, that Nature's productions should be far "truer" in character than man's productions; that they should be infinitely better adapted to the most complex conditions of life, and should plainly bear the stamp of far higher workmanship?

It may metaphorically be said that natural selection is daily and hourly scrutinising, throughout the world, the slightest variations; rejecting those that are bad, preserving and adding up all that are good; silently and insensibly working, *whenever and wherever opportunity offers,* at the improvement of each organic being in relation to its organic and inorganic conditions of life. We see nothing of these slow changes in progress, until the hand of time has marked the lapse of ages, and then so imperfect is our view into long-past geological ages, that we see only that the forms of life are now different from what they formerly were.

In order that any great amount of modification should be effected in a species, a variety when once formed must again, perhaps after a long interval of time, vary or present individual differences of the same favourable nature as before; and these must be again preserved, and so onwards step by step. Seeing that individual differences of the same kind perpetually recur, this can hardly be considered as an unwarrantable assumption. But whether it is true, we can judge only by seeing how far the hypothesis accords with and explains the general phenomena of nature. On the other hand, the ordinary belief that the amount of possible variation is a strictly limited quantity is likewise a simple assumption.

Although natural selection can act only through and for the good of each being, yet characters and structures, which we are apt to consider as of very trifling importance, may thus be acted on. When we see leaf-eating insects green, and bark-feeders mottled-grey; the alpine ptarmigan white in winter, the red-grouse the colour of heather, we must believe that these tints are of service to these birds and insects in preserving them from danger. Grouse, if not destroyed at some period of their lives would increase in countless numbers; they are known to suffer largely from birds of prey; and hawks are guided by eyesight to their prey — so much so, that on parts of the Continent persons are warned not to keep white pigeons, as being the most liable to destruction. Hence natural selection might be effective in giving the proper colour to each kind of grouse, and in keeping that colour, when once acquired, true and constant. Nor ought we to think that the occasional destruction of an animal of any particular colour would produce little effect: we should remember how essential it is in a flock of white sheep to destroy a lamb with the faintest trace of black. We have seen how the colour of the hogs, which feed on the "paint-root" in Virginia, determines whether they shall live or die. In plants, the down on the fruit and the colour of the flesh are considered by botanists as characters of the most trifling importance; yet we hear from an excellent horticulturist, Downing, that in the United States, smooth-skinned fruits suffer far more from a beetle, a Curculio, than those with down; that purple plums suffer far more from a certain disease than yellow plums; whereas another disease attacks yellow-fleshed peaches far more than those with other coloured flesh. If, with all the aids of art, these slight differences make a great difference in cultivating the several varieties, assuredly, in a state of nature, where the trees would have to struggle with other trees, and with a host of enemies, such differences would effectually settle which variety, whether a smooth or downy, a yellow or purple fleshed fruit, should succeed.

In looking at many small points of difference between species, which, as far as our ignorance permits us to judge, seem quite unimportant, we must not forget that climate, food, &c., have no doubt produced some direct effect. It is also necessary to bear in mind that, owing to the law of correlation, when one part varies, and the variations are accumulated through natural selection, other modifications, often of the most unexpected nature, will ensue.

As we see that those variations which, under domestication, appear at any particular period of life, tend to reappear in the offspring at the same period; — for instance, in the shape, size, and flavour of the seeds of the many varieties of our culinary and agricultural plants; in the caterpillar and cocoon stages of the varieties of the silk-worm; in the eggs of poultry, and in the colour of the down of their chickens; in the horns of our sheep and cattle when nearly adult; — so in a state of nature natural selection will be enabled to act on and modify organic beings at any age, by the accumulation of variations profitable at that age, and by their inheritance at a corresponding age. If it profit a plant to have its seeds more and more widely disseminated by the wind, I can see no greater difficulty in this being effected through natural selection, than in the cotton-planter increasing and improving by selection the down in the pods on his cotton-trees. Natural selection may modify and adapt the larva of an insect to a score of contingencies, wholly different from those which concern the mature insect; and these modifications may effect, through correlation, the structure of the adult. So, conversely, modifications in the adult may affect the structure of the larva; but in all cases natural selection will ensure that they shall not be injurious; for if they were so, the species would become extinct.

Natural selection will modify the structure of the young in relation to the parent, and of the parent in relation to the young.

In social animals it will adapt the structure of each individual for the benefit of the whole community; if the community profits by the selected change. What natural selection cannot do, is to modify the structure of one species, without giving it any advantage, for the good of another species; and though statements to this effect may be found in works of natural history, I cannot find one case which will bear investigation. A structure used only once in an animal's life, if of high importance to it, might be modified to any extent by natural selection; for instance, the great jaws possessed by certain insects, used exclusively for opening the cocoon — or the hard tip to the beak of unhatched birds, used for breaking the egg. It has been asserted, that of the best short-beaked tumbler-pigeons a greater number perish in the egg than are able to get out of it; so that fanciers assist in the act of hatching. Now if nature had to make the beak of a full-grown pigeon very short for the bird's own advantage, the process of modification would be very slow, and there would be simultaneously the most rigorous selection of all the young birds within the egg, which had the most powerful and hardest beaks, for all with weak beaks would inevitably perish; or, more delicate and more easily broken shells might be selected, the thickness of the shell being known to vary like every other structure.

It may be well here to remark that with all beings there must be much fortuitous destruction, which can have little or no influence on the course of natural selection. For instance a vast number of eggs or seeds are annually devoured, and these could be modified through natural selection only if they varied in some manner which protected them from their enemies. Yet many of these eggs or seeds would perhaps, if not destroyed, have yielded individuals better adapted to their conditions of life than any of those which happened to survive. So again a vast number of mature animals and plants, whether or not they be the best adapted to their conditions, must be annually destroyed by accidental causes, which would not be in the least degree mitigated by certain changes of structure or constitution which would in other ways be beneficial to the species. But let the destruction of the adults be ever so heavy, if the number which can exist in any district be not wholly kept down by such causes, — or again let the destruction of eggs or seeds be so great that only a hundredth or a thousandth part are developed, — yet of those which do survive, the best adapted individuals, supposing that there is any variability in a favourable direction, will tend to propagate their kind in larger numbers than the less well adapted. If the numbers be wholly kept down by the causes just indicated, as will often have been the case, natural selection will be powerless in certain beneficial directions; but this is no valid objection to its efficiency at other times and in other ways; for we are far from having any reason to suppose that many species ever undergo modification and improvement at the same time in the same area.

### *Sexual Selection*

Inasmuch as peculiarities often appear under domestication in one sex and become hereditarily attached to that sex, so no doubt it will be under nature. Thus it is rendered possible for the two sexes to be modified through natural selection in relation to different habits of life, as is sometimes the case; or for one sex to be modified in relation to the other sex, as commonly occurs. This leads me to say a few words on what I have called Sexual Selection. This form of selection depends, not on a struggle for existence in relation to other organic beings or to external conditions, but on a struggle between the individuals of one sex, generally the males, for the possession of the other sex. The result is not death to the unsuccessful competitor, but few or no offspring. Sexual selection is, therefore, less rigorous than natural selection. Generally, the most vigorous males, those which are best fitted for their places in nature, will leave most progeny. But in many cases, victory depends not so much on general vigor, as on having special weapons, confined to the male sex. A hornless stag or spurless cock would have a poor chance of leaving numerous offspring. Sexual selection, by always allowing the victor to breed, might surely give indomitable courage, length to the spur, and strength to the wing to strike in the spurred leg, in nearly the same manner as does the brutal cock-fighter by the careful selection of his best cocks. How low in the scale of nature the law of battle descends, I know not; male alligators have been described as fighting, bellowing, and whirling round, like Indians in a war-dance, for the possession of the females; male salmons have been observed fighting all day long; male stag-beetles sometimes bear wounds from the huge mandibles of other males; the males of certain hymenopterous insects have been frequently seen by that inimitable observer M. Fabre, fighting for a particular female who sits by, an apparently unconcerned beholder of the struggle, and then retires with the conqueror. The war is, perhaps, severest between the males of polygamous animals, and these seem oftenest provided with special weapons. The males of carnivorous animals are already well armed; though to them and to others, special means of defence may be given through means of sexual selection, as the mane of the lion, and the hooked jaw to the male salmon; for the shield may be as important for victory, as the sword or spear.

Amongst birds, the contest is often of a more peaceful character. All those who have attended to the subject, believe that there is the severest rivalry between the males of many species to attract, by singing, the females. The rock-thrush of Guiana, birds of paradise, and some others, congregate; and successive males display with the most elaborate care, and show off in the best manner, their gorgeous plumage; they likewise perform strange antics before the females, which, standing by as spectators, at last choose the most attractive partner. Those who have closely attended to birds in confinement well know that they often take individual preferences and dislikes: thus Sir R. Heron has described how a pied peacock was eminently attractive to all his hen birds. I cannot here enter on the necessary details; but if man can in a short time give beauty and an elegant carriage to his bantams, according to his standard of beauty, I can see no good reason to doubt that female birds, by selecting, during thousands of generations, the most melodious or beautiful males, according to their standard of beauty, might produce a marked effect. Some well-known laws, with respect to the plumage of male and female birds, in comparison with the plumage of the young, can partly be explained through the action of sexual selection on variations occurring at different ages, and transmitted to the males alone or to both sexes at corresponding ages; but I have not space here to enter on this subject.

Thus it is, as I believe, that when the males and females of any animal have the same general habits of life, but differ in structure, colour, or ornament, such differences have been mainly caused by sexual selection: that is, by individual males having had, in successive generations, some slight advantage over other males, in their weapons, means of defence, or charms, which they have transmitted to their male offspring alone. Yet, I would not wish to attribute all sexual differences to this agency: for we see in our domestic animals peculiarities arising and becoming attached to the male sex, which apparently have not been augmented through selection by man. The tuft of hair on the breast of the wild turkey-cock cannot be of any use, and it is doubtful whether it can be ornamental in the eyes of the female bird;—indeed, had the tuft appeared under domestication, it would have been called a monstrosity.

### *Illustrations of the Action of Natural Selection, or the Survival of the Fittest*

In order to make it clear how, as I believe, natural selection acts, I must beg permission to give one or two imaginary illus-

"Natural Selection"

trations. Let us take the case of a wolf, which preys on various animals, securing some by craft, some by strength, and some by fleetness; and let us suppose that the fleetest prey, a deer for instance, had from any change in the country increased in numbers, or that other prey had decreased in numbers, during that season of the year when the wolf was hardest pressed for food. Under such circumstances the swiftest and slimmest wolves would have the best chance of surviving and so be preserved or selected, — provided always that they retained strength to master their prey at this or some other period of the year, when they were compelled to prey on other animals. I can see no more reason to doubt that this would be the result, than that man should be able to improve the fleetness of his greyhounds by careful and methodical selection, or by that kind of unconscious selection which follows from each man trying to keep the best dogs without any thought of modifying the breed. I may add, that, according to Mr. Pierce, there are two varieties of the wolf inhabiting the Catskill Mountains, in the United States, one with a light greyhound-like form, which pursues deer, and the other more bulky, with shorter legs, which more frequently attacks the shepherd's flocks.

It should be observed that, in the above illustration, I speak of the slimmest individual wolves, and not of any single strongly-marked variation having been preserved. In former editions of this work I sometimes spoke as if this latter alternative had frequently occurred. I saw the great importance of individual differences, and this led me fully to discuss the results of unconscious selection by man, which depends on the preservation of all the more or less valuable individuals, and on the destruction of the worst. I saw, also, that the preservation in a state of nature of any occasional deviation of structure, such as a monstrosity, would be a rare event; and that, if at first preserved, it would generally be lost by subsequent intercrossing with ordinary individuals. Nevertheless, until reading an able and valuable article in the 'North British Review' (1867), I did not appreciate how rarely single variations, whether slight or strongly-marked, could be perpetuated. The author takes the case of a pair of animals, producing during their lifetime two hundred offspring, of which, from various causes of destruction, only two on an average survive to procreate their kind. This is rather an extreme estimate for most of the higher animals, but by no means so for many of the lower organisms. He then shows that if a single individual were born, which varied in some manner, giving it twice as good a chance of life as that of the other individuals, yet the chances would be strongly against its survival. Supposing it to survive and to breed, and that half its young inherited the favourable variation; still, as the Reviewer goes on to show, the young would have only a slightly better chance of surviving and breeding; and this chance would go on decreasing in the succeeding generations. The justice of these remarks cannot, I think, be disputed. If, for instance, a bird of some kind could procure its food more easily by having its beak curved, and if one were born with its beak strongly curved, and which consequently flourished, nevertheless there would be a very poor chance of this one individual perpetuating its kind to the exclusion of the common form; but there can hardly be a doubt, judging by what we see taking place under domestication, that this result would follow from the preservation during many generations of a large number of individuals with more or less strongly curved beaks, and from the destruction of a still larger number with the straightest beaks.

It should not, however, be overlooked that certain rather strongly marked variations, which no one would rank as mere individual differences, frequently recur owing to a similar organisation being similarly acted on — of which fact numerous instances could be given with our domestic productions. In such cases, if the varying individual did not actually transmit to its offspring its newly-acquired character, it would undoubtedly transmit to them, as long as the existing conditions remained the same, a still stronger tendency to vary in the same manner.

There can also be little doubt that the tendency to vary in the same manner has often been so strong that all the individuals of the same species have been similarly modified without the aid of any form of selection. Or only a third, fifth, or tenth part of the individuals may have been thus affected, of which fact several instances could be given. Thus Graba estimates that about one-fifth of the guillemots in the Faroe Islands consist of a variety so well marked, that it was formerly ranked as a distinct species under the name of Uria lacrymans. In cases of this kind, if the variation were of a beneficial nature, the original form would soon be supplanted by the modified form, through the survival of the fittest.

To the effects of intercrossing in eliminating variations of all kinds, I shall have to recur; but it may be here remarked that most animals and plants keep to their proper homes, and do not needlessly wander about; we see this even with migratory birds, which almost always return to the same spot. Consequently each newly-formed variety would generally be at first local, as seems to be the common rule with varieties in a state of nature; so that similarly modified individuals would soon exist in a small body together, and would often breed together. If the new variety were successful in its battle for life, it would slowly spread from a central district, competing with and conquering the unchanged individuals on the margins of an ever-increasing circle.

It may be worth while to give another and more complex illustration of the action of natural selection. Certain plants excrete sweet juice, apparently for the sake of eliminating something injurious from the sap: this is effected, for instance, by glands at the base of the stipules in some Leguminosæ, and at the backs of the leaves of the common laurel. This juice, though small in quantity, is greedily sought by insects; but their visits do not in any way benefit the plant. Now, let us suppose that the juice or nectar was excreted from the inside of the flowers of a certain number of plants of any species. Insects in seeking the nectar would get dusted with pollen, and would often transport it from one flower to another. The flowers of two distinct individuals of the same species would thus get crossed; and the act of crossing, as can be fully proved, gives rise to vigorous seedlings which consequently would have the best chance of flourishing and surviving. The plants which produced flowers with the largest glands or nectaries, excreting most nectar, would oftenest be visited by insects, and would oftenest be crossed; and so in the long-run would gain the upper hand and form a local variety. The flowers, also, which had their stamens and pistils placed, in relation to the size and habits of the particular insects which visited them, so as to favour in any degree the transportal of the pollen, would likewise be favoured. We might have taken the case of insects visiting flowers for the sake of collecting pollen instead of nectar; and as pollen is formed for the sole purpose of fertilisation, its destruction appears to be a simple loss to the plant; yet if a little pollen were carried, at first occasionally and then habitually, by the pollen-devouring insects from flower to flower, and a cross thus effected, although nine-tenths of the pollen were destroyed it might still be a great gain to the plant to be thus robbed; and the individuals which produced more and more pollen, and had larger anthers, would be selected.

When our plant, by the above process long continued, had been rendered highly attractive to insects, they would, unintentionally on their part, regularly carry pollen from flower to flower; and that they do this effectually, I could easily show by many striking facts. I will give only one, as likewise illustrating one step in the separation of the sexes of plants. Some holly-trees bear only male flowers, which have four stamens producing a rather small quantity of pollen, and a rudimentary pistil; other holly-trees bear only female flowers; these have a full-sized pistil, and four stamens with shrivelled anthers, in which not a grain of pollen can be detected. Having found a female tree exactly sixty yards from a male tree, I put the stigmas of twenty flowers, taken from different branches, under the microscope, and on all, without exception, there were a few pollen-grains, and on some a profusion. As the wind had set for several days from the female to the male tree, the pollen could not thus have been carried. The weather had been cold and boisterous, and therefore not favourable to bees, nevertheless every female flower which I examined had been effectually fertilised by the bees, which had flown from tree to tree in search of nectar. But to return to our imaginary case: as soon as the plant had been rendered so highly attractive to insects that pollen was regularly carried from flower to flower, another process might commence. No naturalist doubts the advantage of what has been called the "physiological division of labour;" hence we may believe that it would be advantageous to a plant to produce stamens alone in one flower or on one whole plant, and pistils alone in another flower or on another plant. In plants under culture and placed under new conditions of life, sometimes the male organs and sometimes the female organs become more or less impotent; now if we suppose this to occur in ever so slight a degree under nature, then, as pollen is already carried regularly from flower to flower, and as a more complete separation of the sexes of our plant would be advantageous on the principle of the division of labour, individuals with this tendency more and more increased, would be continually favoured or selected, until at last a complete separation of the sexes might be effected. It would take up too much space to show the various steps, through dimorphism and other means, by which the separation of the sexes in plants of various kinds is apparently now in progress; but I may add that some of the species of holly in North America, are, according to Asa Gray, in an exactly intermediate condition, or, as he expresses it, are more or less diœciously polygamous.

Let us now turn to the nectar-feeding insects; we may suppose the plant, of which we have been slowly increasing the nectar by continued selection, to be a common plant; and that certain insects depended in main part on its nectar for food. I could give many facts showing how anxious bees are to save time: for instance, their habit of cutting holes and sucking the nectar at the bases of certain flowers, which, with a very little more trouble, they can enter by the mouth. Bearing such facts in mind, it may be believed that under certain circumstances individual differences in the curvature or length of the proboscis, &c., too slight to be appreciated by us, might profit a bee or other insect, so that certain individuals would be able to obtain their food more quickly than others; and thus the communities to which they belonged would flourish and throw off many swarms inheriting the same peculiarities. The tubes of the corolla of the common red and incarnate clovers (Trifolium pratense and incarnatum) do not on a hasty glance appear to differ in length; yet the hive-bee can easily suck the nectar out of the incarnate clover, but not out of the common red clover, which is visited by humble-bees alone; so that whole fields of red clover offer in vain an abundant supply of precious nectar to the hive-bee. That this nectar is much liked by the hive-bee is certain; for I have repeatedly seen, but only in the autumn, many hive-bees sucking the flowers through holes bitten in the base of the tube by humble-bees. The difference in the length of the corolla in the two kinds of clover, which determines the visits of the hive-bee, must be very trifling; for I have been assured that when red clover has been mown, the flowers of the second crop are somewhat smaller, and that these are visited by many hive-bees. I do not know whether this statement is accurate; nor whether another published statement can be trusted, namely, that the Ligurian bee which is generally considered a mere variety of the common hive-bee, and which freely crosses with it, is able to reach and suck the nectar of the red clover. Thus, in a country where this kind of clover abounded, it might be a great advantage to the hive-bee to have a slightly longer or differently constructed proboscis. On the other hand, as the fertility of this clover absolutely depends on bees visiting the flowers, if humble-bees were to become rare in any country, it might be a great advantage to the plant to have a shorter or more deeply divided corolla, so that the hive-bees should be enabled to suck its flowers. Thus I can understand how a flower and a bee might slowly become, either simultaneously or one after the other, modified and adapted to each other in the most perfect manner, by the continued preservation of all the individuals which presented slight deviations of structure mutually favorable to each other.

I am well aware that this doctrine of natural selection, exemplified in the above imaginary instances, is open to the same objections which were first urged against Sir Charles Lyell's noble views on "the modern changes of the earth, as illustrative of geology;" but we now seldom hear the agencies which we see still at work, spoken of as trifling or insignificant, when used in explaining the excavation of the deepest valleys or the formation of long lines of inland cliffs. Natural selection acts only by the preservation and accumulation of small inherited modifications, each profitable to the preserved being; and as modern geology has almost banished such views as the excavation of a great valley by a single diluvial wave, so will natural selection banish the belief of the continued creation of new organic beings, or of any great and sudden modification in their structure.

## *On the Intercrossing of Individuals*

I must here introduce a short digression. In the case of animals and plants with separated sexes, it is of course obvious that two individuals must always (with the exception of the curious and not well-understood cases of parthenogenesis) unite for each birth; but in the case of hermaphrodites this is far from obvious. Nevertheless there is reason to believe that with all hermaphrodites two individuals, either occasionally or habitually, concur for the reproduction of their kind. This view was long ago doubtfully suggested by Sprengel, Knight and Kölreuter. We shall presently see its importance; but I must here treat the subject with extreme brevity, though I have the materials prepared for an ample discussion. All vertebrate animals, all insects, and some other large groups of animals, pair for each birth. Modern research has much diminished the number of supposed hermaphrodites, and of real hermaphrodites a large number pair; that is, two individuals regularly unite for reproduction, which is all that concerns us. But still there are many hermaphrodite animals which certainly do not habitually pair, and a vast majority of plants are hermaphrodites. What reason, it may be asked, is there for supposing in these cases that two individuals ever concur in reproduction? As it is impossible here to enter on details, I must trust to some general considerations alone.

In the first place, I have collected so large a body of facts, and made so many experiments, showing, in accordance with the almost universal belief of breeders, that with animals and plants a cross between different varieties, or between individuals of the same variety but of another strain, gives vigour and fertility to the offspring; and on the other hand, that *close* interbreeding diminishes vigour and fertility; that these facts alone incline me to believe that it is a general law of nature that no organic being fertilises itself for a perpetuity of generations; but that a cross with another individual is occasionally — perhaps at long intervals of time — indispensable.

On the belief that this is a law of nature, we can, I think, understand several large classes of facts, such as the following, which on any other view are inexplicable. Every hybridizer knows how unfavourable exposure to wet is to the fertilisation of a flower, yet what a multitude of flowers have their anthers and stigmas fully exposed to the weather! If an occasional cross be indispensable, notwithstanding that the plant's own anthers and pistil stand so near each other as almost to insure self-fertilisation, the fullest freedom for the entrance of pollen from another individual will explain the above state of exposure of the organs. Many flowers, on the other hand, have their organs of fructification closely enclosed, as in the great papilionaceous or pea-family; but these almost invariably present beautiful and curious adaptations in relation to the visits of insects. So necessary are the visits of bees to many papilionaceous flowers, that their fertility is greatly diminished if these visits be prevented. Now, it is scarcely possible for insects to fly from flower to flower, and not to carry pollen from one to the other, to the great good of the plant. Insects act like a camel-hair pencil, and it is sufficient, to ensure fertilisation, just to touch with the same brush the anthers of one flower and then the stigma of another; but it must not be supposed that bees would thus produce a multitude of hybrids between distinct species; for if a plant's own pollen and that from another species are placed on the same stigma, the former is so prepotent that it invariably and completely destroys, as has been shown by Gärtner, the influence of the foreign pollen.

When the stamens of a flower suddenly spring towards the pistil, or slowly move one after the other towards it, the contrivance seems adapted solely to ensure self-fertilisation; and no doubt it is useful for this end: but the agency of insects is often required to cause the stamens to spring forward, as Kölreuter has shown to be the case with the barberry; and in this very genus, which seems to have a special contrivance for self-fertilisation, it is well known that, if closely allied forms or varieties are planted near each other, it is hardly possible to raise pure seedlings, so largely do they naturally cross. In numerous other cases, far from self-fertilisation being favoured, there are special contrivances which effectually prevent the stigma receiving pollen from its own flower, as I could show from the works of Sprengel and others, as well as from my own observations: for instance, in Lobelia fulgens, there is a real beautiful and elaborate contrivance by which all the infinitely numerous pollen-granules are swept out of the conjoined anthers of each flower, before the stigma of that individual flower is ready to receive them; and as this flower is never visited, at least in my garden, by insects, it never sets a seed, though by placing pollen from one flower on the stigma of another, I raise plenty of seedlings. Another species of Lobelia which is visited by bees, seeds freely in my garden. In very many other cases, though there is no special mechanical contrivance to prevent the stigma receiving pollen from the same flower, yet, as Sprengel, and more recently Hildebrand, and others, have shown, and as I can confirm, either the anthers burst before the stigma is ready for fertilisation, or the stigma is ready before the pollen of that flower is ready, so that these so-named dichogamous plants have in fact separated sexes, and must habitually be crossed. So it is with the reciprocally dimorphic and trimorphic plants previously alluded to. How strange are these facts! How strange that the pollen and stigmatic surface of the same flower, though placed so close together, as if for the very purpose of self-fertilisation, should be in so many cases mutually useless to each other! How simply are these facts explained on the view of an occasional cross with a distinct individual being advantageous or indispensable!

If several varieties of the cabbage, radish, onion, and of some other plants, be allowed to seed near each other, a large majority of the seedlings thus raised turn out, as I have found, mongrels: for instance, I raised 233 seedling cabbages from some plants of different varieties growing near each other, and of these only 78 were true to their kind, and some even of these were not perfectly true. Yet the pistil of each cabbage-flower is surrounded not only by its own six stamens but by those of the many other flowers on the same plant; and the pollen of each flower readily gets on its own stigma without insect agency; for I have found that plants carefully protected from insects produce the full number of pods. How, then, comes it that such a vast number of the seedlings are mongrelized? It must arise from the pollen of a distinct *variety* having a prepotent effect over the flower's own pollen; and that this is part of the general law of good being derived from the intercrossing of distinct individuals of the same species. When distinct *species* are crossed the case is reversed, for a plant's own pollen is almost always

(Paper Aug 1842) (useless)

Geology shows us the vast succession of organisms have inhabited this earth. They appeared to have come & disappeared suddenly in groups — But in later periods we have reason to believe they have come & disappeared from on the scene one by one, & we must believe that some have disappeared within late periods. We are thus led to ask whether their appearance be not rather due to some regular cause or law of nature & not to infinitely numerous separate miracles. — Looking further we see the fossils of any one country are more particularly related to the living organisms of that country, than to any other; we ask can they not be descended from those fossils? — We see in the same continent & different parts of the continent which separated by space, change of temp, great rivers or mountains inhabited by different species, which have evident relationship —

Affinity — unity of type — foetal state — abortive organs — hybrids like mongrels — difficulty of testing species from variation — if species given up, genera must. — We know that variation within certain limits is possible, we ask for limits of the variation who can answer? —

(This page was thought of as introduction)

Facsimile of a manuscript page in the handwriting of Charles Darwin prepotent over foreign pollen; but to this subject we shall return in a future chapter.

In the case of a large tree covered with innumerable flowers, it may be objected that pollen could seldom be carried from tree to tree, and at most only from flower to flower on the same tree; and flowers on the same tree can be considered as distinct individuals only in a limited sense. I believe this objection to be valid, but that nature has largely provided against it by giving to trees a strong tendency to bear flowers with separated sexes. When the sexes are separated, although the male and female flowers may be produced on the same tree, pollen must be regularly carried from flower to flower; and this will give a better chance of pollen being occasionally carried from tree to tree. The trees belonging to all Orders have their sexes more often separated than other plants, I find to be the case in this country; and at my request, Dr. Hooker tabulated the trees of New Zealand, and Dr. Asa Gray those of the United States, and the result was as I anticipated. On the other hand, Dr. Hooker informs me that the rule does not hold good in Australia: but if most of the Australian trees are dichogamous, the same result would follow as if they bore flowers with separated sexes. I have made these few remarks on trees simply to call attention to the subject.

Turning for a brief space to animals: various terrestrial species are hermaphrodites, such as the land-mollusca and earthworms; but these all pair. As yet I have not found a single terrestrial animal which can fertilise itself. This remarkable fact, which offers so strong a contrast with terrestrial plants, is intelligible on the view of an occasional cross being indispensable; for owing to the nature of the fertilising element there are no means, analogous to the action of insects and of the wind with plants, by which an occasional cross could be effected with terrestrial animals without the concurrence of two individuals. Of aquatic animals, there are many self-fertilising hermaphrodites; but here the currents of water offer an obvious means for an occasional cross. As in the case of flowers, I have as yet failed, after consultation with one of the highest authorities, namely, Professor Huxley, to discover a single hermaphrodite animal with the organs of reproduction so perfectly enclosed that access from without, and the occasional influence of a distinct individual, can be shown to be physically impossible. Cirripedes long appeared to me to present, under this point of view, a case of great difficulty; but I have been enabled, by a fortunate chance, to prove that two individuals, though both are self-fertilising hermaphrodites, do sometimes cross.

It must have struck most naturalists as a strange anomaly that, both with animals and plants, some species of the same family and even of the same genus, though agreeing closely with each other in their whole organisation, are hermaphrodites, and some unisexual. But if, in fact, all hermaphrodites do occasionally intercross, the difference between them and unisexual species is, as far as function is concerned, very small.

From these several considerations and from the many special facts which I have collected, but which I am unable here to give, it appears that with animals and plants an occasional intercross between distinct individuals is a very general, if not universal, law of nature.

### *Circumstances favourable for the production of new forms through Natural Selection*

This is an extremely intricate subject. A great amount of variability, under which term individual differences are always included, will evidently be favourable. A large number of individuals, by giving a better chance within any given period for the appearance of profitable variations, will compensate for a lesser amount of variability in each individual, and is, I believe, a highly important element of success. Though Nature grants long periods of time for the work of natural selection, she does not grant an indefinite period; for as all organic beings are striving to seize on each place in the economy of nature, if any one species does not become modified and improved in a corresponding degree with its competitors, it will be exterminated. Unless favourable variations be inherited by some at least of the offspring, nothing can be effected by natural selection. The tendency to reversion may often check or prevent the work; but as this tendency has not prevented man from forming by selection numerous domestic races, why should it prevail against natural selection?

In the case of methodical selection, a breeder selects for some definite object, and if the individuals be allowed freely to intercross, his work will completely fail. But when many men, without intending to alter the breed, have a nearly common standard of perfection, and all try to procure and breed from the best animals, improvement surely but slowly follows from this unconscious process of selection, notwithstanding that there is no separation of selected individuals. Thus it will be under nature, for within a confined area, with some place in the natural polity not perfectly occupied, all the individuals varying in the right direction, though in different degrees, will tend to be preserved. But if the area be large, its several districts will almost certainly present different conditions of life; and then, if the same species undergoes modification in different districts, the newly-formed varieties will intercross on the confines of each. But we shall see in the sixth chapter that intermediate varieties, inhabiting intermediate districts, will in the long run generally be supplanted by one of the adjoining varieties. Intercrossing will chiefly affect those animals which unite for each birth and wander much, and which do not breed at a very quick rate. Hence with animals of this nature, for instance, birds, varieties will generally be confined to separated countries; and this I find to be the case. With hermaphrodite organisms which cross only occasionally, and likewise with animals which unite for each birth, but which wander little and can increase at a rapid rate, a new and improved variety might be quickly formed on any one spot, and might there maintain itself in a body and afterwards spread, so that the individuals of the new variety would chiefly cross together. On this principle, nurserymen always prefer saving seed from a large body of plants, as the chance of intercrossing is thus lessened.

Even with animals which unite for each birth, and which do not propagate rapidly, we must not assume that free intercrossing would always eliminate the effects of natural selection; for I can bring forward a considerable body of facts showing that within the same area, two varieties of the same animal may long remain distinct, from haunting different stations, from breeding at slightly different seasons, or from the individuals of each variety preferring to pair together.

Intercrossing plays a very important part in nature by keeping the individuals of the same species, or of the same variety, true and uniform in character. It will obviously thus act far more efficiently with those animals which unite for each birth; but, as already stated, we have reason to believe that occasional intercrosses take place with all animals and plants. Even if these take place only at long intervals of time, the young thus produced will gain so much in vigour and fertility over the offspring from long-continued self-fertilisation, that they will have a better chance of surviving and propagating their kind; and thus in the long run the influence of crosses, even at rare intervals, will be great. With respect to organic beings extremely low in the scale, which do not propagate sexually, nor conjugate, and which cannot possibly intercross, uniformity of character can be retained by them under the same conditions of life, only through the principle of inheritance, and through natural selection which will destroy any individuals departing from the proper type. If the conditions of life change and the form undergoes modification, uniformity of character can be given to the modified offspring, solely by natural selection preserving similar favourable variations.

Isolation, also, is an important element in the modification of species through natural selection. In a confined or isolated area, if not very large, the organic and inorganic conditions of life will generally be almost uniform; so that natural selection will tend to modify all the varying individuals of the same species in the same manner. Intercrossing with the inhabitants of the surrounding districts will, also, be thus prevented. Moritz Wagner has lately published an interesting essay on this subject, and has shown that the service rendered by isolation in preventing crosses between newly-formed varieties is probably greater even than I supposed. But from reasons already assigned I can by no means agree with this naturalist, that migration and isolation are necessary elements for the formation of new species. The importance of isolation is likewise great in preventing, after any physical change in the conditions, such as of climate, elevation of the land, &c., the immigration of better adapted organisms; and thus new places in the natural economy of the district will be left open to be filled up by the modification of the old inhabitants. Lastly, isolation will give time for a new variety to be improved at a slow rate; and this may sometimes be of much importance. If, however, an isolated area be very small, either from being surrounded by barriers, or from having very peculiar physical conditions, the total number of the inhabitants will be small; and this will retard the production of new species, through natural selection by decreasing the chances of favourable variations arising.

The mere lapse of time by itself does nothing, either for or against natural selection. I state this because it has been erroneously asserted that the element of time has been assumed by me to play an all-important part in modifying species, as if all the forms of life were necessarily undergoing change through some innate law. Lapse of time is only so far important, and its importance in this respect is great, that it gives a better chance of beneficial variations arising and of their being selected, accumulated, and fixed. It likewise tends to increase the direct action of the physical conditions of life, in relation to the constitution of each organism.

If we turn to nature to test the truth of these remarks, and look at any small isolated area, such as an oceanic island, although the number of species inhabiting it is small, as we shall see in our chapter on Geographical Distribution; yet of these species a very large proportion are endemic, — that is, have been produced there and nowhere else in the world. Hence an oceanic island at first sight seems to have been highly favourable for the production of new species. But we may thus deceive ourselves, for to ascertain whether a small isolated area, or a large open area like a continent, has been most favourable for the production of new organic forms, we ought to make the comparison within equal times; and this we are incapable of doing.

Although isolation is of great importance in the production of new species, on the whole I am inclined to believe that largeness of area is still more important, especially for the production of species which shall prove capable of enduring for a long period, and of spreading widely. Throughout a great and open area, not only will there be a better chance of favourable variations, arising from the large number of individuals of the same species there supported, but the conditions of life are much more complex from the large number of already existing species; and if some of these many species become modified and improved, others will have to be improved in a corresponding degree, or they will be exterminated. Each new form, also, as soon as it has been much improved, will be able to spread over the open and continuous area, and will thus come into competition with many other forms. Moreover, great areas, though now continuous, will often, owing to former oscillations of level, have existed in a broken condition; so that the good effects of isolation will generally, to a certain extent, have concurred. Finally, I conclude that, although small isolated areas have been in some respects highly favourable for the production of new species, yet that the course of modification will generally have been more rapid on large areas; and what is more important, that the new forms produced on large areas, which already have been victorious over many competitors, will be those that will spread most widely, and will give rise to the greatest number of new varieties and species. They will thus play a more important part in the changing history of the organic world.

In accordance with this view, we can, perhaps, understand some facts which will be again alluded to in our chapter on Geographical Distribution; for instance, the fact of the productions of the smaller continent of Australia now yielding before those of the larger Europæo-Asiatic area. Thus, also, it is that continental productions have everywhere become so largely naturalised on islands. On a small island, the race for life will have been less severe, and there will have been less modification and less extermination. Hence, we can understand how it is that the flora of Madeira, according to Oswald Heer, resembles to a certain extent the extinct tertiary flora of Europe. All fresh-water basins, taken together, make a small area compared with that of the sea or of the land. Consequently, the competition between fresh-water productions will have been less severe than elsewhere; new forms will have been then more slowly produced, and old forms more slowly exterminated. And it is in fresh-water basins that we find seven genera of Ganoid fishes, remnants of a once preponderant order: and in fresh water we find some of the most anomalous forms now known in the world as the Ornithorhynchus and Lepidosiren which, like fossils, connect to a certain extent orders at present widely sundered in the natural scale. These anomalous forms may be called living fossils; they have endured to the present day, from having inhabited a confined area, and from having been exposed to less varied, and therefore less severe, competition.

To sum up, as far as the extreme intricacy of the subject permits, the circumstances favourable and unfavourable for the production of new species through natural selection. I conclude that for terrestrial productions a large continental area, which has undergone many oscillations of level, will have been the most favourable for the production of many new forms of life, fitted to endure for a long time and to spread widely. Whilst the area existed as a continent, the inhabitants will have been numerous in individuals and kinds, and will have been subjected to severe competition. When converted by subsidence into large separate islands, there will still have existed many individuals of the same species on each island: intercrossing on the confines of the range of each new species will have been checked: after physical changes of any kind, immigration will have been prevented, so that new places in the polity of each island will have had to be filled up by the modification of the old inhabitants; and time will have been allowed for the varieties in each to become well modified and perfected. When, by renewed elevation, the islands were reconverted into a continental area, there will again have been very severe competition: the most favoured or improved varieties will have been enabled to spread: there will have been much extinction of the less improved forms, and the relative proportional numbers of the various inhabitants of the reunited continent will again have been changed; and again there will have been a fair field for natural selection to improve still further the inhabitants, and thus to produce new species.

That natural selection generally acts with extreme slowness I fully admit. It can act only when there are places in the natural polity of a district which can be better occupied by the modification of some of its existing inhabitants. The occurrence of such places will often depend on physical changes, which generally take place very slowly, and on the immigration of better adapted forms being prevented. As some few of the old inhabitants become modified, the mutual relations of others will often be disturbed; and this will create new places, ready to be filled up by better adapted forms, but all this will take place very slowly. Although all the individuals of the same species differ in some slight degree from each other, it would often be long before differences of the right nature in various parts of the organisation might occur. The result would often be greatly retarded by free intercrossing. Many will exclaim that these several causes are amply sufficient to neutralise the power of natural selection. I do not believe so. But I do believe that natural selection will generally act very slowly, only at long intervals of time, and only on a few of the inhabitants of the same region. I further believe that these slow, intermittent results accord well with what geology tells us of the rate and manner at which the inhabitants of the world have changed.

Slow though the process of selection may be, if feeble man can do much by artificial selection, I can see no limit to the amount of change, to the beauty and complexity of the coadaptations between all organic beings, one with another and with their physical conditions of life, which may have been affected in the long course of time through nature's power of selection, that is by the survival of the fittest.

### *Extinction caused by Natural Selection*

This subject will be more fully discussed in our chapter on Geology; but it must here be alluded to from being intimately connected with natural selection. Natural selection acts solely through the preservation of variations in some way advantageous, which consequently endure. Owing to the high geometrical rate of increase of all organic beings, each area is already fully stocked with inhabitants; and it follows from this, that as the favoured forms increase in number, so, generally, will the less favoured decrease and become rare. Rarity, as geology tells us, is the precursor to extinction. We can see that any form which is represented by few individuals will run a good chance of utter extinction, during great fluctuations in the nature of the seasons, or from a temporary increase in the number of its enemies. But we may go further than this; for, as new forms are produced, unless we admit that specific forms can go on indefinitely increasing in number, many old forms must become extinct. That the number of specific forms has not indefinitely increased, geology plainly tells us; and we shall presently attempt to show why it is that the number of species throughout the world has not become immeasurably great.

We have seen that the species which are most numerous in individuals have the best chance of producing favourable variations within any given period. We have evidence of this, in the facts stated in the second chapter showing that it is the common and diffused or dominant species which offer the greatest number of recorded varieties. Hence, rare species will be less quickly modified or improved within any given period; they will consequently be beaten in the race for life by the modified and improved descendants of the commoner species.

From these several considerations I think it inevitably follows, that as new species in the course of time are formed through natural selection, others will become rarer and rarer, and finally extinct. The forms which stand in closest competition with those undergoing modification and improvement will naturally suffer most. And we have seen in the chapter on the Struggle for Existence that it is the most closely-allied forms, — varieties of the same species, and species of the same genus or of related genera, — which, from having nearly the same structure, constitution, and habits, generally come into the severest competition with each other; consequently, each new variety or species, during the progress of its formation, will generally press hardest on its nearest kindred, and tend to exterminate them. We see the same process of extermination amongst our domesticated productions, through the selection of improved forms by man. Many curious instances could be given showing how quickly new breeds of cattle, sheep, and other animals, and varieties of flowers, take the place of older and inferior kinds. In Yorkshire, it is historically known that the ancient black cattle were displaced by the long-horns, and that these "were swept away by the short-horns" (I quote the words of an agricultural writer) "as if by some murderous pestilence."

## *Divergence of Character*

The principle, which I have designated by this term, is of high importance, and explains, as I believe, several important facts. In the first place, varieties, even strongly-marked ones, though having somewhat of the character of species — as is shown by the hopeless doubts in many cases how to rank them — yet certainly differ far less from each other than do good and distinct species. Nevertheless, according to my view, varieties are species in the process of formation, or are, as I have called them, incipient species. How, then, does the lesser difference between varieties become augmented into the greater difference between species? That this does habitually happen, we must infer from most of the innumerable species throughout nature presenting well-marked differences; whereas varieties, the supposed prototypes and parents of future well-marked species, present slight and ill-defined differences. Mere chance, as we may call it, might cause one variety to differ in some character from its parents, and the offspring of this variety again to differ from its parent in the very same character and in a greater degree; but this alone would never account for so habitual and large a degree of difference as that between the species of the same genus.

As has always been my practice, I have sought light on this head from our domestic productions. We shall here find something analogous. It will be admitted that the production of races so different as short-horn and Hereford cattle, race and cart horses, the several breeds of pigeons, &c., could never have been effected by the mere chance accumulation of similar variations during many successive generations. In practice, a fancier is, for instance, struck by a pigeon having a slightly shorter beak; another fancier is struck by a pigeon having a rather longer beak; and on the acknowledged principle that "fanciers do not and will not admire a medium standard, but like extremes," they both go on (as has actually occurred with the sub-breeds of the tumbler-pigeon) choosing and breeding from birds with longer and longer beaks, or with shorter and shorter beaks. Again, we may suppose that at an early period of history, the men of one nation or district required swifter horses, whilst those of another required stronger and bulkier horses. The early differences would be very slight; but, in the course of time, from the continued selection of swifter horses in the one case, and of stronger ones in the other, the differences would become greater, and would be noted as forming two sub-breeds. Ultimately, after the lapse of centuries, these sub-breeds would become converted into two well-established and distinct breeds. As the differences became greater, the inferior animals with intermediate characters, being neither swift nor very strong, would not have been used for breeding, and will thus have tended to disappear. Here, then, we see in man's productions the action of what may be called the principle of divergence, causing differences, at first barely appreciable, steadily to increase, and the breeds to diverge in character, both from each other and from their common parent.

But how, it may be asked, can any analogous principle apply in nature? I believe it can and does apply most efficiently (though it was a long time before I saw how), from the simple circumstance that the more diversified the descendants from any one species become in structure, constitution, and habits, by so much will they be better enabled to seize on many and widely diversified places in the polity of nature, and so be enabled to increase in numbers.

We can clearly discern this in the case of animals with simple habits. Take the case of a carnivorous quadruped, of which the number that can be supported in any country has long ago arrived at its full average. If its natural power of increase be allowed to act, it can succeed in increasing (the country not undergoing any change in conditions) only by its varying descendants seizing on places at present occupied by other animals: some of them, for instance, being enabled to feed on new kinds of prey, either dead or alive; some inhabiting new stations, climbing trees, frequenting water, and some perhaps becoming less carnivorous. The more diversified in habits and structure the descendants of our carnivorous animals become, the more places they will be enabled to occupy. What applies to one animal will apply throughout all time to all animals — that is, if they vary — for otherwise natural selection can effect nothing. So it will be with plants. It has been experimentally proved, that if a plot of ground be sown with one species of grass, and a similar plot be sown with several distinct genera of grasses, a greater number of plants and a greater weight of dry herbage can be raised in the latter than in the former case. The same has been found to hold good when one variety and several mixed varieties of wheat have been sown on equal spaces of ground. Hence, if any one species of grass were to go on varying, and the varieties were continually selected which differed from each other in the same manner, though in a very slight degree, as do the distinct species and genera of grasses, a greater number of individual plants of this species, including its modified descendants, would succeed in living on the same piece of ground. And we know that each species and each variety of grass is annually sowing almost countless seeds; and is thus striving, as it may be said, to the utmost to increase in number. Consequently, in the course of many thousand generations, the most distinct varieties of any one species of grass would have the best chance of succeeding and of increasing in numbers, and thus of supplanting the less distinct varieties; and varieties, when rendered very distinct from each other, take the rank of species.

The truth of the principle that the greatest amount of life can be supported by great diversification of structure, is seen under many natural circumstances. In an extremely small area, especially if freely open to immigration, and where the contest between individual and individual must be very severe, we always find great diversity in its inhabitants. For instance, I found that a piece of turf, three feet by four in size, which had been exposed for many years to exactly the same conditions, supported twenty species of plants, and these belonged to eighteen genera and to eight orders, which shows how much these plants differed from each other. So it is with the plants and insects on small and uniform islets; also in small ponds of fresh water. Farmers find that they can raise most food by a rotation of plants belonging to the most different orders: nature follows what may be called a simultaneous rotation. Most of the animals and plants which live close round any small piece of ground, could live on it (supposing its nature not to be in any way peculiar), and may be said to be striving to the utmost to live there; but, it is seen, that where they come into the closest competition, the advantages of diversification of structure, with the accompanying differences of habit and constitution, determine that the inhabitants, which thus jostle each other most closely, shall, as a general rule, belong to what we call different genera and orders.

The same principle is seen in the naturalisation of plants through man's agency in foreign lands. It might have been expected that the plants which would succeed in becoming naturalised in any land would generally have been closely allied to the indigenes; for these are commonly looked at as specially created and adapted for their own country. It might also, perhaps, have been expected that naturalised plants would have belonged to a few groups more especially adapted to certain stations in their new homes. But the case is very different; and Alph. de Candolle has well remarked, in his great and admirable work, that floras gain by naturalisation, proportionally with the number of the native genera and species far more in new genera than in new species. To give a single instance: in the last edition of Dr. Asa Gray's 'Manual of the Flora of the Northern United States,' 260 naturalised plants are enumerated, and these belong to 162 genera. We thus see that these naturalised plants are of a highly diversified nature. They differ, moreover, to a large extent, from the indigenes, for out of the 162 naturalised genera, no less than 100 genera are not there indigenous, and thus a large proportional addition is made to the genera now living in the United States.

By considering the nature of the plants or animals which have in any country struggled successfully with the indigenes and have there become naturalised, we may gain some crude idea in what manner some of the natives would have to be modified, in order to gain an advantage over their compatriots; and we may at least infer that diversification of structure, amounting to new generic differences, would be profitable to them.

The advantage of diversification of structure in the inhabitants of the same region is, in fact, the same as that of the physiological division of labour in the organs of the same individual body — a subject so well elucidated by Milne Edwards. No physiologist doubts that a stomach adapted to digest vegetable matter alone, or flesh alone, draws most nutriment from these substances. So in the general economy of any land, the more widely and perfectly the animals and plans are diversified for different habits of life, so will a greater number of individuals be capable of there supporting themselves. A set of animals, with their organisation but little diversified, could hardly compete with a set more perfectly diversified in structure. It may be doubted, for instance, whether the Australian marsupials, which are divided into groups differing but little from each other, and feebly representing, as Mr. Waterhouse and others have remarked, our carnivorous, ruminant, and rodent mammals, could successfully compete with these well-developed orders. In the Australian mammals, we see the process of diversification in an early and incomplete stage of development.

### *The Probable Effects of the Action of Natural Selection through Divergence of Character and Extinction, on the Descendants of a Common Ancestor.*

After the foregoing discussion, which has been much compressed, we may assume that the modified descendants of any one species will succeed so much the better as they become more diversified in structure, and are thus enabled to encroach on places occupied by other beings. Now let us see how this principle of benefit being derived from divergence of character, combined with the principles of natural selection and of extinction, tends to act.

The accompanying diagram will aid us in understanding this rather perplexing subject. Let A to L represent the species of a genus large in its own country; these species are supposed to resemble each other in unequal degrees, as is so generally the case in nature, and as is represented in the diagram by the letters standing at unequal distances. I have said a large genus, because as we saw in the second chapter, on an average more species vary in large genera than in small genera; and the varying species of the large genera present a greater number of varieties. We have, also, seen that the species, which are the commonest and the most widely diffused, vary more than do the rare and restricted species. Let (A) be a common, widely-diffused, and varying species, belonging to a genus large in its own country. The branching and diverging dotted lines of unequal lengths proceeding from (A), may represent its varying offspring. The variations are supposed to be extremely slight, but of the most diversified nature; they are not supposed all to appear simultaneously, but often after long intervals of time; nor are they all supposed to endure for equal periods. Only those variations which are in some way profitable will be preserved or naturally selected. And here the importance of the principle of benefit derived from divergence of character comes in; for this will generally lead to the most different or divergent variations (represented by the outer dotted lines) being preserved and accumulated by natural selection. When a dotted line reaches one of the horizontal lines, and is there marked by a small numbered letter, a sufficient amount of variation is supposed to have been accumulated to form it into a fairly well-

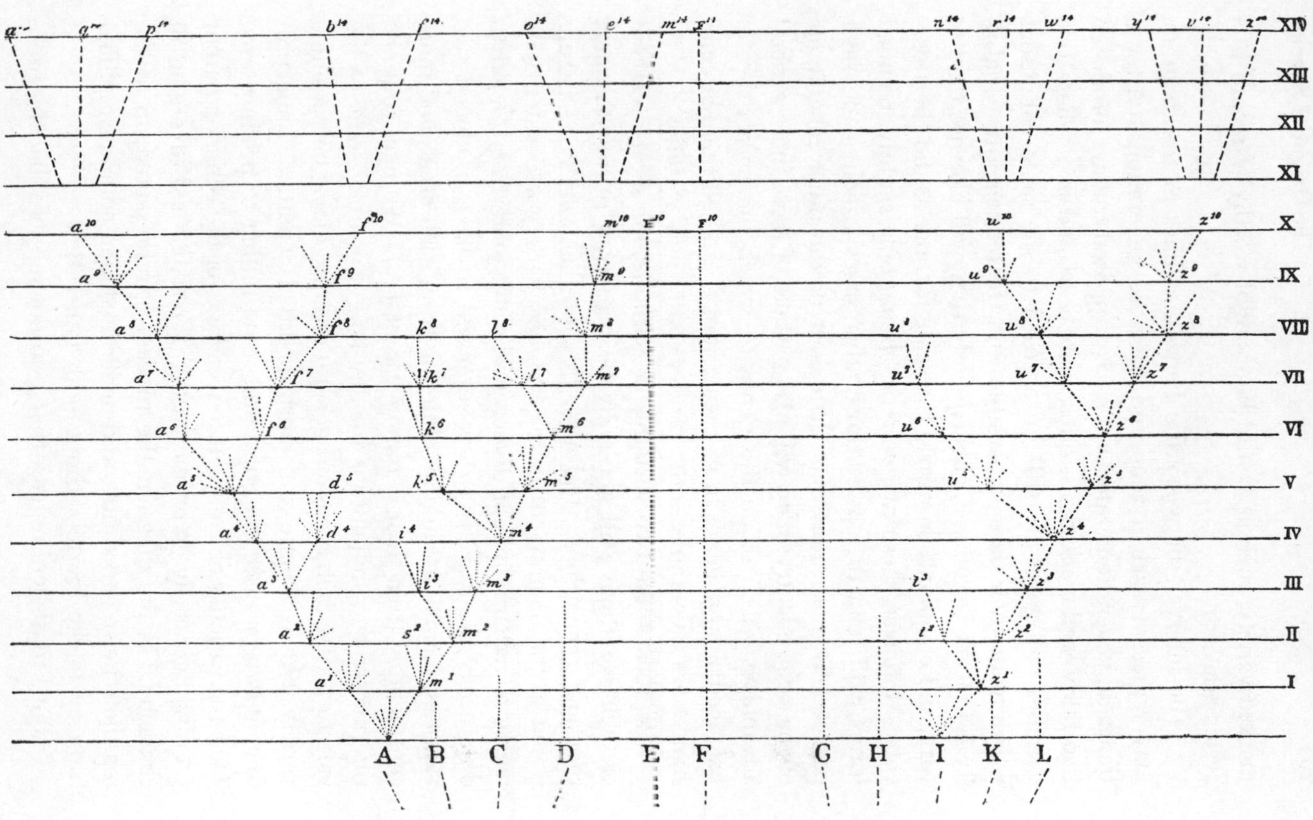

XIV
XIII
XII
XI
X
IX
VIII
VII
VI
V
IV
III
II
I
A B C D E F G H I K L

marked variety, such as would be thought worthy of record in a systematic work.

The intervals between the horizontal lines in the diagram, may represent each a thousand or more generations. After a thousand generations, species (A) is supposed to have produced two fairly well-marked varieties, namely $a^1$ and $m^1$. These two varieties will generally still be exposed to the same conditions which made their parents variable, and the tendency to variability is in itself hereditary; consequently they will likewise tend to vary, and commonly in nearly the same manner as did their parents. Moreover, these two varieties, being only slightly modified forms, will tend to inherit those advantages which made their parent (A) more numerous than most of the other inhabitants of the same country; they will also partake of those more general advantages which made the genus to which the parent-species belonged, a large genus in its own country. And all these circumstances are favourable to the production of new varieties.

If, then, these two varieties be variable, the most divergent of their variations will generally be preserved during the next thousand generations. And after this interval, variety $a^1$ is supposed in the diagram to have produced variety $a^2$, which will, owing to the principle of divergence, differ more from (A) than did variety $a^1$. Variety $m^1$ is supposed to have produced two varieties, namely $m^2$ and $s^2$, differing from each other, and more considerably from their common parent (A). We may continue the process by similar steps for any length of time; some of the varieties, after each thousand generations, producing only a single variety, but in a more and more modified condition, some producing two or three varieties, and some failing to produce any. Thus the varieties or modified descendants of the common parent (A), will generally go on increasing in number and diverging in character. In the diagram the process is represented up to the ten-thousandth generation, and under a condensed and simplified form up to the fourteen-thousandth generation.

But I must here remark that I do not suppose that the process ever goes on so regularly as is represented in the diagram, though in itself made somewhat irregular, nor that it goes on continuously; it is far more probable that each form remains for long periods unaltered, and then again undergoes modification. Nor do I suppose that the most divergent varieties are invariably preserved: a medium form may often long endure, and may or may not produce more than one modified descendant; for natural selection will always act according to the nature of the places which are either unoccupied or not perfectly occupied by other beings; and this will depend on infinitely complex relations. But as a general rule, the more diversified in structure the descendants from any one species can be rendered, the more places they will be enabled to seize on, and the more their modified progeny will increase. In our diagram the line of succession is broken at regular intervals by small numbered letters marking the successive forms which have become sufficiently distinct to be recorded as varieties. But these breaks are imaginary, and might have been inserted anywhere, after intervals long enough to allow the accumulation of a considerable amount of divergent variation.

As all the modified descendants from a common and widely-diffused species, belonging to a large genus, will tend to partake of the same advantages which made their parent successful in life, they will generally go on multiplying in number as well as diverging in character: this is represented in the diagram by the several divergent branches proceeding from (A). The modified offspring from the later and more highly improved branches in the lines of descent, will, it is probable, often take the place of, and so destroy, the earlier and less improved branches: this is represented in the diagram by some of the lower branches not reaching to the upper horizontal lines. In some cases no doubt the process of modification will be confined to a single line of descent and the number of modified descendants will not be increased; although the amount of divergent modification may have been augmented. This case would be represented in the diagram, if all the lines proceeding from (A) were removed, excepting that from $a^1$ to $a^{10}$. In the same way the English race-horse and English pointer have apparently both gone on slowly diverging in character from their original stocks, without either having given off any fresh branches or races.

After ten thousand generations, species (A) is supposed to have produced three forms, $a^{10}$, $f^{10}$, and $m^{10}$, which, from having diverged in character during the successive generations, will have come to differ largely, but perhaps unequally, from each other and from their common parent. If we suppose the amount of change between each horizontal line in our diagram to be excessively small, these three forms may still be only well-marked varieties; but we have only to suppose the steps in the process of modification to be more numerous or greater in amount, to convert these three forms into doubtful or at least into well-defined species. Thus the diagram illustrates the steps by which the small differences distinguishing varieties are increased into the larger differences distinguishing species. By continuing the same process for a greater number of generations (as shown in the diagram in a condensed and simplified manner), we get eight species, marked by the letters between $a^{14}$ and $m^{14}$, all descended from (A). Thus, as I believe, species are multiplied and genera are formed.

In a large genus it is probable that more than one species would vary. In the diagram I have assumed that a second species (I) has produced, by analogous steps, after ten thousand generations, either two well-marked varieties ($w^{10}$ and $z^{10}$) or two species, according to the amount of change supposed to be represented between the horizontal lines. After fourteen thousand generations, six new species, marked by the letters $n^{14}$ to $z^{14}$, are supposed to have been produced. In any genus, the species which are already very different in character from each other, will generally tend to produce the greatest number of modified descendants; for these will have the best chance of seizing on new and widely different places in the polity of nature: hence in the diagram I have chosen the extreme species (A), and the nearly extreme species (I), as those which have largely varied, and have given rise to new varieties and species. The other nine species (marked by capital letters) of our original genus, may for long but unequal periods continue to transmit unaltered descendants; and this is shown in the diagram by the dotted lines unequally prolonged upwards.

But during the process of modification, represented in the diagram, another of our principles, namely that of extinction, will have played an important part. As in each fully stocked country natural selection necessarily acts by the selected form having some advantage in the struggle for life over other forms, there will be a constant tendency in the improved descendants of any one species to supplant and exterminate in each stage of descent their predecessors and their original progenitor. For it should be remembered that the competition will generally be most severe between those forms, which are most nearly related to each other in habits, constitution, and structure. Hence all the intermediate forms between the earlier and later states, that is between the less and more improved states of the same species, as well as the original parent-species itself, will generally tend to become extinct. So it probably will be with many whole collateral lines of descent, which will be conquered by later and improved lines. If, however, the modified offspring of a species get into some distinct country, or become quickly adapted to some quite new station, in which offspring and progenitor do not come into competition, both may continue to exist.

If, then, our diagram be assumed to represent a considerable amount of modification, species (A) and all the earlier varieties will have become extinct, being replaced by eight new species ($a^{14}$ to $m^{14}$); and species (I) will be replaced by six ($n^{14}$ to $z^{14}$) new species.

But we may go further than this. The original species of our genus were supposed to resemble each other in unequal degrees, as is so generally the case in nature; species (A) being more nearly related to B, C, and D, than to the other species; and species (I) more to G, H, K, L, than to the others. These two species (A) and (I) were also supposed to be very common and widely diffused species, so that they must originally have had some advantage over most of the other species of the genus. Their modified descendants, fourteen in number at the fourteen-thousandth generation, will probably have inherited some of the same advantages: they have also been modified and improved in a diversified manner at each stage of descent, so as to have become adapted to many related places in the natural economy of their country. It seems, therefore, extremely probable that they will have taken the places of, and thus exterminated not only their parents (A) and (I), but likewise some of the original species which were most nearly related to their parents. Hence very few of the original species will have transmitted offspring to the fourteen-thousandth generation. We may suppose that only one, (F), of the two species (E and F) which were least closely related to the other nine original species, has transmitted descendants to this late stage of descent.

The new species in our diagram descended from the original eleven species, will now be fifteen in number. Owing to the divergent tendency of natural selection, the extreme amount of difference in character between species $a^{14}$ and $z^{14}$ will be much greater than that between the most distinct of the original eleven species. The new species, moreover, will be allied to each other in a widely different manner. Of the eight descendants from (A) the three marked $a^{14}$, $q^{14}$, $p^{14}$, will be nearly related from having recently branched off from $a^{10}$, $b^{14}$, and $f^{14}$, from having diverged at an earlier period from $a^5$, will be in some degree distinct from the three first-named species; and lastly, $o^{14}$, $e^{14}$, and $m^{14}$, will be nearly related one to the other, but, from having diverged at the first commencement of the process of modification, will be widely different from the other five species, and may constitute a sub-genus or a distinct genus.

The six descendants from (I) will form two sub-genera or

genera. But as the original species (I) differed largely from (A), standing nearly at the extreme end of the original genus, the six descendants from (I) will, owing to inheritance alone, differ considerably from the eight descendants from (A); the two groups, moreover, are supposed to have gone on diverging in different directions. The intermediate species, also (and this is a very important consideration), which connected the original species (A) and (I), have all become, excepting (F), extinct, and have left no descendants. Hence the six new species descended from (I), and the eight descendants from (A), will have to be ranked as very distinct genera, or even as distinct sub-families.

Thus it is, as I believe, that two or more genera are produced by descent with modification, from two or more species of the same genus. And the two or more parent-species are supposed to be descended from some one species of an earlier genus. In our diagram, this is indicated by the broken lines, beneath the capital letters, converging in sub-branches downwards towards a single point; this point represents a species, the supposed progenitor of our several new sub-genera and genera.

It is worth while to reflect for a moment on the character of the new species $F^{14}$, which is supposed not to have diverged much in character, but to have retained the form of (F), either unaltered or altered only in a slight degree. In this case, its affinities of the other fourteen new species will be of a curious and circuitous nature. Being descended from a form which stood between the parent-species (A) and (I), now supposed to be extinct and unknown, it will be in some degree intermediate in character between the two groups descended from these two species. But as these two groups have gone on diverging in character from the type of their parents, the new species ($F^{14}$) will not be directly intermediate between them, but rather between types of the two groups; and every naturalist will be able to call such cases before his mind.

In the diagram, each horizontal line has hitherto been supposed to represent a thousand generations, but each may represent a million or more generations; it may also represent a section of the successive strata of the earth's crust including extinct remains. We shall, when we come to one chapter on Geology, have to refer again to this subject, and I think we shall then see that the diagram throws light on the affinities of extinct beings, which, though generally belonging to the same orders, families, or genera, with those now living, yet are often, in some degree, intermediate in character between existing groups; and we can understand this fact, for the extinct species lived at various remote epochs when the branching lines of descent had diverged less.

I see no reason to limit the process of modification, as now explained, to the formation of genera alone. If, in the diagram, we suppose the amount of change, represented by each successive group of diverging dotted lines to be great, the forms marked $a^{14}$ to $p^{14}$, those marked $b^{14}$ and $f^{14}$, and those marked $o^{14}$ to $m^{14}$, will form three very distinct genera. We shall also have two very distinct genera descended from (I), differing widely from the descendants of (A). These two groups of genera will thus form two distinct families, or orders, according to the amount of divergent modification supposed to be represented in the diagram. And the two new families, or orders, are descended from two species of the original genus, and these are supposed to be descended from some still more ancient and unknown form.

We have seen that in each country it is the species belonging to the larger genera which oftenest present varieties or incipient species. This, indeed, might have been expected; for, as natural selection acts through one form having some advantage over other forms in the struggle for existence, it will chiefly act on those which already have some advantage; and the largeness of any group shows that its species have inherited from a common ancestor some advantage in common. Hence, the struggle for the production of new and modified descendants will mainly lie between the larger groups which are all trying to increase in number. One large group will slowly conquer another large group, reduce its numbers, and thus lessen its chance of further variation and improvement. Within the same large group, the later and more highly perfected sub-groups, from branching out and seizing on many new places in the polity of Nature, will constantly tend to supplant and destroy the earlier and less improved sub-groups. Small and broken groups and sub-groups will finally disappear. Looking to the future, we can predict that the groups of organic beings which are now large and triumphant, and which are least broken up, that is, which have as yet suffered least extinction, will, for a long period, continue to increase. But which groups will ultimately prevail, no man can predict; for we know that many groups formerly most extensively developed, have now become extinct. Looking still more remotely to the future, we may predict that, owing to the continued and steady increase of the larger groups, a multitude of smaller groups will become utterly extinct, and leave no modified descendants; and consequently that, of the species living at any one period, extremely few will transmit descendants to a remote futurity. I shall have to return to this subject in the chapter on Classification, but I may add that as, according to this view, extremely few of the more ancient species have transmitted descendants to the present day, and, as all the descendants of the same species form a class, we can understand how it is that there exist so few classes in each main division of the animal and vegetable kingdoms. Although few of the most ancient species have left modified descendants, yet, at remote geological periods, the earth may have been almost as well peopled with species of many genera, families, orders, and classes, as at the present time.

### *On the Degree to which Organization tends to advance*

Natural Selection acts exclusively by the preservation and accumulation of variations, which are beneficial under the organic and inorganic conditions to which each creature is exposed at all periods of life. The ultimate result is that each creature tends to become more and more improved in relation to its conditions. This improvement inevitably leads to the gradual advancement of the organisation of the greater number of living beings throughout the world. But here we enter on a very intricate subject, for naturalists have not defined to each other's satisfaction what is meant by an advance in organisation. Amongst the vertebrata the degree of intellect and an approach in structure to man clearly come into play. It might be thought that the amount of change which the various parts and organs pass through in their development from the embryo to maturity would suffice as a standard of comparison; but there are cases, as with certain parasitic crustaceans, in which several parts of the structure become less perfect, so that the mature animal cannot be called higher than its larva. Von Baer's standard seems the most widely applicable and the best, namely, the amount of differentiation of the parts of the same organic being, in the adult state as I should be inclined to add, and their specialisation for different functions; or, as Milne Edwards would express it, the completeness of the division of physiological labour. But we shall see how obscure this subject is if we look, for instance, to fishes, amongst which some naturalists rank those as highest which, like the sharks, approach nearest to amphibians; whilst other naturalists rank the common bony or teleostean fishes as the highest, inasmuch as they are most strictly fish-like and differ most from the other vertebrate classes. We see still more plainly the obscurity of the subject by turning to plants, amongst which the standard of intellect is of course quite excluded; and here some botanists rank those plants as highest which have every organ, as sepals, petals, stamens, and pistils, fully developed in each flower; whereas other botanists, probably with more truth, look at the plants which have their several organs much modified and reduced in number as the highest.

If we take as the standard of high organisation, the amount

of differentiation and specialisation of the several organs in each being when adult (and this will include the advancement of the brain for intellectual purposes), natural selection clearly leads towards this standard: for all physiologists admit that the specialisation of organs, inasmuch as in this state they perform their functions better, is an advantage to each being; and hence the accumulation of variations tending towards specialisation is within the scope of natural selection. On the other hand, we can see, bearing in mind that all organic beings are striving to increase at a high ratio and to seize on every unoccupied or less well occupied place in the economy of nature, that it is quite possible for natural selection gradually to fit a being to a situation in which several organs would be superfluous or useless: in such cases there would be retrogression in the scale of organisation. Whether organisation on the whole has actually advanced from the remotest geological periods to the present day will be more conveniently discussed in our chapter on Geological Succession.

But it may be objected that if all organic beings thus tend to rise in the scale, how is it that throughout the world a multitude of the lowest forms still exist; and how is it that in each great class some forms are far more highly developed than others? Why have not the more highly developed forms everywhere supplanted and exterminated the lower? Lamarck, who believed in an innate and inevitable tendency towards perfection in all organic beings, seems to have felt this difficulty so strongly, that he was led to suppose that new and simple forms are continually being produced by spontaneous generation. Science has not as yet proved the truth of this belief, whatever the future may reveal. On our theory the continued existence of lowly organisms offers no difficulty; for natural selection, or the survival of the fittest, does not necessarily include progressive development — it only takes advantage of such variations as arise and are beneficial to each creature under its complex relations of life. And it may be asked what advantage, as far as we can see, would it be to an infusorian animalcule — to an intestinal worm — or even to an earthworm, to be highly organised. If it were no advantage, these forms would be left, by natural selection, unimproved or but little improved, and might remain for indefinite ages in their present lowly condition. And geology tells us that some of the lowest forms, as the infusoria and rhizopods, have remained for an enormous period in nearly their present state. But to suppose that most of the many now existing low forms have not in the least advanced since the first dawn of life would be extremely rash; for every naturalist who has dissected some of the beings now ranked as very low in the scale, must have been struck with their really wondrous and beautiful organisation.

Nearly the same remarks are applicable if we look to the different grades of organisation within the same great group; for instance, in the vertebrata, to the co-existence of mammals and fish — amongst mammalia, to the co-existence of man and the ornithorhynchus — amongst fishes, to the co-existence of the shark and the lancelot (Amphioxus), which latter fish in the extreme simplicity of its structure approaches the invertebrate classes. But mammals and fish hardly come into competition with each other; the advancement of the whole class of mammals, or of certain members in this class, to the highest grade would not lead to their taking the place of fishes. Physiologists believe that the brain must be bathed by warm blood to be highly active, and this requires aërial respiration; so that warm-blooded mammals when inhabiting the water lie under a disadvantage in having to come continually to the surface to breathe. With fishes, members of the shark family would not tend to supplant the lancelet; for the lancelet, as I hear from Fritz Müller, has as sole companion and competitor on the barren sandy shore of South Brazil, an anomalous annelid. The three lowest orders of mammals, namely, marsupials, edentata, and rodents, co-exist in South America in the same region with numerous monkeys, and probably interfere little with each other. Although organisation, on the whole, may have advanced and be still advancing throughout the world, yet the scale will always present many degrees of perfection; for the high advancement of certain whole classes, or of certain members of each class, does not at all necessarily lead to the extinction of those groups with which they do not enter into close competition. In some cases, as we shall hereafter see, lowly organised forms appear to have been less preserved to the present day, from inhabiting confined or peculiar stations, where they have been subjected to less severe competition, and where their scanty numbers have retarded the chance of favourable variations arising.

Finally, I believe that many lowly organised forms now exist throughout the world, from various causes. In some cases variations or individual differences of a favourable nature may never have arisen for natural selection to act on and accumulate. In no case, probably, has time sufficed for the utmost possible amount of development. In some few cases there has been what we must call retrogression of organisation. But the main cause lies in the fact that under very simple conditions of life a high organisation would be of no service, — possibly would be of actual disservice, as being of a more delicate nature, and more liable to be put out of order and injured.

Looking to the first dawn of life, when all organic beings, as we may believe, presented the simplest structure, how, it has been asked, could the first steps in the advancement or differentiation of parts have arisen? Mr. Herbert Spencer would probably answer that, as soon as simple unicellular organism came by growth or division to be compounded of several cells, or became attached to any supporting surface, his law "that homologous units of any order become differentiated in proportion as their relations to incident forces become different" would come into action. But as we have no facts to guide us, speculation on the subject is almost useless. It is, however, an error to suppose that there would be no struggle for existence, and, consequently, no natural selection, until many forms had been produced: variations in a single species inhabiting an isolated station might be beneficial, and thus the whole mass of individuals might be modified, or two distinct forms might arise. But, as I remarked towards the close of the Introduction, no one ought to feel surprise at much remaining as yet unexplained on the origin of species, if we make due allowance for our profound ignorance on the mutual relations of the inhabitants of the world at the present time, and still more so during past ages.

### *Convergence of Character*

Mr. H. C. Watson thinks that I have overrated the importance of divergence of character (in which, however, he apparently believes), and that convergence, as it may be called, has likewise played a part. If two species, belonging to two distinct though allied genera, had both produced a large number of new and divergent forms, it is conceivable that these might approach each other so closely that they would have all to be classed under the same genus; and thus the descendants of two distinct genera would converge into one. But it would in most cases be extremely rash to attribute to convergence a close and general similarity of structure in the modified descendants of widely distinct forms. The shape of a crystal is determined solely by the molecular forces, and it is not surprising that dissimilar substances should sometimes assume the same form; but with organic beings we should bear in mind that the form of each depends on an infinitude of complex relations, namely on the variations which have arisen, these being due to causes far too intricate to be followed out, — on the nature of the variations which have been preserved or selected, and this depends on the surrounding physical conditions, and in a still higher degree on the surrounding organisms with which each being has come into competition, — and lastly, on inheritance (in itself a fluctuating element) from innumerable progenitors, all of which have had their forms determined through equally complex relations. It is incredible that the descendants of two organisms, which had originally differed in a marked manner, should ever afterwards converge so closely as to lead to a near approach to identity throughout their whole organisation. If this had occurred, we should meet with the same form, independently of genetic connection, recurring in widely separated geological formations; and the balance of evidence is opposed to any such an admission.

Mr. Watson has also objected that the continued action of natural selection, together with divergence of character, would tend to make an indefinite number of specific forms. As far as mere inorganic conditions are concerned, it seems probable that a sufficient number of species would soon become adapted to all considerable diversities of heat, moisture, &c.; but I fully admit that the mutual relations of organic beings are more important; and as the number of species in any country goes on increasing, the organic conditions of life must become more and more complex. Consequently there seems at first sight no limit to the amount of profitable diversification of structure, and therefore no limit to the number of species which might be produced. We do not know that even the most prolific area is fully stocked with specific forms: at the Cape of Good Hope and in Australia, which support such an astonishing number of species, many European plants have become naturalised. But geology shows us, that from an early part of the tertiary period the number of species of shells, and that from the middle part of this same period the number of mammals, has not greatly or at all increased. What then checks an indefinite increase in the number of species? The amount of life (I do not mean the number of specific forms) supported on an area must have a limit, depending so largely as it does on physical conditions; therefore, if an area be inhabited by very many species, each or nearly each species will be represented by few individuals; and such species will be liable to extermination from accidental fluctuations in the nature of the seasons or in the number of their enemies. The process of extermination in such cases would be rapid, whereas the production of new species must always be slow. Imagine the extreme case of as many species as individuals in England, and the first severe winter or very dry summer would exterminate thousands on thousands of species. Rare species, and each species will become rare if the number of species in any country becomes indefinitely increased, will, on the principle often explained, present within a given period few favourable variations; consequently, the process of giving birth to new specific forms would thus be retarded. When any species becomes very rare, close interbreeding will help to exterminate it; authors have thought that this comes into play in accounting for the deterioration of the Aurochs in Lithuania, of Red Deer in Scotland, and of Bears in Norway, &c. Lastly, and this I am inclined to think is the most important element, a dominant species, which has already beaten many competitors in its own home, will tend to spread and supplant many others. Alph. de Candolle has shown that those species which spread widely, tend generally to spread *very* widely; consequently, they will tend to supplant and exterminate several species in several areas, and thus check the inordinate increase of specific forms throughout the world. Dr. Hooker has recently shown that in the S.E. corner of Australia, where, apparently, there are many invaders from different quarters of the globe, the endemic Australian species have been greatly reduced in number. How much weight to attribute to these several considerations I will not pretend to say; but conjointly they must limit in each country the tendency to an indefinite augmentation of specific forms.

### *Summary of Chapter*

If under changing conditions of life organic beings present individual differences in almost every part of their structure, and this cannot be disputed; if there be, owing to their geometrical rate of increase, a severe struggle for life at some age, season, or year, and this certainly cannot be disputed; then, considering the infinite complexity of the relations of all organic beings to each other and to their conditions of life, causing an infinite diversity in structure, constitution, and habits, to be advantageous to them, it would be a most extraordinary fact if no variations had ever occurred useful to each being's own welfare, in the same manner as so many variations have occurred useful to man. But if variations useful to any organic being ever do occur, assuredly individuals thus characterised will have the best chance of being preserved in the struggle for life; and from the strong principle of inheritance, these will tend to produce offspring similarly characterised. This principle of preservation, or the survival of the fittest, I have called Natural Selection. It leads to the improvement of each creature in relation to its organic and inorganic conditions of life; and consequently, in most cases, to what must be regarded as an advance in organisation. Nevertheless, low and simple forms will long endure if well fitted for their simple conditions of life.

Natural selection, on the principle of qualities being inherited at corresponding ages, can modify the egg, seed, or young, as easily as the adult. Amongst many animals, sexual selection will have given its aid to ordinary selection, by assuring to the most vigorous and best adapted males the greatest number of offspring. Sexual selection will also give characters useful to the males alone, in their struggles or rivalry with other males; and these characters will be transmitted to one sex or to both sexes, according to the form of inheritance which prevails.

Whether natural selection has really thus acted in adapting the various forms of life to their several conditions and stations, must be judged by the general tenor and balance of evidence given in the following chapters. But we have already seen how it entails extinction; and how largely extinction has acted in the world's history, geology plainly declares. Natural selection, also leads to divergence of character; for the more organic beings diverge in structure, habits, and constitution, by so much the more can a large number be supported on the area, — of which we see proof by looking to the inhabitants of any small spot, and to the productions naturalised in foreign lands. Therefore, during the modification of the descendants of any one species, and during the incessant struggle of all species to increase in numbers, the more diversified the descendants become, the better will be their chance of success in the battle for life. Thus the small differences distinguishing varieties of the same species, steadily tend to increase, till they equal the greater differences between species of the same genus, or even of distinct genera.

We have seen that it is the common, the widely-diffused and widely-ranging species, belonging to the larger genera within each class, which vary most; and these tend to transmit to their modified offspring that superiority which now makes them dominant in their own countries. Natural selection, as has just been remarked, leads to divergence of character and to much extinction of the less improved and intermediate forms of life. On these principles, the nature of the affinities, and the generally well-defined distinctions between the innumerable organic beings in each class throughout the world, may be explained. It is a truly wonderful fact — the wonder of which we are apt to overlook from familiarity — that all animals and all plants throughout all time and space should be related to each other in groups, subordinate to groups, in the manner which we everywhere behold — namely, varieties of the same species most closely related, species of the same genus less closely and unequally related, forming sections and sub-genera, species of distinct genera much less closely related, and genera related in different degrees, forming sub-families, families, orders, sub-classes and classes. The several subordinate groups in any class cannot be ranked in a single file, but seen clustered round points, and these round other points, and so on in almost endless cycles. If species had been independently created, no explanation would have been possible of this kind of classification; but it is explained through inheritance and the complex action of natural selection, entailing extinction and divergence of character, as we have seen illustrated in the diagram.

The affinities of all the beings of the same class have sometimes been represented by a great tree. I believe this simile largely speaks the truth. The green and budding twigs may represent existing species; and those produced during former years may represent the long succession of extinct species. At each period of growth all the growing twigs have tried to branch out on all sides, and to overtop and kill the surrounding twigs and branches, in the same manner as species and groups of species have at all times overmastered other species in the great battle for life. The limbs divided into great branches, and these into lesser and lesser branches, were themselves once, when the tree was young, budding twigs, and this connection of the former and present buds by ramifying branches may well represent the classification of all extinct and living species in groups subordinate to groups. Of the many twigs which flourished when the tree was a mere bush, only two or three, now grown into great branches, yet survive and bear the other branches; so with the species which lived during long-past geological periods, very few have left living and modified descendants. From the first growth of the tree, many a limb and branch has decayed and dropped off; and these fallen branches of various sizes may represent those whole orders, families, and genera which have now no living representatives, and which are known to us only in a fossil state. As we here and there see a thin straggling branch springing from a fork low down in a tree, and which by some chance has been favoured and is still alive on its summit, so we occasionally see an animal like the Ornithorhynchus or Lepidosiren, which in some small degree connects by its affinities two large branches of life, and which has apparently been saved from fatal competition by having inhabited a protected station. As buds give rise by growth to fresh buds, and these, if vigorous, branch out and overtop on all sides many a feebler branch, so by generation I believe it has been with the great Tree of Life, which fills with its dead and broken branches the crust of the earth, and covers the surface with its ever-branching and beautiful ramifications.

# *Difficulties of the Theory*

Long before the reader has arrived at this part of my work, a crowd of difficulties will have occurred to him. Some of them are so serious that to this day I can hardly reflect on them without being in some degree staggered; but, to the best of my judgment, the greater number are only apparent, and those that are real are not, I think, fatal to the theory.

These difficulties and objections may be classed under the following heads: — First, why, if species have descended from other species by fine gradations, do we not everywhere see innumerable transitional forms? Why is not all nature in confusion, instead of the species being, as we see them, well defined?

Secondly, is it possible that an animal having, for instance, the structure and habits of a bat, could have been formed by the modification of some other animal with widely different habits and structure? Can we believe that natural selection could produce, on the one hand, an organ of trifling importance, such as the tail of a giraffe, which serves as a fly-flapper, and, on the other hand, an organ so wonderful as the eye?

Thirdly, can instincts be acquired and modified through natural selection? What shall we say to the instinct which leads the bee to make cells, and which has practically anticipated the discoveries of profound mathematicians?

Fourthly, how can we account for species, when crossed, being sterile and producing sterile offspring, whereas, when varieties are crossed, their fertility is unimpaired?

The two first heads will here be discussed; some miscellaneous objections in the following chapter; Instinct and Hybridism in the two succeeding chapters.

*On the Absence or Rarity of Transitional Varieties.*—As natural selection acts solely by the preservation of profitable modifications, each new form will tend in a fully-stocked country to take the place of, and finally to exterminate, its own less improved parent-form and other less favoured forms with which it comes into competition. Thus extinction and natural selection go hand in hand. Hence, if we look at each species as descended from some unknown form, both the parent and all the transitional varieties will generally have been exterminated by the very process of the formation and perfection of the new form.

But, as by this theory innumerable transitional forms must have existed, why do we not find them embedded in countless numbers in the crust of the earth? It will be more convenient to discuss this question in the chapter on the Imperfection of the Geological Record; and I will here only state that I believe the answer mainly lies in the record being incomparably less perfect than is generally supposed. The crust of the earth is a vast museum; but the natural collections have been imperfectly made, and only at long intervals of time.

But it may be urged that when several closely-allied species inhabit the same territory, we surely ought to find at the present time many transitional forms. Let us take a simple case: in travelling from north to south over a continent, we generally meet at successive intervals with closely allied or representative species, evidently filling nearly the same place in the natural economy of the land. These representative species often meet and interlock; and as the one becomes rarer and rarer, the other becomes more and more frequent, till the one replaces the other. But if we compare these species where they intermingle, they are generally as absolutely distinct from each other in every detail of structure as are specimens taken from the metropolis inhabited by each. By my theory these allied species are descended from a common parent; and during the process of modification, each has become adapted to the conditions of life of its own region, and has supplanted and exterminated its original parent-form and all the transitional varieties between its past and present states. Hence we ought not to expect at the present time to meet with numerous transitional varieties in each region, though they must have existed there, and may be embedded there in a fossil condition. But in the intermediate region, having intermediate conditions of life, why do we not now find closely-linking intermediate varieties? This difficulty for a long time quite confounded me. But I think it can be in large part explained.

In the first place we should be extremely cautious in inferring, because an area is now continuous, that it has been continuous during a long period. Geology would lead us to believe that most continents have been broken up into islands even during the later tertiary periods; and in such islands distinct species might have been separately formed without the possibility of intermediate varieties existing in the intermediate zones. By changes in the form of the land and of climate, marine areas now continuous must often have existed within recent times in a far less continuous and uniform condition than at present. But I will pass over this way of escaping from the difficulty; for I believe that many perfectly defined species have been formed on strictly continuous areas; though I do not doubt that the formerly broken condition of areas now continuous, has played an important part in the formation of new species, more especially with freely-crossing and wandering animals.

In looking at species as they are now distributed over a wide area, we generally find them tolerably numerous over a large territory, then becoming somewhat abruptly rarer and rarer on the confines, and finally disappearing. Hence the neutral territory, between two representative species is generally narrow in comparison with the territory proper to each. We see the same fact in ascending mountains, and sometimes it is quite remarkable how abruptly, as Alph. de Candolle has observed, a common alpine species disappears. The same fact has been noticed by E. Forbes in sounding the depths of the sea with the dredge. To those who look at climate and the physical conditions of life as the all-important elements of distribution, these facts ought to cause surprise, as climate and height or depth graduate away insensibly. But when we bear in mind that almost every species, even in its metropolis, would increase immensely in numbers, were it not for other competing species; that nearly all either prey on or serve as prey for others; in short, that each organic being is either directly or indirectly related in the most important manner to other organic beings, — we see that the range of the inhabitants of any country by no means exclusively depends on insensibly changing physical conditions, but in a large part on the presence of other species, on which it lives, or by which it is destroyed, or with which it comes into competition; and as these species are already defined objects, not blending one into another by insensible gradations, the range of any one species, depending as it does on the range of others, will tend to be sharply defined. Moreover, each species on the confines of its range, where it exists in lessened numbers, will, during fluctuations in the number of its enemies or of its prey, or in the nature of the seasons, be extremely liable to utter extermination; and thus its geographical range will come to be still more sharply defined.

As allied or representative species, when inhabiting a continuous area, are generally distributed in such a manner that each has a wide range, with a comparatively narrow neutral territory between them, in which they become rather suddenly rarer and rarer; then, as varieties do not essentially differ from species, the same rule will probably apply to both; and if we take a varying species inhabiting a very large area, we shall have to adapt two varieties to two large areas, and a third variety to a narrow intermediate zone. The intermediate variety, consequently, will exist in lesser numbers from inhabiting a narrow and lesser area; and practically, as far as I can make out, this rule holds good with varieties in a state of nature. I have met with striking instances of the rule in the case of varieties intermediate between well-marked varieties in the genus Balamus. And it would appear from information given me by Mr. Watson, Dr. Asa Gray, and Mr. Wollaston, that generally, when varieties intermediate between two other forms occur, they are much rarer numerically than the forms which they connect. Now, if we may trust these facts and inferences, and conclude that varieties linking two other varieties together generally have existed in lesser numbers than the forms which they connect, then we can understand why intermediate varieties should not endure for very long periods: — why, as a general rule, they should be exterminated and disappear, sooner than the forms which they originally linked together.

For any form existing in lesser numbers would, as already remarked, run a greater chance of being exterminated than the one existing in large numbers; and in this particular case the intermediate form would be eminently liable to the inroads of closely-allied forms existing on both sides of it. But it is a far more important consideration, that during the process of further modification, by which two varieties are supposed to be converted and perfected into two distinct species, the two which exist in larger numbers, from inhabiting larger areas, will have a great advantage over the intermediate variety, which exists in smaller numbers in a narrow and intermediate zone. For forms existing in larger numbers will have a better chance, within any given period, of presenting further favourable variations for natural selection to seize on, than will the rarer forms which exist in lesser numbers. Hence, the more common forms, in the race for life, will tend to beat and supplant the less common forms, for these will be more slowly modified and improved. It is the same principle which, as I believe, accounts for the common species in each country, as shown in the second chapter, presenting on an average a greater number of well-marked varieties than do the rarer species. I may illustrate what I mean by supposing three varieties of sheep to be kept, one adapted to an extensive mountainous region; a second to a comparatively narrow, hilly tract; and a third to the wide plains at the base; and that the inhabitants are all trying with equal steadiness and skill to improve their stocks by selection; the chances in this case will be strongly in favour of the great holders on the mountains or on the plains, improving their breeds more quickly than the small holders on the intermediate narrow, hilly tract; and consequently the improved mountain or plain breed will soon take the place of the less improved hill breed; and thus the two breeds, which originally existed in greater numbers, will come into close contact with each other, without the interposition of the supplanted, intermediate hill variety.

To sum up, I believe that species come to be tolerably well-defined objects, and do not at any one period present an inextricable chaos of varying and intermediate links; first, because new varieties are very slowly formed, for variation is a slow process, and natural selection can do nothing until favourable individual differences or variations occur, and until a place in the natural polity of the country can be better filled by some modification of some one or more of its inhabitants. And such new places will depend on slow changes of climate, or on the occasional immigration of new inhabitants, and, probably, in a still more important degree, on some of the old inhabitants becoming slowly modified, with the new forms thus produced, and the old ones acting and reacting on each other. So that, in any one region and at any one time, we ought to see only a few species presenting slight modifications of structure in some degree permanent; and this assuredly we do see.

Secondly, areas now continuous must often have existed within the recent period as isolated portions, in which many forms, more especially amongst the classes which unite for each birth and wander much, may have separately been rendered sufficiently distinct to rank as representative species. In this case, intermediate varieties between the several representative species and their common parent, must formerly have existed within each isolated portion of the land, but these links during the process of natural selection will have been supplanted and exterminated, so that they will no longer be found in a living state.

Thirdly, when two or more varieties have been formed in different portions of a strictly continuous area, intermediate varieties will, it is probable, at first have been formed in the intermediate zones, but they will generally have had a short duration. For these intermediate varieties will, from reasons already assigned (namely from what we know of the actual distribution of closely allied or representative species, and likewise of acknowledged varieties), exist in the intermediate zones in lesser numbers than the varieties which they tend to connect. From this cause alone the intermediate varieties will be liable to accidental extermination; and during the process of further modification through natural selection, they will almost certainly be beaten and supplanted by the forms which they connect; for these from existing in greater numbers will, in the aggregate, present more varieties, and thus be further improved through natural selection and gain further advantages.

Lastly, looking not to any one time, but to all time, if my theory be true, numberless intermediate varieties, linking closely together all the species of the same group, must assuredly have existed; but the very process of natural selection constantly tends, as has been so often remarked, to exterminate the parent-forms and the intermediate links. Consequently evidence of their former existence could be found only amongst fossil remains, which are preserved, as we shall attempt to show in a future chapter, in an extremely imperfect and intermittent record.

*On the Origin and Transitions of Organic Beings with peculiar Habits and Structure.* — It has been asked by the opponents of such views as I hold, how, for instance, could a land carnivorous animal have been converted into one with aquatic habits; for how could the animal in its transitional state have subsisted? It would be easy to show that there now exist carnivorous animals presenting close intermediate grades from strictly terrestrial to aquatic habits; and as each exists by a struggle for life, it is clear that each must be well adapted to its place in nature. Look at the Mustela vison of North America, which has webbed feet, and which resembles an otter in its fur, short legs, and form of tail. During the summer this animal dives for and preys on fish, but during the long winter it leaves the frozen waters, and preys, like other pole-cats, on mice and land animals. If a different case had been taken, and it had been asked how an insectivorous quadruped could possibly have been converted into a flying bat, the question would have been far more difficult to answer. Yet I think such difficulties have little weight.

Here, as on other occasions, I lie under a heavy disadvantage, for, out of the many striking cases which I have collected, I can only give one or two instances of transitional habits and structures in allied species; and of diversified habits, either constant or occasional, in the same species. And it seems to me that nothing less than a long list of such cases is sufficient to lessen the difficulty in any particular case like that of the bat.

Look at the family of squirrels; here we have the finest gradation from animals with their tails only slightly flattened, and from others, as Sir J. Richardson has remarked, with the posterior part of their bodies rather wide and with the skin on their flanks rather full, to the so-called flying squirrels; and flying squirrels have their limbs and even the base of the tail united by a broad expanse of skin, which serves as a parachute and allows them to glide through the air to an astonishing distance from tree to tree. We cannot doubt that each structure is of use to each kind of squirrel in its own country, by enabling it to escape birds or beasts of prey, to collect food more quickly, or, as there is reason to believe, to lessen the danger from occasional falls. But it does not follow from this fact that the structure of each squirrel is the best that is possible to conceive under all possible conditions. Let the climate and vegetation change, let other competing rodents or new beasts of prey immigrate, or old ones become modified, and all analogy would lead us to believe that some at least of the squirrels would decrease in numbers or become exterminated, unless they also become modified and improved in structure in a corresponding manner. Therefore, I can see no difficulty, more especially under changing conditions of life, in the continued preservation of individuals with fuller and fuller flank-membranes, each modification being useful, each being propagated, until, by the accumulated effects of this process of natural selection, a perfect so-called flying squirrel was produced.

Now look at the Galeopithecus or so-called flying lemur, which formerly was ranked amongst bats, but is now believed to belong to the Insectivora. An extremely wide flank-membrane stretches from the corners of the jaw to the tail, and includes the limbs with the elongated fingers. This flank-membrane is furnished with an extensor muscle. Although no graduated links of structure, fitted for gliding through the air, now connect the Galeopithecus with the other Insectivora, yet there is no difficulty in supposing that such links formerly existed, and that each was developed in the same manner as with the less perfectly gliding squirrels; each grade of structure having been useful to its possessor. Nor can I see any insuperable difficulty in further believing that the membrane connected fingers and fore-arm of the Galeopithecus might have been greatly lengthened by natural selection; and this, as far as the organs of flight are concerned, would have converted the animal into a bat. In certain bats in which the wing-membrane extends from the top of the shoulder to the tail and includes the hind-legs, we perhaps see traces of an apparatus originally fitted for gliding through the air rather than for flight.

If about a dozen genera of birds were to become extinct, who would have ventured to surmise that birds might have existed which used their wings solely as flappers, like the logger-headed duck (Micropterus of Eyton); as fins in the water and as front-legs on the land, like the penguin; as sails, like the ostrich; and functionally for no purpose, like the Apteryx? Yet the structure of each of these birds is good for it, under the conditions of life to which it is exposed, for each has to live by a struggle; but it is not necessarily the best possible under all possible conditions. It must not be inferred from these remarks that any of the grades of wing-structure here alluded to, which perhaps may all be the result of disuse, indicate the steps by which birds actually acquired their perfect power of flight; but they serve to show what diversified means of transition are at least possible.

Seeing that a few members of such water-breathing classes as the Crustacea and Mollusca are adapted to live on the land; and seeing that we have flying birds and mammals, flying insects of the most diversified types, and formerly had flying reptiles, it is conceivable that flying-fish, which now glide far through the air, slightly rising and turning by the aid of their fluttering fins, might have been modified into perfectly winged animals. If this had been effected, who would have ever imagined that in an early transitional state they had been the inhabitants of the open ocean, and had used their incipient organs of flight exclusively, as far as we know, to escape being devoured by other fish?

When we see any structure highly perfected for any particular habit, as the wings of a bird for flight, we should bear in mind that animals displaying early transitional grades of the structure will seldom have survived to the present day, for they will have been supplanted by their successors, which were gradually rendered more perfect through natural selection. Furthermore, we may conclude that transitional states between structures fitted for very different habits of life will rarely have been developed at an early period in great numbers and under many subordinate forms. Thus, to return to our imaginary illustration of the flying-fish, it does not seem probable that fishes capable of true flight would have been developed under many subordinate forms, for taking prey of many kinds in many ways, on the land and in the water, until their organs of flight had come to a high stage of perfection, so as to have given them a decided advantage over other animals in the battle for life. Hence the chance of discovering species with transitional grades of structure in a fossil condition will always be less, from their having existed in lesser numbers, than in the case of species with fully developed structures.

I will now give two or three instances both of diversified and of changed habits in the individuals of the same species. In either case it would be easy for natural selection to adapt the structure of the animal to its changed habits, or exclusively to one of its several habits. It is, however, difficult to decide, and immaterial for us, whether habits generally change first and structure afterwards; or whether slight modifications of structure lead to changed habits; both probably often occurring almost simultaneously. Of cases of changed habits it will suffice merely to allude to that of the many British insects which now feed on exotic plants, or exclusively on artificial substances. Of diversified habits innumerable instances could be given: I have often watched a tyrant flycatcher (Saurophagus sulphuratus) in South America, hovering over one spot and then proceeding to another, like a kestrel, and at other times standing stationary on the margin of water, and then dashing into it like a kingfisher at a fish. In our own country the larger titmouse (Parus major) may be seen climbing branches, almost like a creeper; it sometimes, like a shrike, kills small birds by blows on the head; and I have many times seen and heard it hammering the seeds of the yew on a branch, and thus breaking them like a nuthatch. In North America the black bear was seen by Hearne swimming for hours with widely open mouth, thus catching, almost like a whale, insects in the water.

As we sometimes see individuals following habits different from those proper to their species and to the other species of the same genus, we might expect that such individuals would occasionally give rise to new species, having anomalous habits, and with their structure either slightly or considerably modified from that of their type. And such instances occur in nature. Can a more striking instance of adaptation be given than that of a woodpecker for climbing trees and seizing insects in the chinks of the bark? Yet in North America there are woodpeckers which feed largely on fruit, and others with elongated wings which chase insects on the wing. On the plains of La Plata, where hardly a tree grows, there is a woodpecker (Colaptes campestris) which has two toes before and two behind, a long pointed tongue, pointed tail-feathers, sufficiently stiff to support the bird in a vertical position on a post, but not so stiff as in the typical woodpeckers, and a straight strong beak. The beak, however, is not so straight or so strong as in the typical woodpeckers, but it is strong enough to bore into wood. Hence this Colaptes in all the essential parts of its structure is a woodpecker. Even in such trifling characters as the colouring, the harsh tone of the voice, and undulatory flight, its close blood-relationship to our common woodpecker is plainly declared; yet, as I can assert, not only from my own observation, but from those of the accurate Azara, in certain large districts it does not climb trees, and it makes its nest in holes in banks! In certain other districts, however, this same woodpecker, as Mr. Hudson states, frequents trees, and bores holes in the trunk for its nest. I may mention as another illustration of the varied habits of this genus, that a Mexican

Colaptes has been described by De Saussure as boring holes into hard wood in order to lay up a store of acorns.

Petrels are the most aërial and oceanic of birds, but in the quiet sounds of Tierra del Fuego, the Puffinuria berardi, in its general habits, in its astonishing power of diving, in its manner of swimming and of flying when made to take flight, would be mistaken by any one for an auk or a grebe; nevertheless it is essentially a petrel, but with many parts of its organisation profoundly modified in relation to its new habits of life; whereas the woodpecker of La Plata has had its structure only slightly modified. In the case of the water-ouzel, the acutest observer by examining its dead body would never have suspected its sub-aquatic habits; yet this bird, which is allied to the thrush family, subsists by diving — using its wings under water, and grasping stones with its feet. All the members of the great order of Hymenopterus insects are terrestrial, excepting the genus Proctotrupes, which Sir John Lubbock has discovered to be aquatic in its habits; it often enters the water and dives about by the use not of its legs but of its wings, and remains as long as four hours beneath the surface; yet it exhibits no modification in structure in accordance with its abnormal habits.

He who believes that each being has been created as we now see it, must occasionally have felt surprise when he has met with an animal having habits and structure not in agreement. What can be plainer than that the webbed feet of ducks and geese are formed for swimming? Yet there are upland geese with webbed feet which rarely go near the water; and no one except Audubon has seen the frigate-bird, which has all its four toes webbed, alight on the surface of the ocean. On the other hand, grebes and coots are eminently aquatic, although their toes are only bordered by membrane. What seems plainer than that the long toes, not furnished with membrane of the Grallatores are formed for walking over swamps and floating plants? — the water-hen and landrail are members of this order, yet the first is nearly as aquatic as the coot, and the second nearly as terrestrial as the quail or partridge. In such cases, and many others could be given, habits have changed without a corresponding change of structure. The webbed feet of the upland goose may be said to have become almost rudimentary in function, though not in structure. In the frigate-bird, the deeply scored membrane between the toes shows that structure has begun to change.

He who believes in separate and innumerable acts of creation may say, that in these cases it has pleased the Creator to cause a being of one type to take the place of one belonging to another type; but this seems to me only re-stating the fact in dignified language. He who believes in the struggle for existence and in the principle of natural selection, will acknowledge that every organic being is constantly endeavouring to increase in numbers; and that if any one being varies ever so little, either in habits or structure, and thus gains an advantage over some other inhabitant of the same country, it will seize on the place of that inhabitant, however different that may be from its own place. Hence it will cause him no surprise that there should be geese and frigate-birds with webbed feet, living on the dry land and rarely alighting on the water, that there should be long-toed corncrakes, living in meadows instead of in swamps; that there should be woodpeckers where hardly a tree grows; that there should be diving thrushes and diving Hymenoptera, and petrels with the habits of auks.

### *Organs of extreme Perfection and Complication*

To suppose that the eye with all its inimitable contrivances for adjusting the focus to different distances, for admitting different amounts of light, and for the correction of spherical and chromatic aberration, could have been formed by natural selection, seems, I freely confess, absurd in the highest degree. When it was first said that the sun stood still and the world turned round, the common sense of mankind declared the doctrine false;

but the old saying of *Vox populi, vox Dei,* as every philosopher knows, cannot be trusted in science. Reason tells me, that if numerous gradations from a simple and imperfect eye to one complex and perfect can be shown to exist, each grade being useful to its possessor, as is certainly the case; if further, the eye ever varies and the variations be inherited, as is likewise certainly the case; and if such variations should be useful to any animal under changing conditions of life, then the difficulty of believing that a perfect and complex eye could be formed by natural selection, though insuperable by our imagination, should not be considered as subversive of the theory. How a nerve comes to be sensitive to light, hardly concerns us more than how life itself originated; but I may remark that, as some of the lowest organisms, in which nerves cannot be detected, are capable of perceiving light, it does not seem impossible that certain sensitive elements in their sarcode should become aggregated and developed into nerves, endowed with this special sensibility.

In searching for the gradations through which an organ in any species has been perfected, we ought to look exclusively to its lineal progenitors; but this is scarcely ever possible, and we are forced to look to other species and genera of the same group, that is to the collateral descendants from the same parent-form, in order to see what gradations are possible, and for the chance of some gradations having been transmitted in an unaltered or little altered condition. But the state of the same organ in distinct classes may incidentally throw light on the steps by which it has been perfected.

The simplest organ which can be called an eye consists of an optic nerve, surrounded by pigment-cells and covered by translucent skin, but without any lens or other refractive body. We may, however, according to M. Jourdain, descend even a step lower and find aggregates of pigment-cells, apparently serving as organs of vision, without any nerves, and resting merely on sarcodic tissue. Eyes of the above simple nature are not capable of distinct vision, and serve only to distinguish light from darkness. In certain star-fishes, small depressions in the layer of pigment which surrounds the nerve are filled, as described by the author just quoted, with transparent gelatinous matter, projecting with a convex surface, like the cornea in the higher animals. He suggests that this serves not to form an image, but only to concentrate the luminous rays and render their perception more easy. In this concentration of the rays we gain the first and by far the most important step towards the formation of a true, picture-forming eye; for we have only to place the naked extremity of the optic nerve, which in some of the lower animals lies deeply buried in the body, and in some near the surface, at the right distance from the concentrating apparatus, and an image will be formed on it.

In the great class of the Articulata, we may start from an optic nerve simply coated with pigment, the latter sometimes forming a sort of pupil, but destitute of a lens or other optical contrivance. With insects it is now known that the numerous facets on the cornea of their great compound eyes form true lenses, and that the cones include curiously modified nervous filaments. But these organs in the Articulata are so much diversified that Müller formerly made three main classes with seven subdivisions, besides a fourth main class of aggregated simple eyes.

When we reflect on these facts, here given much too briefly, with respect to the wide, diversified, and graduated range of structure in the eyes of the lower animals; and when we bear in mind how small the number of all living forms must be in comparison with those which have become extinct, the difficulty ceases to be very great in believing that natural selection may have converted the simple apparatus of an optic nerve, coated with pigment and invested by transparent membrane, into an optical instrument as perfect as is possessed by any member of the Articulate Class.

He who will go thus far, ought not to hesitate to go one step further, if he finds on finishing this volume that large bodies of facts, otherwise inexplicable, can be explained by the theory of modification through natural selection; he ought to admit that with a structure even as perfect as an eagle's eye might thus be formed, although in this case he does not know the transitional states. It has been objected that in order to modify the eye and still preserve it as a perfect instrument, many changes would have to be effected simultaneously, which, it is assumed, could not be done through natural selection; but as I have attempted to show in my work on the variation of domestic animals, it is not necessary to suppose that the modifications were all simultaneous, if they were extremely slight and gradual. Different kinds of modification would, also, serve for the same general purpose: as Mr. Wallace has remarked, "if a lens has too short or too long a focus, it may be amended either by an alteration of curvature, or an alteration of density; if the curvature be irregular, and the rays do not converge to a point, then any increased regularity of curvature will be an improvement. So the contraction of the iris and the muscular movements of the eye are neither of them essential to vision, but only improvements which might have been added and perfected at any stage of the construction of the instrument." Within the highest division of the animal kingdom, namely, the Vertebrata, we can start from an eye so simple, that it consists, as in the lancelet, of a little sack of transparent skin, furnished with a nerve and lined with pigment, but destitute of any other apparatus. In fishes and reptiles, as Owen has remarked, "the range of gradations of dioptric structures is very great." It is a significant fact that even in man, according to the high authority of Virchow, the beautiful crystalline lens is formed in the embryo by an accumulation of epidermic cells, lying in a sack-like fold of the skin; and the vitreous body is formed from embryonic sub-cutaneous tissue. To arrive, however, at a just conclusion regarding the formation of the eye, with all its marvellous yet not absolutely perfect characters, it is indispensable that the reason should conquer the imagination;

but I have felt the difficulty far too keenly to be surprised at others hesitating to extend the principle of natural selection to so startling a length.

It is scarcely possible to avoid comparing the eye with a telescope. We know that this instrument has been perfected by the long-continued efforts of the highest human intellects; and we naturally infer that the eye has been formed by a somewhat analogous process. But may not this inference be presumptuous? Have we any right to assume that the Creator works by intellectual powers like those of man? If we must compare the eye to an optical instrument, we ought in imagination to take a thick layer of transparent tissue, with spaces filled with fluid, and with a nerve sensitive to light beneath, and then suppose every part of this layer to be continually changing slowly in density, so as to separate into layers of different densities and thicknesses, placed at different distances from each other, and with the surfaces of each layer slowly changing in form. Further we must suppose that there is a power, represented by natural selection or the survival of the fittest, always intently watching each slight alteration in the transparent layers; and carefully preserving each which, under varied circumstances, in any way or in any degree, tends to produce a distincter image. We must suppose each new state of the instrument to be multiplied by the million; each to be preserved until a better one is produced, and then the old ones to be all destroyed. In living bodies, variation will cause the slight alterations, generation will multiply them almost infinitely, and natural selection will pick out with unerring skill each improvement. Let this process go on for millions of years; and during each year on millions of individuals of many kinds; and may we not believe that a living optical instrument might thus be formed as superior to one of glass, as the works of the Creator are to those of man?

### *Modes of Transition*

If it could be demonstrated that any complex organ existed, which could not possibly have been formed by numerous, successive, slight modifications, my theory would absolutely break down. But I can find out no such case. No doubt many organs exist of which we do not know the transitional grades, more especially if we look to much-isolated species, round which, according to the theory, there has been much extinction. Or again, if we take an organ common to all the members of a class, for in this latter case the organ must have been originally formed at a remote period, since which all the many members of the class have been developed; and in order to discover the early transitional grades through which the organ has passed, we should have to look to very ancient ancestral forms, long since become extinct.

We should be extremely cautious in concluding that an organ could not have been formed by transitional gradations of some kind. Numerous cases could be given amongst the lower animals [*sic*] of the same organ performing at the same time wholly distinct functions; thus in the larva of the dragon-fly and in the fish Cobites the alimentary canal respires, digests, and excretes. In the Hydra, the animal may be turned inside out, and the exterior surface will then digest and the stomach respire. In such cases natural selection might specialise, if any advantage were thus gained, the whole or part of an organ, which had previously performed two functions, for one function alone, and thus by insensible steps greatly change its nature. Many plants are known which regularly produce at the same time different constructed flowers; and if such plants were to produce one kind alone, a great change would be effected with comparative suddenness in the character of the species. It is, however, probable that the two sorts of flowers borne by the same plant were originally differentiated by finely graduated steps, which may still be followed in some few cases.

Again, two distinct organs, or the same organ under two very different forms, may simultaneously perform in the same individual the same function, and this is an extremely important means of transition: to give one instance, — there are fish with gills or branchiæ that breathe the air dissolved in the water, at the same time that they breathe free air in their swimbladders, this latter organ being divided by highly vascular partitions and having a ductus pneumaticus for the supply of air. To give another instance from the vegetable kingdom: plants climb by three distinct means, by spirally twining, by clasping a support with their sensitive tendrils, and by the emission of aërial rootlets; these three means are usually found in distinct groups, but some few species exhibit two of the means, or even all three, combined in the same individual. In all such cases one of the two organs might readily be modified and perfected so as to perform all the work, being aided during the progress of modification by the other organ; and then this other organ might be modified for some other and quite distinct purpose, or be wholly obliterated.

The illustration of the swimbladder in fishes is a good one, because it shows us clearly the highly important fact that an organ originally constructed for one purpose, namely, flotation, may be converted into one for a widely different purpose, namely, respiration. The swimbladder has, also, been worked in as an accessory to the auditory organs of certain fishes. All physiologists admit that the swimbladder is homologous, or "ideally similar" in position and structure with the lungs of the higher vertebrate animals: hence there is no reason to doubt that the swimbladder has actually been converted into lungs, or an organ used exclusively for respiration.

According to this view it may be inferred that all vertebrate animals with true lungs are descended by ordinary generation from an ancient and unknown prototype, which was furnished with a floating apparatus or swimbladder. We can thus, as I infer from Owen's interesting description of these parts, understand the strange fact that every particle of food and drink which we swallow has to pass over the orifice of the trachea, with some risk of falling into the lungs, notwithstanding the beautiful contrivance by which the glottis is closed. In the higher Vertebrate the branchiæ have wholly disappeared — but in the embryo the slits on the sides of the neck and the loop-like course of the arteries still mark their former position. But it is conceivable that the now utterly lost branchiæ might have been gradually worked in by natural selection for some distinct purpose: for instance, Landois has shown that the wings of insects are developed from the tracheæ; it is therefore highly probable that in this great class organs which once served for respiration have been actually converted into organs for flight.

In considering transitions of organs, it is so important to bear in mind the probability of conversion from one function to another, that I will give another instance. Pedunculated cirripedes have two minute folds of skin, called by me the ovigerous frena, which serve, through the means of a sticky secretion, to retain the eggs until they are hatched within the sack. These cirripedes have no branchiæ, the whole surface of the body and of the sack, together with the small frena, serving for respiration. The Balanidæ or sessile cirripedes, on the other hand, have no ovigerous frena, the eggs lying loose at the bottom of the sack, within the well-enclosed shell; but they have, in the same relative position with the frena, large, much-folded membranes, which freely communicate with the circulatory lacunæ of the sack and body, and which have been considered by all naturalists to act as branchiæ. Now I think no one will dispute that the ovigerous frena in the one family are strictly homologous with the branchiæ of the other family; indeed, they graduate into each other. Therefore it need not be doubted that the two little folds of skin, which originally served as ovigerous frena, but which, likewise, very slightly aided in the act of respiration, have been gradually converted by natural selection into branchiæ, simply through an increase in their size and the obliteration of their adhesive glands. If all pedunculated cirripedes had become extinct, and they have suffered far more extinction than have sessile cirripedes, who would ever have imagined that the branchiæ in this latter family had originally existed as organs for preventing the ova from being washed out of the sack?

There is another possible mode of transmission, namely, through the acceleration or retardation of the period of reproduction. This has lately been insisted on by Prof. Cope and others in the United States. It is now known that some animals are capable of reproduction at a very early age, before they have acquired their perfect characters; and if this power became thoroughly well developed in a species, it seems probable that the adult stage of development would sooner or later be lost; and in this case, especially if the larva differed much from the mature forms, the character of the species would be greatly changed and degraded. Again, not a few animals, after arriving at maturity, go on changing in character during nearly their whole lives. With mammals, for instance, the form of the skull is often much altered with age, of which Dr. Murie has given some striking instances with seals; every one knows how the horns of stags become more and more branched, and the plumes of some birds become more finely developed, as they grow older. Prof. Cope states that the teeth of certain lizards change much in shape with advancing years; with crustaceans not only many trivial, but some important parts assume a new character, as recorded by Fritz Müller, after maturity. In all such cases, — and many could be given, — if the age for reproduction were retarded, the character of the species, at least in its adult state, would be modified; nor is it improbable that the previous and earlier stages of development would in some cases be hurried through and finally lost. Whether species have often or ever been modified through this comparatively sudden mode of transition, I can form no opinion; but if this has occurred, it is probable that the differences between the young and the mature, and between the mature and the old, were primordially acquired by graduated steps.

### *Special Difficulties of the Theory of Natural Selection*

Although we must be extremely cautious in concluding that any organ could not have been produced by successive, small, transitional gradations, yet undoubtedly serious cases of difficulty occur.

One of the most serious is that of neuter insects, which are often differently constructed from either the males or fertile females; but this case will be treated of in the next chapter. The electric organs of fishes offer another case of special difficulty; for it is impossible to conceive by what steps these wondrous organs have been produced. But this is not surprising, for we do not even know of what use they are. In the Gymnotus and Torpedo they no doubt serve as powerful means of defence, and perhaps for securing prey; yet in the Ray, as observed by Matteucci, an analogous organ in the tail manifests but little electricity, even when the animal is greatly irritated; so little, that it can hardly be of any use for the above purposes. Moreover, in the Ray, besides the organ just referred to, there is, as Dr. R. M'Donnell has shown, another organ near the head, not known to be electrical, but which appears to be the real homologue of the electric battery in the Torpedo. It is generally admitted that there exists between these organs and ordinary muscle a close analogy, in intimate structure, in the distribution of the nerves, and in the manner in which they are acted on by various reagents. It should, also, be especially observed that muscular contraction is accompanied by an electrical discharge; and, as Dr. Radcliffe insists, "in the electrical apparatus of the torpedo during rest, there would seem to be a charge in every respect like that which is met with in muscle and nerve during rest, and the discharge of the torpedo, instead of being peculiar, may be only another form of the discharge which depends upon the action of muscle and motor nerve." Beyond this we cannot at present go in the way of explanation; but as we know so little about the uses of these organs, and as we know nothing about the habits and structure of the progenitors of the existing electric fishes, it would be extremely bold to maintain that no serviceable transitions are possible by which these organs might have been gradually developed.

These organs appear at first to offer another and far more serious difficulty; for they occur in about a dozen kinds of fish, of which several are widely remote in their affinities. When the same organ is found in several members of the same class, especially if in members having very different habits of life, we may generally attribute its presence to inheritance from a common ancestor; and its absence in some of the members to loss through disuse or natural selection. So that, if the electric organs had been inherited from some one ancient progenitor, we might have expected that all electric fishes would have been specially related to each other; but this is far from the case. Nor does geology at all lead to the belief that most fishes formerly possessed electric organs, which their modified descendants have now lost. But when we look at the subject more closely, we find in the several fishes provided with electric organs, that these are situated in different parts of the body, — that they differ in construction, as in the arrangement of the plates, and, according to Pacini, in the process or means by which the electricity is excited — and lastly, in being supplied with nerves proceeding from different sources, and this is perhaps the most important of all the differences. Hence in the several fishes furnished with electric organs, these cannot be considered as homologous, but only as analogous in function. Consequently there is no reason to suppose that they have been inherited from a common progenitor; for had this been the case they would have closely resembled each other in all respects. Thus the difficulty of an organ, apparently the same, arising in several remotely allied species, disappears, leaving only the lesser yet still great difficulty; namely, by what graduated steps these organs have been developed in each separate group of fishes.

The luminous organs which occur in a few insects, belonging to widely different families, and which are situated in different parts of the body, offer, under our present state of ignorance, a difficulty almost exactly parallel with that of the electric organs. Other similar cases could be given; for instance in plants, the very curious contrivance of a mass of pollen-grains, borne on a foot-stalk with an adhesive gland, is apparently the same in Orchis and Asclepias, — genera almost as remote as is possible amongst flowering plants; but here again the parts are not homologous. In all cases of beings, far removed from each other in the scale of organisation, which are furnished with similar and peculiar organs, it will be found that although the general appearance and function of the organs may be the same, yet fundamental differences between them can always be detected. For instance, the eyes of cephalopods or cuttle-fish and of vertebrate animals appear wonderfully alike; and in such widely sundered groups no part of this resemblance can be due to inheritance from a common progenitor. Mr. Mivart has advanced this case as one of special difficulty, but I am unable to see the force of his argument. An organ for vision must be formed of transparent tissue, and must include some sort of lens for throwing an image at the back of a darkened chamber. Beyond this superficial resemblance, there is hardly any real similarity between the eyes of cuttle-fish and vertebrates, as may be seen by consulting Hensen's admirable memoir on these organs in the Cephalopoda. It is impossible for me here to enter on details, but I may specify a few of the points of difference. The crystalline lens in the higher cuttle-fish consists of two parts, placed one behind the other like two lenses, both having a very different structure and disposition to what occurs in the vertebrata. The retina is wholly different, with an actual inversion of the elemental parts, and with a large nervous ganglion included within the membranes of the eye. The relations of the muscles are as different as it is possible to conceive, and so in other points. Hence it is not a little difficult to decide how far even the same terms ought to be employed in describing the eyes of the Cephalopoda and Vertebrata. It is, of course, open to any one to deny that the eye in either case could have been developed through the natural selection of successive slight variations; but if this be admitted in the one case, it is clearly possible in the other; and fundamental differences of structure in the visual organs of two groups might have been anticipated, in accordance with this view of their manner of formation. As two men have sometimes independently hit on the same invention, so in the several foregoing cases it appears that natural selection, working for the good of each being, and taking advantage of all favourable variations, has produced similar organs, as far as function is concerned, in distinct organic beings, which owe none of their structure in common to inheritance from a common progenitor.

Fritz Müller, in order to test the conclusions arrived at in this volume, has followed out with much care a nearly similar line of argument. Several families of crustaceans include a few species, possessing an air-breathing apparatus and fitted to live out of the water. In two of these families, which were more especially examined by Müller, and which are nearly related to each other, the species agree most closely in all important characters; namely, in their sense organs, circulating system, in the position of the tufts of hair within their complex stomachs, and lastly in the whole structure of the water-breathing branchiæ, even to the microscopical hooks by which they are cleansed. Hence it might have been expected that in the few species belonging to both families which live on the land, the equally important air-breathing apparatus would have been the same; for why should this one apparatus, given for the same purpose, have been made to differ, whilst all the other important organs were closely similar or rather identical.

Fritz Müller argues that this close similarity in so many points of structure must, in accordance with the views advanced by me, be accounted for by inheritance from a common progenitor. But as the vast majority of the species in the above two families, as well as most other crustaceans, are aquatic in their habits, it is improbable in the highest degree, that their common progenitor should have been adapted for breathing air. Müller was thus led carefully to examine the apparatus in the air-breathing species; and he found it to differ in each in several important points, as in the position of the orifices, in the manner in which they are opened and closed, and in some accessory details. Now such differences are intelligible, and might even have been expected, on the supposition that species belonging to distinct families had slowly become adapted to live more and more out of water, and to breathe the air. For these species, from belonging to distinct families, would have differed to a certain extent, and in accordance with the principle that the nature of each variation depends on two factors, viz., the nature of the organism and that of the surrounding conditions, their variability assuredly would not have been exactly the same. Consequently natural selection would have had different materials or variations to work on, in order to arrive at the same functional result; and the structures thus acquired would almost necessarily have differed. On the hypothesis of separate acts of creation the whole case remains unintelligible. This line of argument seems to have had great weight in leading Fritz Müller to accept the views maintained by me in this volume.

Another distinguished zoologist, the late Professor Claparède, has argued in the same manner, and has arrived at the same result. He shows that there are parasitic mites (Acaridæ), belonging to distinct sub-families and families, which are furnished with hair-claspers. These organs must have been independently developed, as they could not have been inherited from a common progenitor; and in the several groups they are formed by the modification of the fore-legs, — of the hind-legs, — of the maxillæ or lips, — and of appendages on the under side of the hind part of the body.

In the foregoing cases, we see the same end gained and the same function performed, in beings not at all or only remotely allied, by organs in appearance, though not in development, closely similar. On the other hand, it is a common rule throughout nature that the same end should be gained, even sometimes in the case of closely-related beings, by the most diversified means. How differently constructed is the feathered wing of a bird and the membrane-covered wing of a bat; and still more so the four wings of a butterfly, the two wings of a fly, and the two wings with the elytra of a beetle. Bivalve shells are made to open and shut, but on what a number of patterns is the hinge constructed, — from the long row of neatly interlocking teeth in a Nucula to the simple ligament of a Mussel! Seeds are disseminated by their minuteness, — by their capsule being converted into a light balloon-like envelope, — by being embedded in pulp or flesh, formed of the most diverse parts, and rendered nutritious, as well as conspicuously coloured, so as to attract and be devoured by birds, — by having hooks and grapnels of many kinds and serrated awns, so as to adhere to the fur of quadrupeds, — and by being furnished with wings and plumes, as different in shape as they are elegant in structure, so as to be wafted by every breeze. I will give one other instance; for this subject of the same end being gained by the most diversified means well deserves attention. Some authors maintain that organic beings have been formed in many ways for the sake of mere variety, almost like toys in a shop, but such a view of nature is incredible. With plants having separated sexes, and with those in which, though hermaphrodites, the pollen does not spontaneously fall on the stigma, some aid is necessary for their fertilisation. With several kinds this is effected by the pollen-grains, which are light and incoherent, being blown by the wind through mere chance on to the stigma; and this is the simplest plan which can well be conceived. An almost equally simple, though very different, plan occurs in many plants in which a symmetrical flower secretes a few drops of nectar, and is consequently visited by insects; and these carry the pollen from the anthers to the stigma.

From this simple stage we may pass through an inexhaustible number of contrivances, all for the same purpose and effected in essentially the same manner, but entailing changes in every part of the flower. The nectar may be stored in variously shaped receptacles, with the stamens and pistils modified in many ways, sometimes forming trap-like contrivances, and sometimes capable of neatly adapted movements through irritability or elasticity. From such structures we may advance till we come to such a case of extraordinary adaptation as that lately described by Dr. Crüger in the Coryanthes. This orchid has part of its labellum or lower lip hollowed out into a great bucket, into which drops of almost pure water continually fall from two secreting horns which stand above it; and when the bucket is half full, the water overflows by a spout on one side. The basal part of the labellum stands over the bucket, and is itself hollowed out into a sort of chamber with two lateral entrances; within this chamber there are curious fleshy ridges. The most ingenious man, if he had not witnessed what takes place, could never have imagined what purpose all these parts serve. But Dr. Crüger saw crowds of large humble-bees visiting the gigantic flowers of this orchid, not in order to suck nectar, but to gnaw off the ridges within the chamber above the bucket; in doing this they frequently pushed each other into the bucket, and their wings being thus wetted they could not fly away, but were compelled to crawl out through the passage formed by the spout or overflow. Dr. Crüger saw a "continual procession" of bees thus crawling out of their involuntary bath. The passage is narrow, and is roofed over by the column, so that a bee, in forcing its way out, first rubs its back against the viscid stigma and then against the viscid glands of the pollen-masses. The pollen-masses are thus glued to the back of the bee which first happens to crawl out through the passage of a lately expanded flower, and are thus carried away. Dr. Crüger sent me a flower in spirits of wine, with a bee which he had killed before it had quite crawled out with a pollen-mass still fastened to its back. When the bee, thus provided, flies to another flower, or to the same flower a second time, and is pushed by its comrades into the bucket and then crawls out by the passage, the pollen-mass necessarily comes first into contact with the viscid stigma, and adheres to it, and the flower is fertilised. Now at last we see the full use of every part of the flower, of the water-secreting horns, of the bucket half full of water, which prevents the bees from flying away, and forces them to crawl out through the spout, and rub against the properly placed viscid pollen-masses and the viscid stigma.

The construction of the flower in another closely allied orchid, namely the Catasetum, is widely different, though serving the same end; and is equally curious. Bees visit these flowers, like those of the Coryanthes, in order to gnaw the labellum; in doing this they inevitably touch a long, tapering, sensitive projection, or, as I have called it, the antenna. This antenna, when touched, transmits a sensation or vibration to a certain membrane which is instantly ruptured; this sets free a spring by which the pollen-mass is shot forth, like an arrow, in the right direction, and adheres by its viscid extremity to the back of the bee. The pollen-mass of the male plant (for the sexes are separate in this orchid) is thus carried to the flower of the female plant where it is brought into contact with the stigma, which is viscid enough to break certain elastic threads, and retaining the pollen, fertilisation is effected.

How, it may be asked, in the foregoing and in innumerable other instances, can we understand the graduated scale of complexity and the multifarious means for gaining the same end. The answer no doubt is, as already remarked, that when two forms vary, which already differ from each other in some slight degree, the variability will not be of the same exact nature, and consequently the results obtained through natural selection for the same general purpose will not be the same. We should also bear in mind that every highly developed organism has passed through many changes; and that each modified structure tends to be inherited, so that each modification will not readily be quite lost, but may be again and again further altered. Hence the structure of each part of each species, for whatever purpose it may serve, is the sum of many inherited changes, through which the species has passed during its successive adaptations to change habits and conditions of life.

Finally then, although in many cases it is most difficult even to conjecture by what transitions organs have arrived at their present state; yet, considering how small the proportion of living and known forms is to the extinct and unknown, I have been astonished how rarely an organ can be named, towards which no transitional grade is known to lead. It certainly is true, that new organs appearing as if created for some special purpose, rarely or never appear in any being; — as indeed is shown by that old, but somewhat exaggerated, canon in natural history of "Natura non facit saltum." We meet with this admission in the writings of almost every experienced naturalist; or as Milne Edwards has well expressed it, Nature is prodigal in variety, but niggard in innovation. Why, on the theory of Creation, should there be so much variety and so little real novelty? Why should all the parts and organs of many independent beings, each supposed to have been separately created for its proper place in nature, be so commonly linked together by graduated steps? Why should not Nature take a sudden leap from structure to structure? On the theory of natural selection, we can clearly understand why she should not; for natural selection acts only by taking advantage of slight successive variations, she can never take a great and sudden leap, but must advance by short and sure, though slow steps.

### *Organs of little apparent Importance, as affected by Natural Selection*

As natural selection acts by life and death, — by the survival of the fittest, and by the destruction of the less well-fitted individuals, — I have sometimes felt great difficulty in understanding the origin or formation of parts of little importance; almost as great, though of a very different kind, as in the case of the most perfect and complex organs.

In the first place, we are much too ignorant in regard to the whole economy of any one organic being, to say what slight modifications would be of importance or not. In a former chapter I have given instances of very trifling characters, such as the down on fruit and the colour of its flesh, the colour of the skin and hair of quadrupeds, which, from being correlated with constitutional differences or from determining the attacks of insects, might assuredly be acted on by natural selection. The tail of the giraffe looks like an artificially constructed fly-flapper; and it seems at first incredible that this could not have been adapted for its present purpose by successive slight modifications, each better and better fitted, for so trifling an object as to drive away flies; yet we should pause before being too positive even in this case, for we know that the distribution and existence of cattle and other animals in South America absolutely depend on their power of resisting the attacks of insects: so that individuals which could by any means defend themselves from these small enemies, would be able to range into new pastures and thus gain a great advantage. It is not that the larger quadrupeds are actually destroyed (except in some rare cases) by flies, but they are incessantly harassed and their strength reduced, so that they are more subject to disease, or not so well enabled in a coming dearth to search for food, or to escape from beasts of prey.

Organs now of trifling importance have probably in some cases been of high importance to an early progenitor, and, after having been slowly perfected at a former period, have been transmitted to existing species in nearly the same state, although now of very slight use; but any actually injurious deviations in their structure would of course have been checked by natural selection. Seeing how important an organ of locomotion the tail is in most aquatic animals, its general presence and use for many purposes in so many land animals, which in their lungs or modified swimbladders betray their aquatic origin, may perhaps be thus accounted for. A well-developed tail having been formed in an aquatic animal, it might subsequently come to be worked in for all sorts of purposes, — as a fly-flapper, an organ of prehension, or as an aid in turning, as in the case of the dog, though the aid in this latter respect must be slight, for the hare, with hardly any tail, can double still more quickly.

In the second place, we may easily err in attributing importance to characters, and in believing that they have been developed through natural selection. We must by no means overlook the effects of the definite action of changed conditions of life, — of so-called spontaneous variations, which seem to depend in a quite subordinate degree on the nature of the conditions, — of the tendency to reversion to long-lost characters, — of the complex laws of growth, such as of correlation, compensation, of the pressure of one part on another, &c., — and finally of sexual selection, by which characters of use to one sex are often gained and then transmitted more or less perfectly to the other sex, though of no use to this sex. But structures thus indirectly gained, although at first of no advantage to a species, may subsequently have been taken advantage of by its modified descendants, under new conditions of life and newly acquired habits.

If green woodpeckers alone had existed, and we did not know that there were many black and pied kinds, I dare say that we should have thought that the green colour was a beautiful adaptation to conceal this tree-frequenting bird from its enemies;

and consequently that it was a character of importance, and had been acquired through natural selection; as it is, the colour is probably in chief part due to sexual selection. A trailing palm in the Malay Archipelago climbs the loftiest trees by the aid of exquisitely constructed hooks clustered around the ends of the branches, and this contrivance, no doubt, is of the highest service to the plant; but as we see nearly similar hooks on many trees which are not climbers, and which, as there is reason to believe from the distribution of the thorn-bearing species in Africa and South America, serve as a defence against browsing quadrupeds, so the spikes on the palm may at first have been developed for this object, and subsequently have been improved and taken advantage of by the plant, as it underwent further modification and became a climber. The naked skin on the head of a vulture is generally considered as a direct adaptation for wallowing in putridity; and so it may be, or it may possibly be due to the direct action of putrid matter; but we should be very cautious in drawing any such inference, when we see that the skin on the head of the clean-feeding male Turkey is likewise naked. The sutures in the skulls of young mammals have been advanced as a beautiful adaptation for aiding parturition, and no doubt they facilitate or may be indispensable for this act; but as sutures occur in the skulls of young birds and reptiles, which have only to escape from a broken egg, we may infer that this structure has arisen from the laws of growth, and has been taken advantage of in the parturition of the higher animals.

We are profoundly ignorant of the cause of each slight variation or individual difference; and we are immediately made conscious of this by reflecting on the differences between the breeds of our domesticated animals in different countries,—more especially in the less civilised countries where there has been but little methodical selection. Animals kept by savages in different countries often have to struggle for their own subsistence, and are exposed to a certain extent to natural selection, and individuals with slightly different constitutions would succeed best under different climates. With cattle susceptibility to the attacks of flies is correlated with colour, as is the liability to be poisoned by certain plants; so that even colour would be thus subjected to the action of natural selection. Some observers are convinced that a damp climate affects the growth of the hair, and that with the hair the horns are correlated. Mountain breeds always differ from lowland breeds; and a mountainous country would probably affect the hind limbs from exercising them more, and possibly even the form of the pelvis; and then by the law of homologous variation, the front limbs and the head would probably be affected. The shape, also, of the pelvis might affect by pressure the shape of certain parts of the young in the womb. The laborious breathing necessary in high regions tends, as we have good reason to believe, to increase the size of the chest; and again correlation would come into play. The effects of lessened exercise together with abundant food on the whole organisation is probably still more important; and this, as H. von Nathusius has lately shown in his excellent Treatise, is apparently one chief cause of the great modification which the breeds of swine have undergone. But we are far too ignorant to speculate on the relative importance of the several known and unknown causes of variation; and I have made these remarks only to show that, if we are unable to account for the characteristic differences of our several domestic breeds, which nevertheless are generally admitted to have arisen through ordinary generation from one or a few parent-stocks, we ought not to lay too much stress on our ignorance of the precise cause of the slight analogous differences between true species.

### *Utilitarian Doctrine, how far true: Beauty, how acquired*

The foregoing remarks lead me to say a few words on the protest lately made by some naturalists, against the utilitarian doctrine that every detail of structure has been produced for the good of its possessor. They believe that many structures have been created for the sake of beauty, to delight man or the Creator (but this latter point is beyond the scope of scientific discussion), or for the sake of mere variety, a view already discussed. Such doctrines, if true, would be absolutely fatal to my theory. I fully admit that many structures are now of no direct use to their possessors, and may never have been of any use to their progenitors; but this does not prove that they were formed solely for beauty or variety. No doubt the definite action of changed conditions, and the various causes of modifications, lately specified, have all produced an effect, probably a great effect, independently of any advantage thus gained. But a still more important consideration is that the chief part of the organisation of every living creature is due to inheritance; and consequently, though each being assuredly is well fitted for its place in nature, many structures have now no very close and direct relation to present habits of life. Thus, we can hardly believe that the webbed feet of the upland goose or of the frigate-bird are of special use to these birds; we cannot believe that the similar bones in the arm of the monkey, in the fore-leg of the horse, in the wing of the bat, and in the flipper of the seal, are of special use to these animals. We may safely attribute these structures to inheritance. But webbed feet no doubt were as useful to the progenitor of the upland goose and of the frigate-bird, as they now are to the most aquatic of living birds. So we may believe that the progenitor of the seal did not possess a flipper, but a foot with five toes fitted for walking or grasping; but we may further venture to believe that the several bones in the limbs of the monkey, horse, and bat, were originally developed, on the principle of utility, probably through the reduction of more numerous bones in the fin of some ancient fish-like progenitor of the whole class. It is scarcely possible to decide how much allowance ought to be made for such causes of change, as the definite action of external conditions, so-called spontaneous variations, and the complex laws of growth; but with these important exceptions, we may conclude that the structure of every living creature either now is, or was formerly, of some direct or indirect use to its possessor.

With respect to the belief that organic beings have been created beautiful for the delight of man, — a belief which it has been pronounced is subversive of my whole theory, — I may first remark that the sense of beauty obviously depends on the nature of the mind, irrespective of any real quality in the admired object; and that the idea of what is beautiful, is not innate or unalterable. We see this, for instance, in the men of different races admiring an entirely different standard of beauty in their women. If beautiful objects had been created solely for man's gratification, it ought to be shown that before man appeared, there was less beauty on the face of the earth than since he came on the stage. Were the beautiful volute and cone shells of the Eocene epoch, and the gracefully sculptured ammonites of the Secondary period, created that man might ages afterwards admire them in his cabinet? Few objects are more beautiful than the minute siliceious cases of the diatomaceæ: were these created that they might be examined and admired under the higher powers of the microscope? The beauty in this latter case, and in many others, is apparently wholly due to symmetry of growth. Flowers rank amongst the most beautiful productions of nature; but they have been rendered conspicuous in contrast with the green leaves, and in consequence at the same time beautiful, so that they may be easily observed by insects. I have come to this conclusion from finding it an invariable rule that when a flower is fertilised by the wind it never has a gaily-coloured corolla. Several plants habitually produce two kinds of flowers; one kind open and coloured so as to attract insects; the other closed, not coloured, destitute of nectar, and never visited by insects. Hence we may conclude that, if insects had not been developed on the face of the earth, our plants would not have been decked with beautiful flowers, but would have produced only such poor flowers as we see on our fir, oak, nut and ash trees, on grasses, spinach, docks, and nettles, which are all fertilised through the agency of the wind. A similar line of argument holds good with fruits; that a ripe strawberry or cherry is as pleasing to the eye as to the palate, — that the gaily-coloured fruit of the spindle-wood tree and the scarlet berries of the holly are beautiful objects, — will be admitted by every one. But this beauty serves merely as a guide to birds and beasts, in order that the fruit may be devoured and the matured seeds disseminated: I infer that this is the case from having as yet found no exception to the rule that seeds are always thus disseminated when embedded within a fruit of any kind (that is within a fleshy or pulpy envelope), if it be coloured of any brilliant tint, or rendered conspicuous by being white or black.

On the other hand, I willingly admit that a great number of male animals, as all our most gorgeous birds, some fishes, reptiles, and mammals, and a host of magnificently coloured butterflies, have been rendered beautiful for beauty's sake; but this has been effected through sexual selection, that is, by the more beautiful males having been continually preferred by the females, and not for the delight of man. So it is with the music of birds. We may infer from all this that a nearly similar taste for beautiful colours and for musical sounds runs through a large part of the animal kingdom. When the female is as beautifully coloured as the male, which is not rarely the case with birds and butterflies, the cause apparently lies in the colours acquired through sexual selection having been transmitted to both sexes, instead of to the males alone. How the sense of beauty in its simplest form — that is, the reception of a peculiar kind of pleasure from certain colours, forms, and sounds — was first developed in the mind of man and of the lower animals, is a very obscure subject. The same sort of difficulty is presented, if we enquire how it is that certain flavours and odors give pleasure, and others displeasure. Habit in all these cases appears to have come to a certain extent into play; but there must be some fundamental cause in the constitution of the nervous system in each species.

Natural selection cannot possibly produce any modification in a species exclusively for the good of another species; though throughout nature one species incessantly takes advantage of, and profits by, the structures of others. But natural selection can and does often produce structures for the direct injury of other animals, as we see in the fang of the adder, and in the ovipositor of the ichneumon, by which its eggs are deposited in the living bodies of other insects. If it could be proved that any part of the structure of any one species had been formed for the exclusive good of another species, it would annihilate my theory, for such could not have been produced through natural selection. Although many statements may be found in works on natural history to this effect, I cannot find even one which seems to me of any weight. It is admitted that the rattlesnake has a poison-fang for its own defence, and for the destruction of its prey; but some authors suppose that at the same time it is furnished with a rattle for its own injury, namely, to warn its prey. I would almost as soon believe that the cat curls the end of its tail when preparing to spring, in order to warn the doomed mouse. It is a much more probable view that the rattlesnake uses its rattle, the cobra expands its frill, and the puff-adder swells whilst hissing so loudly and harshly, in order to alarm the many birds and beasts which are known to attack even the most venomous species. Snakes act on the same principle which makes the hen ruffle her feathers and expand her wings when a dog approaches her chickens; but I have not space here to enlarge on the many ways by which animals endeavour to frighten away their enemies.

Natural selection will never produce in a being any structure more injurious than beneficial to that being, for natural selection acts solely by and for the good of each. No organ will be formed, as Paley has remarked, for the purpose of causing pain or for doing an injury to its possessor. If a fair balance be struck between the good and evil caused by each part, each will be found on the whole advantageous. After the lapse of time, under changing conditions of life, if any part comes to be injurious, it will be modified; or if it be not so, the being will become extinct as myriads have become extinct.

Natural selection tends only to make each organic being as perfect as, or slightly more perfect than, the other inhabitants of the same country with which it comes into competition. And we see that this is the standard of perfection attained under nature. The endemic productions of New Zealand, for instance, are perfect one compared with another; but they are now rapidly yielding before the advancing legions of plants and animals introduced from Europe. Natural selection will not produce absolute perfection, nor do we always meet, as far as we can judge, with this high standard under nature. The correction for the aberration of light is said by Müller not to be perfect even in that most perfect organ, the human eye. Helmholtz, whose judgment no one will dispute, after describing in the strongest terms the wonderful powers of the human eye, adds these remarkable words: "That which we have discovered in the way of inexactness and imperfection in the optical machine and in the image on the retina, is as nothing in comparison with the incongruities which we have just come across in the domain of the sensations. One might say that nature has taken delight in accumulating contradictions in order to remove all foundation from the theory of a pre-existing harmony between the external and internal worlds." If our reason leads us to admire with enthusiasm a multitude of inimitable contrivances in nature, this same reason tells us, though we may easily err on both sides, that some other contrivances are less perfect. Can we consider the sting of the bee as perfect, which, when used against many kinds of enemies, cannot be withdrawn, owing to the backward serratures, and thus inevitably causes the death of the insect by tearing out its viscera?

If we look at the sting of the bee, as having existed in a remote progenitor, as a boring and serrated instrument, like that in so many members of the same great order, and that it has since been modified but not perfected for its present purpose, with the poison originally adapted for some other object, such as to produce galls, since intensified, we can perhaps understand how it is that the use of the sting should so often cause the insect's own death: for if on the whole the power of stinging be useful to the social community, it will fulfil all the requirements of natural selection, though it may cause the death of some few members. If we admire the truly wonderful power of scent by which the males of many insects find their females, can we admire the production for this single purpose of thousands of drones, which are utterly useless to the community for any other purpose, and which are ultimately slaughtered by their industrious and sterile sisters? It may be difficult, but we ought to admire the savage instinctive hatred of the queen-bee, which urges her to destroy the young queens, her daughters, as soon as they are born, or to perish herself in the combat; for undoubtedly this is for the good of the community; and maternal love or maternal hatred, though the latter fortunately is most rare, is all the same to the inexorable principle of natural selection. If we admire the several ingenious contrivances, by which orchids and many other plants are fertilised through insect agency, can we consider as equally perfect the elaboration of dense clouds of pollen by our fir-trees, so that a few granules may be wafted by chance on to the ovules?

## *Summary: the Law of Unity of Type and of the Conditions of Existence embraced by the Theory of Natural Selection*

We have in this chapter discussed some of the difficulties and objections which may be urged against the theory. Many of them are serious; but I think that in the discussion light has been thrown on several facts, which on the belief of independent acts of creation are utterly obscure. We have seen that species at any one period are not indefinitely variable, and are not linked together by a multitude of intermediate gradations, partly because the process of natural selection is always very slow, and at any one time acts only on a few forms; and partly because the very process of natural selection implies the continual supplanting and extinction of preceding and intermediate gradations. Closely allied species, now living on a continuous area, must often have been formed when the area was not continuous, and when the conditions of life did not insensibly graduate away from one part to another. When two varieties are formed in two districts of a continuous area, an intermediate variety will often be formed, fitted for an intermediate zone; but from reasons assigned, the intermediate variety will usually exist in lesser numbers than the two forms which it connects; consequently the two latter, during the course of further modification, from existing in greater numbers, will have a great advantage over the less numerous intermediate variety, and will thus generally succeed in supplanting and exterminating it.

We have seen in this chapter how cautious we should be in concluding that the most different habits of life could not graduate into each other; that a bat, for instance, could not have been formed by natural selection from an animal which at first only glided through the air.

We have seen that a species under new conditions of life may change its habits; or it may have diversified habits, with some very unlike those of its nearest congeners. Hence we can understand, bearing in mind that each organic being is trying to live wherever it can live, how it has arisen that there are upland geese with webbed feet, ground woodpeckers, diving thrushes, and petrels with the habits of auks.

Although the belief that an organ so perfect as the eye could have been formed by natural selection, is enough to stagger any one; yet in the case of any organ, if we know of a long series of gradations in complexity, each good for its possessor, then, under changing conditions of life, there is no logical impossibility in the acquirement of any conceivable degree of perfection through natural selection. In the cases in which we know of no intermediate or transitional states, we should be extremely cautious in concluding that none can have existed, for the metamorphoses of many organs show what wonderful changes in function are at least possible. For instance, a swimbladder has apparently been converted into an air-breathing lung. The same organ having performed simultaneously very different functions, and then having been in part or in whole specialised for one function; and two distinct organs having performed at the same time the same function, the one having been perfected whilst aided by the other, must often have largely facilitated transitions.

We have seen that in two beings widely remote from each other in the natural scale, organs serving for the same purpose and in external appearance closely similar may have been separately and independently formed; but when such organs are closely examined, essential differences in their structure can almost always be detected; and this naturally follows from the principle of natural selection. On the other hand, the common rule throughout nature is infinite diversity of structure for gaining the same end; and this again naturally follows from the same great principle.

In many cases we are far too ignorant to be enabled to assert that a part or organ is so unimportant for the welfare of a species, that modifications in its structure could not have been slowly accumulated by means of natural selection. In many other cases, modifications are probably the direct results of the laws of variation or of growth, independently of any good having been thus gained. But even such structures have often, as we may feel assured, been subsequently taken advantage of, and still further modified, for the good of species under new conditions of life. We may, also, believe that a part formerly of high importance has frequently been retained (as the tail of an aquatic animal by its terrestrial descendants), though it has become of such small importance that it could not, in its present state, have been acquired by means of natural selection.

Natural selection can produce nothing in one species for the exclusive good or injury of another; though it may well produce parts, organs, and excretions highly useful or even indispensable, or again highly injurious to another species, but in all cases at the same time useful to the possessor. In each well-stocked country natural selection acts through the competition of the inhabitants, and consequently leads to success in the battle for life, only in accordance with the standard of that particular country. Hence the inhabitants of one country, generally the smaller one, often yield to the inhabitants of another and generally the larger country. For in the larger country there will have existed more individuals and more diversified forms, and the competition will have been severer, and thus the standard of perfection will have been rendered higher. Natural selection will not necessarily lead to absolute perfection; nor, as far as we can judge by our limited faculties, can absolute perfection be everywhere predicated.

On the theory of natural selection we can clearly understand the full meaning of that old canon in natural history, "Natura non facit saltum." This canon, if we look to the present inhabitants alone of the world, is not strictly correct; but if we include all those of past times, whether known or unknown, it must on this theory be strictly true.

It is generally acknowledged that all organic beings have been formed on two great laws — Unity of Type, and the Conditions of Existence. By unity of type is meant that fundamental agreement in structure which we see in organic beings of the same class, and which is quite independent of their habits of life. On my theory, unity of type is explained by unity of descent. The expression of conditions of existence, so often insisted on by the illustrious Cuvier, is fully embraced by the principle of natural selection. For natural selection acts by either now adapting the varying parts of each being to its organic and inorganic conditions of life; or by having adapted them during past periods of time: the adaptations being aided in many cases by the increased use or disuse of parts, being affected by the direct action of the external conditions of life, and subjected in all cases to the several laws of growth and variation. Hence, in fact, the law of the Conditions of Existence is the higher law; as it includes, through the inheritance of former variations and adaptations, that of Unity of Type.

# *The Argument for Natural Selection and Evolution*

As this whole volume is one long argument, it may be convenient to the reader to have the leading facts and inferences briefly recapitulated.

That many and serious objections may be advanced against the theory of descent with modification through variation and natural selection, I do not deny. I have endeavoured to give to them their full force. Nothing at first can appear more difficult to believe than that the more complex organs and instincts have been perfected, not by means superior to, though analogous with, human reason, but by the accumulation of innumerable slight variations, each good for the individual possessor. Nevertheless, this difficulty, though appearing to our imagination insuperably great, cannot be considered real if we admit the following propositions, namely, that all parts of the organisation and instincts offer, at least, individual differences — that there is a struggle for existence leading to the preservation of profitable deviations of structure or instinct — and, lastly, that gradations in the state of perfection of each organ may have existed, each good of its kind. The truth of these propositions cannot, I think, be disputed.

It is, no doubt, extremely difficult even to conjecture by what gradations many structures have been perfected, more especially amongst broken and failing groups of organic beings, which have suffered much extinction, but we see so many strange gradations in nature, that we ought to be extremely cautious in saying that any organ or instinct, or any whole structure, could not have arrived at its present state by many graduated steps. There are, it must be admitted, cases of special difficulty opposed to the theory of natural selection; and one of the most curious of these is the existence in the same community of two or three defined castes of workers or sterile female ants; but I have attempted to show how these difficulties can be mastered.

With respect to the almost universal sterility of species when first crossed, which forms so remarkable a contrast with the almost universal fertility of varieties when crossed, I must refer the reader to the recapitulation of the facts given at the end of the ninth chapter, which seem to me conclusively to show that this sterility is no more a special endowment than is the incapacity of two distinct kinds of trees to be grafted together; but that it is incidental on differences confined to the reproductive systems of the intercrossed species. We see the truth of this conclusion in the vast difference in the results of crossing the same two species reciprocally, — that is, when one species is first used as the father and then as the mother. Analogy from the consideration of dimorphic and trimorphic plants clearly leads to the same conclusion, for when the forms are illegitimately united, they yield few or no seed, and their offspring are more or less sterile; and these forms belong to the same undoubted species, and differ from each other in no respect except in their reproductive organs and functions.

Although the fertility of varieties when intercrossed and of their mongrel offspring has been asserted by so many authors to be universal, this cannot be considered as quite correct after the facts given on the high authority of Gärtner and Kölreuter. Most of the varieties which have been experimented on have been produced under domestication; and as domestication (I do not mean mere confinement) almost certainly tends to eliminate that sterility which, judging from analogy, would have affected the parent-species if intercrossed, we ought not to expect that domestication would likewise induce sterility in their modified descendants when crossed. This elimination of sterility apparently follows from the same cause which allows our domestic animals to breed freely under diversified circumstances; and this again apparently follows from their having been gradually accustomed to frequent changes in their conditions of life.

A double and parallel series of facts seems to throw much light on the sterility of species, when first crossed, and of their hybrid offspring. On the one side, there is good reason to believe that slight changes in the conditions of life give vigour and fertility to all organic beings. We know also that a cross between the distinct individuals of the same variety, and between distinct varieties, increases the number of their offspring, and certainly gives to them increased size and vigour. This is chiefly owing to the forms which are crossed having been exposed to somewhat different conditions of life; for I have ascertained by a laborious series of experiments that if all the individuals of the same variety be subjected during several generations to the same conditions, the good derived from crossing is often much diminished or wholly disappears. This is one side of the case. On the other side, we know that species which have long been exposed to nearly uniform conditions, when they are subjected under confinement to new and greatly changed conditions, either perish, or if they survive, are rendered sterile, though retaining perfect health. This does not occur, or only in a very slight degree, with our domesticated productions, which have long been exposed to fluctuating conditions. Hence when we find that hybrids produced by a cross between two distinct species are few in number, owing to their perishing soon after conception or at a very early age, or if surviving that they are rendered more or less sterile, it seems highly probable that this result is due to their having been in fact subjected to a great change in their conditions of life, from being compounded of two distinct organisations. He who will explain in a definite manner why, for instance, an elephant or a fox will not breed under confinement in its native country, whilst the domestic pig or dog will breed freely under the most diversified conditions, will at the same time be able to give a definite answer to the question why two distinct species, when crossed, as well as their hybrid offspring, are generally rendered more or less sterile, whilst two domesticated varieties when crossed and their mongrel offspring are perfectly fertile.

Turning to geographical distribution, the difficulties encountered on the theory of descent with modification are serious enough. All the individuals of the same species, and all the species of the same genus, or even higher group, are descended from common parents; and therefore, in however distant and isolated parts of the world they may now be found, they must in the course of successive generations have travelled from some one point to all the others. We are often wholly unable even to conjecture how this could have been effected. Yet, as we have reason to believe that some species have retained the same specific form for very long periods of time, immensely long as measured by years, too much stress ought not to be laid on the occasional wide diffusion of the same species; for during very long periods there will always have been a good chance for wide migration by many means. A broken or interrupted range may often be accounted for by the extinction of the species in the intermediate regions. It cannot be denied that we are as yet very ignorant as to the full extent of the various climatal and geographical changes which have affected the earth during modern periods; and such changes will often have facilitated migration. As an example, I have attempted to show how potent has been the influence of the Glacial period on the distribution of the same and of allied species throughout the world. We are as yet profoundly ignorant of the many occasional means of transport. With respect to distinct species of the same genus inhabiting distant and isolated regions, as the process of modification has necessarily been slow, all the means of migration will have been possible during a very long period; and consequently the difficulty of the wide diffusion of the species of the same genus is in some degree lessened.

As according to the theory of natural selection an interminable number of intermediate forms must have existed, linking together all the species in each group by gradations as fine as are our existing varieties, it may be asked: Why do we not see these linking forms all around us? Why are not all organic beings blended together in an inextricable chaos? With respect to existing forms, we should remember that we have no right to expect (excepting in rare cases) to discover *directly* connecting links between them, but only between each and some extinct and supplanted form. Even on a wide area, which has during a long period remained continuous, and of which the climatic and other conditions of life change insensibly in proceeding from a district occupied by one species into another district occupied by a closely allied species, we have no just right to expect often to find intermediate varieties in the intermediate zones. For we have reason to believe that only a few species of a genus ever undergo change; the other species becoming utterly extinct and leaving no modified progeny. Of the species which do change, only a few within the same country change at the same time; and all modifications are slowly effected. I have also shown that the intermediate varieties which probably at first existed in the intermediate zones, would be liable to be supplanted by the allied forms on either hand; for the latter, from existing in greater numbers, would generally be modified and improved at a quicker rate than the intermediate varieties, which existed in lesser numbers; so that the intermediate varieties would, in the long run, be supplanted and exterminated.

On this doctrine of the extermination of an infinitude of connecting links, between the living and extinct inhabitants of the world, and at each successive period between the extinct and still older species, why is not every geological formation charged with such links? Why does not every collection of fossil remains afford plain evidence of the gradation and mutation of the forms of life? Although geological research has undoubtedly revealed the former existence of many links, bringing numerous forms of life much closer together, it does not yield the infinitely many fine gradations between past and present species required on the theory; and this is the most obvious of the many objections which may be urged against it. Why, again, do whole groups of allied species appear, though this appearance is often false, to have come in suddenly on the successive geological stages? Although we now know that organic beings appeared on this globe, at a period incalculably remote, long before the lowest bed of the Cambrian system was deposited, why do we not find beneath this system great piles of strata stored with the remains of the progenitors of the Cambrian fossils? For on the theory, such strata must somewhere have been deposited at these ancient and utterly unknown epochs of the world's history.

I can answer these questions and objections only on the supposition that the geological record is far more imperfect than most geologists believe. The number of specimens in all our museums is absolutely as nothing compared with the countless generations of countless species which have certainly existed. The parent-form of any two or more species would not be in all its characters directly intermediate between its modified offspring, any more than the rock-pigeon is directly intermediate in crop and tail between its descendants, the pouter and fantail pigeons. We should not be able to recognise a species as the parent of another and modified species, if we were to examine the two ever so closely, unless we possessed most of the intermediate links; and owing to the imperfection of the geological record, we have no just right to expect to find so many links. If two or three, or even more linking forms were discovered, they would simply be ranked by many naturalists as so many new species, more especially if found in different geological sub-stages, let their differences be ever so slight. Numerous existing doubtful forms could be named which are probably varieties; but who will pretend that in future ages so many fossil links will be discovered, that naturalists will be able to decide whether or not these doubtful forms ought to be called varieties? Only a small portion of the world has been geologically explored. Only organic beings of certain classes can be preserved in a fossil condition, at least in any great number. Many species when once formed never undergo any further change but become extinct without leaving modified descendants; and the periods, during which species have undergone modification, though long as measured by years, have probably been short in comparison with the periods during which they retain the same form. It is the dominant and widely ranging species which vary most frequently and vary most, and varieties are often at first local — both causes rendering the discovery of intermediate links in any one formation less likely. Local varieties will not spread into other and distant regions until they are considerably modified and improved; and when they have spread, and are discovered in a geological formation, they appear as if suddenly created there, and will be simply classed as new species. Most formations have been intermittent in their accumulation; and their duration has probably been shorter than the average duration of specific forms. Successive formations are in most cases separated from each other by blank intervals of time of great length; for fossiliferous formations thick enough to resist future degradations can as a general rule be accumulated only where much sediment is deposited on the subsiding bed of the sea. During the alternate periods of elevation and of stationary level the record will generally be blank. During these latter periods there will probably be more variability in the forms of life; during periods of subsidence, more extinction.

With respect to the absence of strata rich in fossils beneath the Cambrian formation, I can recur only to the hypothesis given in the tenth chapter; namely, that though our continents and oceans have endured for an enormous period in nearly their present relative positions, we have no reason to assume that this has always been the case; consequently formations much older than any now known may lie buried beneath the great oceans. With respect to the lapse of time not having been sufficient since our planet was consolidated for the assumed amount of organic change, and this objection, as urged by Sir William Thompson, is probably one of the gravest as yet advanced, I can only say, firstly, that we do not know at what rate species change as measured by years, and secondly, that many philosophers are not as yet willing to admit that we know enough of the constitution of the universe and of the interior of our globe to speculate with safety on its past duration.

That the geological record is imperfect all will admit; but that it is imperfect to the degree required by our theory, few will be inclined to admit. If we look to long enough intervals of time, geology plainly declares that species have all changed; and they have changed in the manner required by the theory, for they have changed slowly and in a graduated manner. We clearly see this in the fossil remains from consecutive formations invariably being much more closely related to each other, than are the fossils from widely seperated formations.

Such is the sum of the several chief objections and difficulties which may be justly urged against the theory; and I have now briefly recapitulated the answers and explanations which, as far as I can see, may be given. I have felt these difficulties far too heavily during many years to doubt their weight. But it deserves especial notice that the more important objections relate to questions on which we are confessedly ignorant; nor do we know how ignorant we are. We do not know all the possible transitional gradations between the simplest and the most perfect organs; it cannot be pretended that we know all the varied means of Distribution during the long lapse of years, or that we know how imperfect is the Geological Record. Serious as these several objections are, in my judgment they are by no means sufficient to overthrow the theory of descent with subsequent modification.

Now let us turn to the other side of the argument. Under domestication we see much variability, caused, or at least excited, by changed conditions of life; but often in so obscure a manner, that we are tempted to consider the variations as spontaneous. Variability is governed by many complex laws, — by correlated growth, compensation, the increased use and disuse of parts, and the definite action of the surrounding conditions. There is much difficulty in ascertaining how largely our domestic productions have been modified; but we may safely infer that the amount has been large, and that modifications can be inherited for long periods. As long as the conditions of life remain the same, we have reason to believe that a modification, which has already been inherited for many generations, may continue to be inherited for an almost infinite number of generations. On the other hand, we have evidence that variability when it has once come into play, does not cease under domestication for a very long period; nor do we know that it ever ceases, for new varieties are still occasionally produced by our oldest domesticated productions.

Variability is not actually caused by man; he only unintentionally exposes organic beings to new conditions of life, and then nature acts on the organisation and causes it to vary. But man can and does select the variations given to him by nature, and thus accumulates them in any desired manner. He thus adapts animals and plants for his own benefit or pleasure. He may do this methodically, or he may do it unconsciously by preserving the individuals most useful or pleasing to him without any intention of altering the breed. It is certain that he can largely influence the character of a breed by selecting, in each successive generation, individual differences so slight as to be inappreciable except by an educated eye. This unconscious process of selection has been the great agency in the formation of the most distinct and useful domestic breeds. That many breeds produced by man have to a large extent the character of natural species, is shown by the inextricable doubts whether many of them are varieties or aboriginally distinct species.

There is no reason why the principles which have acted so efficiently under domestication should not have acted under nature. In the survival of favoured individuals and races, during the constantly-recurrent Struggle for Existence, we see a powerful and ever-acting form of Selection. The struggle for existence inevitably follows from the high geometrical ratio of increase which is common to all organic beings. This high rate of increase is proved by calculation, — by the rapid increase of many animals and plants during a succession of peculiar seasons, and when naturalised in new countries. More individuals are born than can possibly survive. A grain in the balance may determine which individuals shall live and which shall die, — which variety or species shall increase in number, and which shall decrease, or finally become extinct. As the individuals of the same species come in all respects into the closest competition with each other, the struggle will generally be most severe between them; it will be almost equally severe between the varieties of the same species, and next in severity between the species of the same genus. On the other hand the struggle will often be severe between beings remote in the scale of nature. The slightest advantage in certain individuals, at any age or during any season, over those with which they come into competition, or better adaptation in however slight a degree to the surrounding physical conditions, will, in the long run, turn the balance.

With animals having separated sexes, there will be in most cases a struggle between the males for the possession of the females. The most vigorous males, or those which have most successfully struggled with their conditions of life, will generally leave most progeny. But success will often depend on the males having special weapons, or means of defence, or charms; and a slight advantage will lead to victory.

As geology plainly proclaims that each land has undergone great physical changes, we might have expected to find that organic beings have varied under nature, in the same way as they have varied under domestication. And if there has been any variability under nature, it would be an unaccountable fact if natural selection had not come into play. It has often been asserted, but the assertion is incapable of proof, that the amount of variation under nature is a strictly limited quantity. Man, though acting on external characters alone and often capriciously, can produce within a short period a great result by adding up mere individual differences in his domestic productions; and every one admits that species present individual differences. But, besides such differences, all naturalists admit that natural varieties exist, which are considered sufficiently distinct to be worthy of record in systematic works. No one has drawn any clear distinction between individual differences and slight varieties; or between more plainly marked varieties and sub-species, and species. On separate continents, and on different parts of the same continent when divided by barriers of any kind, and on outlying islands, what a multitude of forms exist, which some experienced naturalists rank as varieties, others as geographical races or sub-species, and others as distinct, though closely allied species!

If then, animals and plants do vary, let it be ever so slightly or slowly, why should not variations or individual differences, which are in any way beneficial, be preserved and accumulated through natural selection, or the survival of the fittest? If man can by patience select variations useful to him, why, under changing and complex conditions of life, should not variations useful to nature's living products often arise, and be preserved or selected? What limit can be put to this power, acting during long ages and rigidly scrutinising the whole constitution, structure, and habits of each creature, — favouring the good and rejecting the bad? I can see no limit to this power, in slowly and beautifully adapting each form to the most complex relations of life. The theory of natural selection, even if we look no farther than this, seems to be in the highest degree probable. I have already recapitulated, as fairly as I could, the opposed difficulties and objections: now let us turn to the special facts and arguments in favour of the theory.

On the view that species are only strongly marked and permanent varieties, and that each species first existed as a variety, we can see why it is that no line of demarcation can be drawn between species, commonly supposed to have been produced by special acts of creation, and varieties which are acknowledged to have been produced by secondary laws. On this same view we can understand how it is that in a region where many species of a genus have been produced, and where they now flourish, these same species should present many varieties; for where the manufactory of species has been active, we might expect, as a general rule, to find it still in action; and this is the case if varieties be incipient species. Moreover, the species of the larger genera, which afford the greater number of varieties or incipient species, retain to a certain degree the character of varieties; for they differ from each other by a less amount of difference than do the species of smaller genera. The closely allied species also of the larger genera apparently have restricted ranges, and in their affinities they are clustered in little groups round other species — in both respects resembling varieties. These are strange relations on the view that each species was independently created, but are intelligible if each existed first as a variety.

As each species tends by its geometrical rate of reproduction to increase inordinately in number; and as the modified descendants of each species will be enabled to increase by as much as they become more diversified in habits and structure, so as to be able to seize on many and widely different places in the economy of nature, there will be a constant tendency in natural selection to preserve the most divergent offspring of any one species. Hence, during a long-continued course of modification, the slight differences characteristic of varieties of the same species, tend to be augmented into the greater differences characteristic of the species of the same genus. New and improved varieties will inevitably supplant and exterminate the older, less improved, and intermediate varieties; and thus species are rendered to a large extent defined and distinct objects. Dominant species belonging to the larger groups within each class tend to give birth to new and dominant forms; so that each large group tends to become still larger, and at the same time more divergent in character. But as all groups cannot thus go on increasing in size, for the world would not hold them, the more dominant groups beat the less dominant. This tendency in the large groups to go on increasing in size and diverging in character, together with the inevitable contingency of much extinction, explains the arrangement of all the forms of life in groups subordinate to groups, all within a few great classes, which has prevailed throughout all time. This grand fact of the grouping of all organic beings under what is called the Natural System, is utterly inexplicable on the theory of creation.

As natural selection acts solely by accumulating slight, successive, favourable variations, it can produce no great or sudden modifications; it can act only by short and slow steps. Hence, the canon of "Natura non facit saltum," which every fresh addition to our knowledge tends to confirm, is on this theory intelligible. We can see why throughout nature the same general end is gained by an almost infinite diversity of means, for every peculiarity when once acquired is long inherited, and structures already modified in many different ways have to be adapted for the same general purpose. We can, in short, see why nature is prodigal in variety, though niggard in innovation. But why this should be a law of nature if each species has been independently created no man can explain.

Many other facts are, as it seems to me, explicable on this theory. How strange it is that a bird, under the form of a woodpecker, should prey on insects on the ground; that upland geese which rarely or never swim, should possess webbed feet; that a thrush-like bird should dive and feed on sub-aquatic insects; and that a petrel should have the habits and structure fitting it for the life of an awk! and so in endless other cases. But on the view of each species constantly trying to increase in number, with natural selection always ready to adapt the slowly varying descendants of each to any unoccupied or ill-occupied place in nature, these facts cease to be strange, or might even have been anticipated.

We can to a certain extent understand how it is that there is so much beauty throughout nature; for this may be largely attributed to the agency of selection. That beauty, according to our sense of it, is not universal, must be admitted by every one who will look at some venomous snakes, at some fishes, and at certain hideous bats with a distorted resemblance to the human face. Sexual selection has given the most brilliant colours, elegant patterns, and other ornaments to the males, and sometimes to both sexes of many birds, butterflies, and other animals. With birds it has often rendered the voice of the male musical to the female, as well as to our ears. Flowers and fruit have been rendered conspicuous by brilliant colours in contrast with the green foliage, in order that the flowers may be readily seen, visited and fertilised by insects, and the seeds disseminated by birds. How it comes that certain colours, sounds, and forms should give pleasure to man and the lower animals, — that is, how the sense of beauty in its simplest form was first acquired, — we do not know any more than how certain odours and flavours were first rendered agreeable.

As natural selection acts by competition, it adapts and improves the inhabitants of each country only in relation to their co-inhabitants; so that we need feel no surprise at the species of any one country, although on the ordinary view supposed to have been created and specially adapted for that country, being beaten and supplanted by the naturalised productions from another land. Nor ought we to marvel if all the contrivances in nature be not, as far as we can judge, absolutely perfect, as in the case even of the human eye; or if some of them be abhorrent to our ideas of fitness. We need not marvel at the sting of the bee, when used against an enemy, causing the bee's own death; at drones being produced in such great numbers for one single act, and being then slaughtered by their sterile sisters; at the astonishing waste of pollen by our fir-trees; at the instinctive hatred of the queen-bee for her own fertile daughters; at the ichneumonidæ feeding within the living bodies of caterpillars; or at other such cases. The wonder indeed is, on the theory of natural selection, that more cases of the want of absolute perfection have not been detected.

The complex and little known laws governing the production of varieties are the same, as far as we can judge, with the laws which have governed the production of distinct species. In both cases physical conditions seem to have produced some direct and definite effect, but how much we cannot say. Thus, when varieties enter any new station, they occasionally assume some of the characters proper to the species of that station. With both varieties and species, use and disuse seem to have produced a considerable effect; for it is impossible to resist this conclusion when we look, for instance, at the logger-headed duck, which has wings incapable of flight, in nearly the same condition as in the domestic duck; or when we look at the burrowing tucu-tucu, which is occasionally blind, and then at certain moles, which are habitually blind and have their eyes covered with skin; or when we look at the blind animals inhabiting the dark caves of America and Europe. With varieties and species, correlated variation seems to have played an important part, so that when one part has been modified other parts have been necessarily modified.

With both varieties and species, reversions to long-lost characters occasionally occur. How inexplicable on the theory of creation is the occasional appearance of stripes on the shoulders and legs of the several species of the horse-genus and of their hybrids! How simply is this fact explained if we believe that these species are all descended from a striped progenitor, in the same manner as the several domestic breeds of the pigeon are descended from the blue and barred rock-pigeon!

On the ordinary view of each species having been independently created, why should specific characters, or those by which the species of the same genus differ from each other, be more variable than generic characters in which they all agree? Why, for instance, should the colour of a flower be more likely to vary in any one species of a genus, if the other species possess differently coloured flowers, than if all possessed the same coloured flowers? If species are only well-marked varieties, of which the characters have become in a high degree permanent, we can understand this fact; for they have already varied since they branched off from a common progenitor in certain characters, by which they have come to be specifically distinct from each other; therefore these same characters would be more likely again to vary than the generic characters which have been inherited without change for an immense period. It is inexplicable on the theory of creation why a part developed in a very unusual manner in one species alone of a genus, and therefore, as we may naturally infer, of great importance to that species, should be eminently liable to variation; but, on our view, this part has undergone, since the several species branched off from a common progenitor, an unusual amount of variability and modification, and therefore we might expect the part generally to be still variable. But a part may be developed in the most unusual manner, like the wing of a bat, and yet not be more variable than any other structure, if the part be common to many subordinate forms, that is, if it has been inherited for a very long period; for in this case, it will have been rendered constant by long-continued natural selection.

Glancing at instincts, marvellous as some are, they offer no greater difficulty than do corporeal structures on the theory of the natural selection of successive slight, but profitable modifications. We can thus understand why nature moves by graduated steps in endowing different animals of the same class with their several instincts. I have attempted to show how much light the principle of gradation throws on the admirable architectural powers of the hive-bee. Habit no doubt often comes into play in modifying instincts; but it certainly is not indispensable, as we see in the case of neuter insects, which leave no progeny to inherit the effects of long-continued habit. On the view of all the species of the same genus having descended from a common parent, and having inherited much in common, we can understand how it is that allied species, when placed under widely different conditions of life, yet follow nearly the same instincts; why the thrushes of tropical and temperate South America, for instance, line their nests with mud like our British species. On the view of instincts having been slowly acquired through natural selection, we need not marvel at some instincts being not perfect and liable to mistakes, and at many instincts causing other animals to suffer.

If species be only well-marked and permanent varieties, we can at once see why their crossed offspring should follow the same complex laws in their degrees and kinds of resemblance to their parents, — in being absorbed into each other by successive crosses, and in other such points, — as do the crossed offspring of acknowledged varieties. This similarity would be a strange fact, if species had been independently created and varieties had been produced through secondary laws.

If we admit that the geological record is imperfect to an extreme degree, then the facts, which the record does give, strongly support the theory of descent with modification. New species have come on the stage slowly and at successive intervals; and the amount of change, after equal intervals of time, is widely different in different groups. The extinction of species and of whole groups of species which has played so conspicuous a part in the history of the organic world, almost inevitably follows from the principle of natural selection; for old forms are supplanted by new and improved forms. Neither single species nor groups of species reappear when the chain of ordinary generation is once broken. The gradual diffusion of dominant forms, with the slow modification of their descendants, causes the forms of life, after long intervals of time, to appear as if they had changed simultaneously throughout the world. The fact of the fossil remains of each formation being in some degree intermediate in character between the fossils in the formations above and below, is simply explained by their intermediate position in the chain of descent. The grand fact that all extinct beings can be classed with all recent beings, naturally follows from the living and the extinct being the offspring of common parents. As species have generally diverged in character during their long course of descent and modification, we can understand why it is that the more ancient forms, or early progenitors of each group, so often occupy a position in some degree intermediate between existing groups. Recent forms are generally looked upon as being, on the whole, higher in the scale of organisation than ancient forms; and they must be higher, in so far as the later and more improved forms have conquered the older and less improved forms in the struggle for life; they have also generally had their organs more specialised for different functions. This fact is perfectly compatible with numerous beings still retaining simple and but little improved structures, fitted for simple conditions of life; it is likewise compatible with some forms having retrograded in organisation, by having become at each stage of descent better fitted for new and degraded habits of life. Lastly, the wonderful law of the long endurance of allied forms on the same continent, — of marsupials in Australia, of edentata in America, and other such cases, — is intelligible, for within the same country the existing and the extinct will be closely allied by descent.

Looking to geographical distribution, if we admit that there has been during the long course of ages much migration from one part of the world to another, owing to former climatal and geographical changes and to the many occasional and unknown means of dispersal, then we can understand, on the theory of descent with modification, most of the great leading facts in Distribution. We can see why there should be so striking a parallelism in the distribution of organic beings throughout space, and in their geological succession throughout time; for in both cases the beings have been connected by the bond of ordinary generation, and the means of modification have been the same. We see the full meaning of the wonderful fact, which has struck every traveller, namely, that on the same continent, under the most diverse conditions, under heat and cold, on mountain and lowland, on deserts and marshes, most of the inhabitants within each great class are plainly related; for they are the descendants of the same progenitors and early colonists. On this same principle of former migration, combined in most cases with modification, we can understand, by the aid of the Glacial period, the identity of some few plants, and the close alliance of many others, on the most distant mountains, and in the northern and southern temperate zones; and likewise the close alliance of some of the inhabitants of the sea in the northern and southern temperate latitudes, though separated by the whole intertropical ocean. Although two countries may present physical conditions as closely similar as the same species ever require, we need feel no surprise at their inhabitants being widely different, if they have been for a long period completely sundered from each other; for as the relation of organism to organism is the most important of all relations, and as the two countries will have received colonists at various periods and in different proportions, from some other country or from each other, the course of modification in the two areas will inevitably have been different.

On this view of migration, with subsequent modification, we see why oceanic islands are inhabited by only few species, but of these, why many are peculiar or endemic forms. We clearly see why species belonging to those groups of animals which cannot cross wide spaces of the ocean, as frogs and terrestrial mammals, do not inhabit oceanic islands; and why, on the other hand, new and peculiar species of bats, animals which can traverse the ocean, are found on islands far distant from any continent. Such cases as the presence of peculiar species of bats on oceanic islands and the absence of all other terrestrial mammals, are facts utterly inexplicable on the theory of independent acts of creation.

The existence of closely allied or representative species in any two areas, implies, on the theory of descent with modification, that the same parent-forms formerly inhabited both areas; and we almost invariably find that wherever many closely allied species inhabit two areas, some identical species are still common to both. Wherever may closely allied yet distinct species occur, doubtful forms and varieties belonging to the same groups likewise occur. It is a rule of high generality that the inhabitants of each area are related to the inhabitants of the nearest source whence immigrants might have been derived. We see this in the striking relation of nearly all plants and animals of the Galapagos archipelago, of Juan Fernandez, and of the other American islands, to the plants and animals of the neighbouring American mainland; and of those of the Cape de Verde archipelago, and of the other African islands to the African mainland. It must be admitted that these facts receive no explanation on the theory of creation.

The fact, as we have seen, that all past and present organic beings can be arranged within a few great classes, in groups subordinate to groups, and with the extinct groups often falling in between the recent groups, is intelligible on the theory of natural selection with its contingencies of extinction and divergence of character. On these same principles we see how it is, that the mutual affinities of the forms within each class are so complex and circuitous. We see why certain characters are far more serviceable than others for classification; — why adaptive characters, though of paramount importance to the beings, are of hardly any importance in classification; why characters derived from rudimentary parts, though of no service to the beings, are often of high classificatory value; and why embryological characters are often the most valuable of all. The real affinities of all organic beings, in contradistinction to their adaptive resemblances, are due to inheritance or community of descent. The Natural Selection is a genealogical arrangement, with the acquired grades of difference, marked by the terms, varieties, species, genera, families, &c.; and we have to discover the lines of descent by the most permanent characters whatever they may be and of however slight vital importance.

The similar framework of bones in the hand of a man, wing of a bat, fin of the porpoise, and leg of the horse, — the same number of vertebra forming the neck of the giraffe and of the elephant, — and innumerable other such facts, at once explain themselves on the theory of descent with slow and slight successive modifications. The similarity of pattern in the wing and in the leg of a bat, though used for such different purpose, — in the jaws and legs of a crab, — in the petals, stamens, and pistils of a flower, is likewise, to a large extent, intelligible on the view of the gradual modification of parts or organs, which were aboriginally alike in an early progenitor in each of these classes. On the principle of successive variations not always supervening at an early age, and being inherited at a corresponding not early period of life, we clearly see why the embryos of mammals, birds, reptiles, and fishes should be so closely similar, and so unlike the adult forms. We may cease marvelling at the embryo of an air-breathing mammal or bird having branchial slits and arteries running in loops, like those of a fish which has to breathe the air dissolved in water by the aid of well-developed branchiæ.

Disuse, aided sometimes by natural selection, will often have reduced organs when rendered useless under changed habits or conditions of life; and we can understand on this view the meaning of rudimentary organs. But disuse and selection will generally act on each creature, when it has come to maturity and has to play its full part in the struggle for existence, and will thus have little power on an organ during early life; hence the organ will not be reduced or rendered rudimentary at this early age. The calf, for instance, has inherited teeth, which never cut through the gums of the upper jaw, from an early progenitor having well-developed teeth; and we may believe, that the teeth in the mature animal were formerly reduced by disuse, owing to the tongue and palate, or lips, having become excellently fitted through natural selection to browse without their aid; whereas in the calf, the teeth have been left unaffected, and on the principle of inheritance at corresponding ages have been inherited from a remote period to the present day. On the view of each organism with all its separate parts having been specially created, how utterly inexplicable is it that organs bearing the plain stamp of inutility, such as the teeth in the embryonic calf or the shrivelled wings under the soldered wing-covers of many beetles, should so frequently occur. Nature may be said to have taken pains to reveal her scheme of modification, by means of rudimentary organs, of embryological and homologous structures, but we are too blind to understand her meaning.

I have now recapitulated the facts and considerations which have thoroughly convinced me that species have been modified, during a long course of descent. This has been effected chiefly through the natural selection of numerous successive, slight, favourable variations; aided in an important manner by the inherited effects of the use and disuse of parts; and in an unimportant manner, that is in relation to adaptive structures, whether past or present, by the direct action of external conditions, and by variations which seem to us in our ignorance to arise spontaneously. It appears that I formerly underrated the frequency and value of these latter forms of variation, as leading to permanent modifications of structure independently of natural selection. But as my conclusions have lately been much misrepresented, and it has been stated that I attribute the modification of species exclusively to natural selection, I may be permitted to remark that in the first edition of this work, and subsequently, I placed in a most conspicuous position — namely, at the close of the Introduction — the following words: "I am convinced that natural selection has been the main but not the exclusive means of modification." This has been of no avail. Great is the power of steady misrepresentation; but the history of science shows that fortunately this power does not long endure.

It can hardly be supposed that a false theory would explain, in so satisfactory a manner as does the theory of natural selection, the several large classes of facts above specified. It has recently been objected that this is an unsafe method of arguing; but it is a method used in judging of the common events of life, and has often been used by the greatest natural philosophers. The undulatory theory of light has thus been arrived at; and the belief in the revolution of the earth on its own axis was until lately supported by hardly any direct evidence. It is no valid objection that science as yet throws no light on the far higher problem of the essence or origin of life. Who can explain what is the essence of the attraction of gravity? No one now objects to following out the results consequent on this unknown element of attraction; notwithstanding that Leibnitz formerly accused Newton of introducing "occult qualities and miracles into philosophy."

I see no good reason why the views given in this volume should shock the religious feelings of any one. It is satisfactory, as showing how transient such impressions are, to remember that the greatest discovery ever made by man, namely, the law of the attraction of gravity, was also attacked by Leibnitz, "as subversive of natural, and inferentially of revealed, religion." A celebrated author and divine has written to me that "he has gradually learnt to see that it is just as noble a conception of the Deity to believe that He created a few original forms capable of self-development into other and needful forms, as to believe that He required a fresh act of creation to supply the voids caused by the action of His laws."

Why, it may be asked, until recently did nearly all the most eminent living naturalists and geologists disbelieve in the mutability of species? It cannot be asserted that organic beings in a state of nature are subject to no variation; it cannot be proved that the amount of variation in the course of long ages is a limited quality; no clear distinction has been, or can be, drawn between species and well-marked varieties. It cannot be maintained that species when intercrossed are invariably sterile, and varieties invariably fertile; or that sterility is a special endowment and sign of creation. The belief that species were immutable productions was almost unavoidable as long as the history of the world was thought to be of short duration; and now that we have acquired some idea of the lapse of time, we are too apt to assume, without proof, that the geological record is so perfect that it would have afforded us plain evidence of the mutation of species, if they had undergone mutation.

But the chief cause of our natural unwillingness to admit that one species has given birth to clear and distinct species, is that we are always slow in admitting great changes of which we do not see the steps. The difficulty is the same as that felt by so many geologists, when Lyell first insisted that long lines of inland cliffs had been formed, and great valleys excavated, by the agencies which we see still at work. The mind cannot possibly grasp the full meaning of the term of even a million years; it cannot add up and perceive the full effects of many slight variations, accumulated during an almost infinite number of generations.

Although I am fully convinced of the truth of the views given in this volume under the form of an abstract, I by no means expect to convince experienced naturalists whose minds are stocked with a multitude of facts all viewed, during a long course of years, from a point of view directly opposite to mine. It is so easy to hide our ignorance under such expressions as the "plan of creation," "unity of design," &c., and to think that we give an explanation when we only re-state a fact. Any one whose disposition leads him to attach more weight to unexplained difficulties than to the explanation of a certain number of facts will certainly reject the theory. A few naturalists, endowed with much flexibility of mind, and who have already begun to doubt the immutability of species, may be influenced by this volume; but I look with confidence to the future, — to young and rising naturalists, who will be able to view both sides of the question with impartiality. Whoever is led to believe that species are mutable will do good service by conscientiously expressing his conviction; for thus only can the load of prejudice by which this subject is overwhelmed be removed.

Several eminent naturalists have of late published their belief that a multitude of reputed species in each genus are not real species; but that other species are real, that is, have been independently created. This seems to me a strange conclusion to arrive at. They admit that a multitude of forms, which till lately they themselves thought were special creations, and which are still thus looked at by the majority of naturalists, and which consequently have all the external characteristic features of true species, — they admit that these have been produced by variation, but they refuse to extend the same view to other and slightly different forms. Nevertheless they do not pretend that they can define, or even conjecture, which are the created forms of life, and which are those produced by secondary laws. They admit variation as a *vera causa* in one case, they arbitrarily reject it in another, without assigning any distinction in the two cases. The day will come when this will be given as a curious illustration of the blindness of preconceived opinion. These authors seem no more startled at a miraculous act of creation than at an ordinary birth. But do they really believe that at innumerable periods in the earth's history certain elemental atoms have been commanded suddenly to flash into living tissues? Do they believe that at each supposed act of creation one individual or many were produced? Were all the infinitely numerous kinds of animals and plants created as eggs or seed, or as full grown? and in the case of mammals, were they created bearing the false marks of nourishment from the mother's womb? Undoubtedly some of these same questions cannot be answered by those who believe in the appearance or creation of only a few forms of life, or of some one form alone. It has been maintained by several authors that it is as easy to believe in the creation of a million beings as of one; but Maupertuis' philosophical axiom "of least action" leads the mind more willingly to admit the smaller number; and certainly we ought not to believe that innumerable beings within each great class have been created with plain, but deceptive, marks of descent from a single parent.

As a record of a former state of things, I have retained in the foregoing paragraphs, and elsewhere, several sentences which imply that naturalists believe in the separate creation of each species; and I have been much censured for having thus expressed myself. But undoubtedly this was the general belief when the first edition of the present work appeared. I formerly spoke to very many naturalists on the subject of evolution, and never once met with any sympathetic agreement. It is probable that some did then believe in evolution, but they were either silent, or expressed themselves so ambiguously that it was not easy to understand their meaning. Now things are wholly changed, and almost every naturalist admits the great principle of evolution. There are, however, some who still think that species have suddenly given birth, through quite unexplained means, to new and totally different forms: but, as I have attempted to show, weighty evidence can be opposed to the admission of great and abrupt modifications. Under a scientific point of view, and as leading to further investigation, but little advantage is gained by believing that new forms are suddenly developed in an inexplicable manner from old and widely different forms, over the belief in the creation of species from the dust of the earth.

It may be asked how far I extend the doctrine of the modification of species. The question is difficult to answer, because the more distinct the forms are which we consider, by so much the arguments in favour of community of descent become fewer in number and less in force. But some arguments of the greatest weight extend very far. All the members of whole classes are connected together by a chain of affinities, and all can be classed on the same principle, in groups subordinate to groups. Fossil remains sometimes tend to fill up very wide intervals between existing orders.

Organs in a rudimentary condition plainly show that an early progenitor had the organ in a fully developed condition; and this in some cases implies an enormous amount of modification in the descendants. Throughout whole classes various structures are formed on the same pattern, and at a very early age the embryos closely resemble each other. Therefore I cannot doubt that the theory of descent with modification embraces all the members of the same great class or kingdom. I believe that animals are descended from at most only four or five progenitors, and plants from an equal or lesser number.

Analogy would lead me one step farther, namely, to the belief that all animals and plants are descended from some one prototype. But analogy may be a deceitful guide. Nevertheless all living things have much in common, in their chemical composition, their cellular structure, their laws of growth, and their liability to injurious influences. We see this even in so trifling a fact as that the same poison often similarly affects plants and animals; or that the poison secreted by the gall-fly produces monstrous growths on the wild rose or oak-tree. With all organic beings excepting perhaps some of the very lowest, sexual production seems to be essentially similar. With all, as far as is at present known the germinal vesicle is the same; so that all organisms start from a common origin. If we look even to the two main divisions — namely, to the animal and vegetable kingdoms — certain low forms are so far intermediate in character that naturalists have disputed to which kingdom they should be referred. As Professor Asa Gray has remarked, "the spores and other reproductive bodies of many of the lower algæ may claim to have first a characteristically animal, and then an unequivocally vegetable existence." Therefore, on the principle of natural selection with divergence of character, it does not seem incredible that, from such low and intermediate form, both animals and plants may have been developed; and, if we admit this, we must likewise admit that all the organic beings which have ever lived on this earth may be descended from some one primordial form. But this inference is chiefly grounded on analogy and it is immaterial whether or not it be accepted. No doubt it is possible, as Mr. G. H. Lewes has urged, that at the first commencement of life many different forms were evolved; but if so we may conclude that only a very few have left modified descendants. For, as I have recently remarked in regard to the members of each great kingdom, such as the Vertebrata Articulata &c., we have distinct evidence in their embryological homologous and rudimentary structures, that within each kingdom all the members are descended from a single progenitor.

When the views advanced by me in this volume, and by Mr. Wallace, or when analogous views on the origin of species are generally admitted, we can dimly foresee that there will be a considerable revolution in natural history. Systematists will be able to pursue their labours as at present; but they will not be incessantly haunted by the shadowy doubt whether this or that form be a true species. This, I feel sure and I speak after experience, will be no slight relief. The endless disputes whether or not some fifty species of British brambles are good species will cease. Systematists will have only to decide (not that this will be easy) whether any form be sufficiently constant and distinct from other forms, to be capable of definition; and if definable, whether the differences be sufficiently important to deserve a specific name. This latter point will become a far more essential consideration than it is at present; for differences, however slight, between any two forms if not blended by intermediate gradations, are looked at by most naturalists as sufficient to raise both forms to the rank of species.

Hereafter we shall be compelled to acknowledge that the only distinction between species and well-marked varieties is, that the latter are known, or believed, to be connected at the present day by intermediate gradations, whereas species were formerly thus connected. Hence, without rejecting the consideration of the present existence of intermediate gradations between any two forms we shall be led to weigh more carefully and to value higher the actual amount of difference between them. It is quite possible that forms now generally acknowledged to be merely varieties may hereafter be thought worthy of specific names; and in this case scientific and common language will come into accordance. In short, we shall have to treat species in the same manner as those naturalists treat genera, who admit that genera are merely artificial combinations made for convenience. This may not be a cheering prospect; but we shall at least be free from the vain search for the undiscovered and undiscoverable essence of the term species.

The other and more general departments of natural history will rise greatly in interest. The terms used by naturalists, of affinity, relationship, community of type, paternity, morphology, adaptive characters, rudimentary and aborted organs, &c., will cease to be metaphorical, and will have a plain signification. When we no longer look at an organic being as a savage looks at a ship, as something wholly beyond his comprehension; when we regard every production of nature as one which has had a long history; when we contemplate every complex structure and instinct as the summing up of many contrivances, each useful to the possessor, in the same way as any great mechanical invention is the summing up of the labour, the experience, the reason, and even the blunders of numerous workmen; when we thus view each organic being, how far more interesting — I speak from experience — does the study of natural history become!

A grand and almost untrodden field of inquiry will be opened, on the causes and laws of variation, on correlation, on the effects of use and disuse, on the direct action of external conditions, and so forth. The study of domestic productions will rise immensely in value. A new variety raised by man will be a more important and interesting subject for study than one more species added to the infinitude of already recorded species. Our classifications will come to be, as far as they can be so made, genealogies; and will then truly give what may be called the plan of creation. The rules for classifying will no doubt become simpler when we have a definite object in view. We possess no pedigrees or armorial bearings; and we have to discover and trace the many diverging lines of descent in our natural genealogies, by characters of any kind which have long been inherited. Rudimentary organs will speak infallibly with respect to the nature of long-lost structures. Species and groups of species which are called aberrant, and which may fancifully be called living fossils, will aid us in forming a picture of the ancient forms of life. Embryology will often reveal to us the structure, in some degree obscured, of the prototype of each great class.

When we feel assured that all the individuals of the same species, and all the closely allied species of most genera, have within a not very remote period descended from one parent, and have migrated from some one birth-place; and when we better know the many means of migration, then, by the light which geology now throws, and will continue to throw, on former changes of climate and of the level of the land, we shall surely be enabled to trace in an admirable manner the former migrations of the inhabitants of the whole world. Even at present, by comparing the differences between the inhabitants of the sea on the opposite sides of a continent, and the nature of the various inhabitants on that continent, in relation to their apparent means of immigration, some light can be thrown on ancient geography.

The noble science of Geology loses glory from the extreme imperfection of the record. The crust of the earth with its imbedded remains must not be looked at as a well-filled museum, but as a poor collection made at hazard and at rare intervals. The accumulation of each great fossiliferous formation will be recognised as having depended on an unusual concurrence of favourable circumstances, and the blank intervals between the successive stages as having been of vast duration. But we shall be able to gauge with some security the duration of these intervals by a comparison of the preceding and succeeding organic forms. We must be cautious in attempting to correlate as strictly contemporaneous two formations, which do not include many identical species, by the general succession of the forms of life. As species are produced and exterminated by slowly acting and still existing causes, and not by miraculous acts of creation; and as the most important of all causes of organic change is one which is almost independent of altered and perhaps suddenly altered physical conditions, namely, the mutual relation of organism to organism, — the improvement of one organism entailing the improvement or the extermination of others; it follows, that the amount of organic change in the fossils of consecutive formations probably serves as a fair measure of the relative though not actual lapse of time. A number of species, however, keeping in a body might remain for a long period unchanged, whilst within the same period several of these species by migrating into new countries and coming into competition with foreign associates, might become modified; so that we must not overrate the accuracy of organic change as a measure of time.

In the future I see open fields for far more important researches. Psychology will be securely based on the foundation already well laid by Mr. Herbert Spencer, that of the necessary acquirement of each mental power and capacity by gradation. Much light will be thrown on the origin of man and his history.

Authors of the highest eminence seem to be fully satisfied with the view that each species has been independently created. To my mind it accords better with what we know of the laws impressed on matter by the Creator, that the production and extinction of the past and present inhabitants of the world should have been due to secondary causes, like those determining the birth and death of the individual. When I view all beings not as special creations, but as the lineal descendants of some few beings which lived long before the first bed of the Cambrian system was deposited, they seem to me to become ennobled. Judging from the past, we may safely infer that not one living species will transmit its unaltered likeness to a distant futurity. And of the species now living very few will transmit progeny of any kind to a far distant futurity; for the manner in which all organic beings are grouped, shows that the greater number of species in each genus, and all the species in many genera, have left no descendants, but have become utterly extinct. We can so far take a prophetic glance into futurity as to foretell that it will be the common and widely-spread species, belonging to the larger and dominant groups within each class, which will ultimately prevail and procreate new and dominant species. As all the living forms of life are the lineal descendants of those which lived long before the Cambrian epoch, we may feel certain that the ordinary succession by generation has never once been broken, and that no cataclysm has desolated the whole world. Hence we may look with some confidence to a secure future of great length. And as natural selection works solely by and for the good of each being, all corporeal and mental endowments will tend to progress towards perfection.

It is interesting to contemplate a tangled bank, clothed with many plants of many kinds, with birds singing on the bushes, with various insects flitting about, and with worms crawling through the damp earth, and to reflect that these elaborately constructed forms, so different from each other, and dependent upon each other in so complex a manner, have all been produced by laws acting around us. These laws, taken in the largest sense, being Growth with Reproduction; Inheritance which is almost implied by reproduction; Variability from the indirect and direct action of the conditions of life, and from use and disuse: a Ratio of Increase so high as to lead to a Struggle for Life, and as a consequence to Natural Selection, entailing Divergence of Character and the Extinction of less-improved forms. Thus, from the war of nature, from famine and death, the most exalted object which we are capable of conceiving, namely, the production of the higher animals, directly follows. There is grandeur in this view of life, with its several powers, having been originally breathed by the Creator into a few forms or into one; and that, whilst this planet has gone cycling on according to the fixed law of gravity, from so simple a beginning endless forms most beautiful and most wonderful have been, and are being evolved.

# *The Descent of Man*[55]

# *The Manner of Development of Man*

It is manifest that man is now subject to much variability. No two individuals of the same race are quite alike. We may compare millions of faces, and each will be distinct. There is an equally great amount of diversity in the proportions and dimensions of the various parts of the body; the length of the legs being one of the most variable points.[1] Although in some quarters of the world an elongated skull, and in other quarters a short skull prevails, yet there is great diversity of shape even within the limits of the same race, as with the aborigines of America and South Australia — the latter a race "probably as pure and homogeneous in blood, customs, and language as any in existence" — and even with the inhabitants of so confined an area as the Sandwich Islands.[2] An eminent dentist assures me that

1 'Investigations in Military and Anthropolog. Statistics of American Soldiers,' by B. A. Gould, 1869, p. 256.

2 With respect to the "Cranial forms of the American aborigines," see Dr. Aitken Meigs in 'Proc. Acad. Nat. Sci.' Philadelphia, May, 1868. On the Australians, see Huxley, in Lyell's 'Antiquity of Man,' 1863, p. 87. On the Sandwich Islanders, Prof. J. Wyman, 'Observations on Crania,' Boston, 1868, p. 18.

there is nearly as much diversity in the teeth as in the features. The chief arteries so frequently run in abnormal courses, that it has been found useful for surgical purposes to calculate from 1040 corpses how often each course prevails.[3] The muscles are eminently variable: thus those of the foot were found by Prof. Turner[4] not to be strictly alike in any two out of fifty bodies; and in some the deviations were considerable. He adds, that the power of performing the appropriate movements must have been modified in accordance with the several deviations. Mr. J. Wood has recorded[5] the occurrence of 295 muscular variations in thirty-six subjects, and in another set of the same number no less than 558 variations, those occurring on both sides of the body being only reckoned as one. In the last set, not one body out of the thirty-six was "found totally wanting in departures from the standard descriptions of the muscular system given in anatomical text books." A single body presented the extraordinary number of twenty-five distinct abnormalities. The same muscle sometimes varies in many ways: thus Prof. Macalister describes[6] no less than twenty distinct variations in the *palmaris accesorius.*

The famous old anatomist, Wolff,[7] insists that the internal viscera are more variable than the external parts: *Nulla particula est quæ non aliter et aliter in aliis se habeat hominibus.* He has even written a treatise on the choice of typical examples of the viscera for representation. A discussion on the beau-ideal of the liver, lungs, kidneys, &c., as of the human face divine, sounds strange in our ears.

The variability or diversity of the mental faculties in men of the same race, not to mention the greater differences between the men of distinct races, is so notorious that not a word need here be said. So it is with the lower animals. All who have had

[3] 'Anatomy of the Arteries,' by R. Quain. Preface, vol. i. 1844.

[4] 'Transact. Royal Soc. Edinburgh,' vol. xxiv. pp. 175, 189.

[5] 'Proc. Royal Soc.' 1867, p. 544; also 1868, pp. 483, 524. There is a previous paper, 1866, p. 229.

[6] 'Proc. R. Irish Academy,' vol. x. 1868, p. 141.

[7] 'Act. Acad. St. Petersburg,' 1778, part ii. p. 217.

PUNCH'S FANCY PORTRAITS.—No. 54.

CHARLES ROBERT DARWIN, LL.D., F.R.S.

IN HIS *DESCENT OF MAN* HE BROUGHT HIS OWN SPECIES DOWN AS LOW AS POSSIBLE—*I.E.*, TO "A HAIRY QUADRUPED FURNISHED WITH A TAIL AND POINTED EARS, AND PROBABLY *ARBOREAL* IN ITS HABITS"—WHICH IS A REASON FOR THE VERY GENERAL INTEREST IN A "FAMILY TREE." HE HAS LATELY BEEN TURNING HIS ATTENTION TO THE "POLITIC WORM."

How Darwin's contemporaries viewed the evolutionist and his theory charge of menageries admit this fact, and we see it plainly in our dogs and other domestic animals. Brehm especially insists that each individual monkey of those which he kept tame in Africa had its own peculiar disposition and temper: he mentions one baboon remarkable for its high intelligence; and the keepers in the Zoological Gardens pointed out to me a monkey, belonging to the New World division, equally remarkable for intelligence. Rengger, also, insists on the diversity in the various mental characters of the monkeys of the same species which he kept in Paraguay; and this diversity, as he adds, is partly innate, and partly the result of the manner in which they have been treated or educated.[8]

I have elsewhere[9] so fully discussed the subject of inheritance, that I need here add hardly anything. A greater number of facts have been collected with respect to the transmission of the most trifling, as well as of the most important characters in man, than in any of the lower animals; though the facts are copious enough with respect to the latter. So in regard to mental qualities, their transmission is manifest in our dogs, horses, and other domestic animals. Besides special tastes and habits, general intelligence, courage, bad and good temper, &c., are certainly transmitted. With man we see similar facts in almost every family; and we now know, through the admirable labours of Mr. Galton,[10] that genius which implies a wonderfully complex combination of high faculties, tends to be inherited; and, on the other hand, it is too certain that insanity and deteriorated mental powers likewise run in families.

With respect to the causes of variability, we are in all cases very ignorant; but we can see that in man as in the lower animals, they stand in some relation to the conditions to which each spe-

[8] Brehm, 'Thierleben,' B. i. s. 58, 87. Rengger, 'Säugethiere von Paraguay,' s. 57.

[9] 'Variation of Animals and Plants under Domestication,' vol. ii. chap. xii.

[10] 'Hereditary Genius: an Inquiry into its Laws and Consequences,' 1869.

cies has been exposed, during several generations. Domesticated animals vary more than those in a state of nature; and this is apparently due to the diversified and changing nature of the conditions to which they have been subjected. In this respect the different races of man resemble domesticated animals, and so do the individuals of the same race, when inhabiting a very wide area, like that of America. We see the influence of diversified conditions in the more civilised nations; for the members belonging to different grades of rank, and following different occupations, present a greater range of character than do the members of barbarous nations. But the uniformity of savages has often been exaggerated, and in some cases can hardly be said to exist.[11] It is, nevertheless, an error to speak of man, even if we look only to the conditions to which he has been exposed, as "far more domesticated"[12] than any other animal. Some savage races, such as the Australians, are not exposed to more diversified conditions than are many species which have a wide range. In another and much more important respect, man differs widely from any strictly domesticated animal, for his breeding has never long been controlled, either by methodical or unconscious selection. No race or body of men has been so completely subjugated by other men, as that certain individuals should be preserved, and thus unconsciously selected, from somehow excelling in utility to their masters. Nor have certain male and female individuals been intentionally picked out and matched, except in the well-known case of the Prussian grenadiers; and in this case man obeyed, as might have been expected, the law of methodical selection; for it is asserted that many tall men were reared in the villages inhabited by the grenadiers and their tall wives. In Sparta, also, a form of selection was followed, for it was enacted

[11] Mr. Bates remarks ('The Naturalist on the Amazons,' 1863, vol. ii. p. 159), with respect to the Indians of the same South American tribe, "no two of them were at all similar in the shape of the head; one man had an oval visage with fine features, and another was quite Mongolian in breadth and prominence of cheek, spread of nostrils, and obliquity of eyes."

[12] Blumenbach, 'Treatises on Anthropolog.,' Eng. translat., 1865, p. 205.

that all children should be examined shortly after birth; the well-formed and vigorous being preserved, the others left to perish.[13]

If we consider all the races of man as forming a single species, his range is enormous; but some separate races, as the Americans and Polynesians, have very wide ranges. It is a well-known law that widely-ranging species are much more variable than species with restricted ranges; and the variability of man may with more truth be compared with that of widely-ranging species, than with that of domesticated animals.

Not only does variability appear to be induced in man and the lower animals by the same general causes, but in both the same parts of the body are effected in a closely analogous manner. This has been proved in such full detail by Godron and Quatrefages, that I need here only refer to their works.[14] Mon-

[13] Mitford's 'History of Greece,' vol. i. p. 282. It appears also from a passage in Xenophon's 'Memorabilia,' B. ii. 4 (to which my attention has been called by the Rev. J. N. Hoare), that it was a well recognised principle with the Greeks, that men ought to select their wives with a view to the health and vigour of their children. The Grecian poet, Theognis, who lived 550 B. C., clearly saw how important selection, if carefully applied, would be for the improvement of mankind. He saw, likewise, that wealth often checks the proper action of sexual selection. He thus writes:

"With kine and horses, Kurnus! we proceed
By reasonable rules, and choose a breed
For profit and increase, at any price:
Of a sound stock, without defect or vice.
But, in the daily matches that we make,
The price is everything: for money's sake,
Men marry: women are in marriage given
The churl or ruffian, that in wealth has thriven,
May match his offspring with the proudest race:
Thus everything is mix'd, noble and base!
If then in outward manner, form, and mind,
You find us a degraded, motley kind,
Wonder no more, my friend! the cause is plain,
And to lament the consequence is vain."

(The works of J. Hookham Frere, vol. ii. 1872, p. 334.)

[14] Godron, 'De l'Espèce,' 1859, tom. ii. livre 3. Quatrefages, 'Unité de l'Espèce Humaine,' 1861. Also Lectures on Anthropology, given in the 'Revue des Cours Scientifiques,' 1866-1868.

strosities, which graduate into slight variations, are likewise so similar in man and the lower animals, that the same classification and the same terms can be used for both, as has been shown by Isidore Geoffroy St.-Hilaire.[15] In my work on the variation of domestic animals, I have attempted to arrange in a rude fashion the laws of variation under the following heads: — The direct and definite action of changed conditions, as exhibited by all or nearly all the individuals of the same species, varying in the same manner under the same circumstances. The effects of the long-continued use or disuse of parts. The cohesion of homologous parts. The variability of multiple parts. Compensation of growth; but of this law I have found no good instance in the case of man. The effects of the mechanical pressure of one part on another; as of the pelvis on the cranium of the infant in the womb. Arrests of development, leading to the diminution or suppression of parts. The reappearance of long-lost characters through reversion. And lastly, correlated variation. All these so-called laws apply equally to man and the lower animals; and most of them even to plants. It would be superfluous here to discuss all of them;[16] but several are so important, that they must be treated at considerable length.

*The Direct and Definite Action of Changed Conditions.* — This is a most perplexing subject. It cannot be denied that changed conditions produce some, and occasionally a considerable effect, on organisms of all kinds; and it seems at first probable that if sufficient time were allowed this would be the invariable result. But I have failed to obtain clear evidence in favour of this conclusion; and valid reasons may be urged on the other side, at least as far as the innumerable structures are

[15] 'Hist. Gén. et Part. des Anomalies de l'Organisation,' in three volumes, tom. i. 1832.

[16] I have fully discussed these laws in my 'Variation of Animals and Plants under Domestication,' vol. ii. chap. xxii. and xxiii. M. J. P. Durand has lately (1868) published a valuable essay 'De l'Influence des Milieux,' &c. He lays much stress, in the case of plants, on the nature of the soil.

concerned, which are adapted for special ends. There can, however, be no doubt that changed conditions induce an almost indefinite amount of fluctuating variability, by which the whole organisation is rendered in some degree plastic.

In the United States, above 1,000,000 soldiers, who served in the late war, were measured, and the States in which they were born and reared were recorded.[17] From this astonishing number of observations it is proved that local influences of some kind act directly on stature; and we further learn that "the State where the physical growth has in great measure taken place, and the State of birth, which indicates the ancestry, seem to exert a marked influence on the stature." For instance, it is established, "that residence in the Western States, during the years of growth, tends to produce increase of stature." On the other hand, it is certain that with sailors, their life delays growth, as shewn "by the great difference between the statures of soldiers and sailors at the ages of seventeen and eighteen years." Mr. B. A. Gould endeavoured to ascertain the nature of the influences which thus act on stature; but he arrived only at negative results, namely that they did not relate to climate, the elevation of the land, soil, nor even "in any controlling degree" to the abundance or the need of the comforts of life. This latter conclusion is directly opposed to that arrived at by Villermé, from the statistics of the height of the conscripts in different parts of France. When we compare the differences in stature between the Polynesian chiefs and the lower orders within the same islands, or between the inhabitants of the fertile volcanic and low barren coral islands of the same ocean,[18] or again between the Fuegians on the eastern and western shores of their country, where the

[17] 'Investigations in Military and Anthrop. Statistics,' &c. 1869, by B. A. Gould, p. 93, 107, 126, 131, 134.

[18] For the Polynesians, see Prichard's 'Physical Hist. of Mankind,' vol. v. 1847, p. 145, 283. Also Godron, 'De l'Espèce,' tom. ii. p. 289. There is also a remarkable difference in appearance between the closely-allied Hindoos inhabiting the Upper Ganges and Bengal; see Elphinstone's 'History of India,' vol. i. p. 324.

means of subsistence are very different, it is scarcely possible to avoid the conclusion that better food and greater comfort do influence stature. But the preceding statements shew how difficult it is to arrive at any precise result. Dr. Beddoe has lately proved that, with the inhabitants of Britain, residence in towns and certain occupations have a deteriorating influence on height; and he infers that the result is to a certain extent inherited, as is likewise the case in the United States. Dr. Beddoe further believes that wherever a "race attains its maximum of physical development, it rises highest in energy and moral vigour."[19]

Whether external conditions produce any other direct effect on man is not known. It might have been expected that differences of climate would have had a marked influence, inasmuch as the lungs and kidneys are brought into activity under a low temperature, and the liver and skin under a high one.[20] It was formerly thought that the colour of the skin and the character of the hair were determined by light or heat; and although it can hardly be denied that some effect is thus produced, almost all observers now agree that the effect has been very small, even after exposure during many ages. But this subject will be more properly discussed when we treat of the different races of mankind. With our domestic animals there are grounds for believing that cold and damp directly affect the growth of the hair; but I have not met with any evidence on this head in the case of man.

*Effects of the increased Use and Disuse of Parts.* — It is well known that use strengthens the muscles in the individual, and complete disuse, or the destruction of the proper nerve, weakens them. When the eye is destroyed, the optic nerve often becomes atrophied. When an artery is tied, the lateral channels increase not only in diameter, but in the thickness and strength of their coats. When one kidney ceases to act from disease, the other

19 'Memoirs, Anthropolog. Soc.' vol. iii. 1867-69, pp. 561, 565, 567.

20 Dr. Brakenridge, 'Theory of Diathesis,' 'Medical Times,' June 19 and July 17, 1869.

increases in size, and does double work. Bones increase not only in thickness, but in length, from carrying a greater weight.[21] Different occupations, habitually followed, lead to changed proportions in various parts of the body. Thus it was ascertained by the United States Commission[22] that the legs of the sailors employed in the late war were longer by 0.217 of an inch than those of the soldiers, though the sailors were on an average shorter men; whilst their arms were shorter by 1.09 of an inch, and therefore, out of proportion, shorter in relation to their lesser height. This shortness of the arms is apparently due to their greater use, and is an unexpected result: but sailors chiefly use their arms in pulling, and not in supporting weights. With sailors, the girth of the neck and the depth of the instep are greater, whilst the circumference of the chest, waist, and hips is less, than in soldiers.

Whether the several foregoing modifications would become hereditary, if the same habits of life were followed during many generations, is not known, but it is probable. Rengger[23] attributes the thin legs and thick arms of the Payaguas Indians to successive generations having passed nearly their whole lives in canoes, with their lower extremities motionless. Other writers have come to a similar conclusion in analogous cases. According to Cranz,[24] who lived for a long time with the Esquimaux, "the natives believe that ingenuity and dexterity in seal-catching (their highest art and virtue) is hereditary; there is really something to it, for the son of a celebrated seal-catcher will distinguish himself, though he lost his father in childhood." But in this case it is mental aptitude, quite as much as bodily structure, which appears to be inherited. It is asserted that the hands

[21] I have given authorities for these several statements in my 'Variation of Animals under Domestication,' vol. ii. pp. 297-300. Dr. Jaeger, "Ueber das Längenwachsthum der Knochen." 'Jenaischen Zeitschrift,' B. v. Heft. i.

[22] 'Investigations,' &c. By B. A. Gould, 1869, p. 288.

[23] 'Säugethiere von Paraguay,' 1830, s. 4.

[24] 'History of Greenland,' Eng. translat. 1767, vol. i. p. 230.

of English labourers are at birth larger than those of the gentry.[25] From the correlation which exists, at least in some cases,[26] between the development of the extremities and of the jaws, it is possible that in those classes which do not labour much with their hands and feet, the jaws would be reduced in size from this cause. That they are generally smaller in refined and civilized men than in hard-working men or savages, is certain. But with savages, as Mr. Herbert Spencer[27] has remarked, the greater use of the jaws in chewing coarse, uncooked food, would act in a direct manner on the masticatory muscles, and on the bones to which they are attached. In infants, long before birth, the skin on the soles of the feet is thicker than on any other part of the body;[28] and it can hardly be doubted that this is due to the inherited effects of pressure during a long series of generations.

It is familiar to every one that watchmakers and engravers are liable to be short-sighted, whilst men living much out of doors, and especially savages, are generally long-sighted.[29] Short-sight and long-sight certainly tend to be inherited.[30] The inferiority of Europeans, in comparison with savages, in eyesight and in the other senses, is no doubt the accumulated and transmitted effect of lessened use during many generations; for Rengger[31] states that he has repeatedly observed Europeans, who had been brought up and spent their whole lives with the

[25] 'Intermarriage.' By Alex. Walker, 1838, p. 377.

[26] 'The Variation of Animals under Domestication,' vol. i. p. 173.

[27] 'Principles of Biology,' vol. i. p. 455.

[28] Paget, 'Lectures on Surgical Pathology,' vol. ii. 1853, p. 209.

[29] It is a singular and unexpected fact that sailors are inferior to landsmen in their mean distance of distinct vision. Dr. B. A. Gould ('Sanitary Memoirs of the War of the Rebellion,' 1869, p. 530), has proved this to be the case; and he accounts for it by the ordinary range of vision in sailors being "restricted to the length of the vessel and the height of the masts."

[30] 'The Variation of Animals under Domestication,' vol. i. p. 8.

[31] 'Säugethiere von Paraguay,' 8, 10. I have had good opportunities for observing the extraordinary power of eyesight in the Fuegians. See also Lawrence ('Lectures on Physiology,' &c., 1822, p. 404) on this same subject. M. Giraud-Teulon has recently collected ('Revue des Cours Scientifiques,' 1870, p. 625) a large and valuable body of evidence proving that the cause of short-sight, *"C'est le travail assidu de près."*

wild Indians, who nevertheless did not equal them in the sharpness of their senses. The same naturalist observes that the cavities in the skull for the reception of the several sense-organs are larger in the American aborigines than in Europeans; and this probably indicates a corresponding difference in the dimensions of the organs themselves. Blumenbach has also remarked on the large size of the nasal cavities in the skulls of the American aborigines, and connects this fact with their remarkably acute power of smell. The Mongolians of the plains of Northern Asia, according to Pallas, have wonderfully perfect senses; and Prichard believes that the great breadth of their skulls across the zygomas follows from their highly-developed sense-organs.[32]

The Quechua Indians inhabit the lofty plateaux of Peru; and Alcide d'Orbigny states[33] that, from continually breathing a highly rarefied atmosphere, they have acquired chests and lungs of extraordinary dimensions. The cells, also, of the lungs are larger and more numerous than in Europeans. These observations have been doubted, but Mr. D. Forbes carefully measured many Aymaras, an allied race, living at the height of between 10,000 and 15,000 feet; and he informs me[34] that they differ conspicuously from the men of all other races seen by him in the circumference and length of their bodies. In his table of measurements, the stature of each man is taken at 1000, and the other measurements are reduced to this standard. It is here seen that the extended arms of the Aymaras are shorter than those of Europeans, and much shorter than those of Negroes. The legs are likewise shorter; and they present this remarkable peculiarity, that in every Aymara measured, the femur is actually shorter than the tibia. On an average, the length of the femur to that of the tibia is as 211 to 252; whilst in two Europeans, measured at the

[32] Prichard, 'Phys. Hist. of Mankind,' on the authority of Blumenbach, vol. i. 1851, p. 311; for the statement by Pallas, vol. iv, 1844, p. 407.

[33] Quoted by Prichard, 'Researches into the Phys. Hist. of Mankind,' vol. v. p. 463.

[34] Mr. Forbes' valuable paper is now published in the 'Journal of the Ethnological Soc. of London,' new series, vol. ii. 1870, p. 193.

same time, the femora to the tibiæ were as 244 to 230; and in three Negroes as 258 to 241. The humerus is likewise shorter relatively to the forearm. This shortening of that part of the limb which is nearest to the body, appears to be, as suggested to me by Mr. Forbes, a case of compensation in relation with the greatly increased length of the trunk. The Aymaras present some other singular points of structure, for instance, the very small projection of the heel.

These men are so thoroughly acclimatised to their cold and lofty abode, that when fomerly carried down by the Spaniards to the low eastern plains, and when now tempted down by high wages to the gold-washings, they suffer a frightful rate of mortality. Nevertheless Mr. Forbes found a few pure families which had survived during two generations: and he observed that they still inherited their characteristic peculiarities. But it was manifest, even without measurement, that these peculiarities had all decreased; and on measurement, their bodies were found not to be so much elongated as those of the men on the high plateau; whilst their femora had become somewhat lengthened, as had their tibiæ, although in a less degree. The actual measurements may be seen by consulting Mr. Forbes's memoir. From these observations, there can, I think, be no doubt that residence during many generations at a great elevation tends, both directly and indirectly, to induce inherited modifications in the proportions of the body.[35]

Although man may not have been much modified during the latter stages of his existence through the increased or decreased use of parts, the facts now given shew that his liability in this respect has not been lost; and we positively know that the same law holds good with the lower animals. Consequently we may infer that when at a remote epoch the progenitors of man were in a transitional state, and were changing from quadrupeds

[35] Dr. Wilckens ('Landwirthschaft. Wochenblatt,' No. 10, 1869) has lately published an interesting Essay shewing how domestic animals, which live in mountainous regions, have their frames modified.

into bipeds, natural selection would probably have been greatly aided by the inherited effects of the increased or diminished use of the different parts of the body.

*Arrests of Development.* — There is a difference between arrested development and arrested growth, for parts in the former state continue to grow whilst still retaining their early condition. Various monstrosities come under this head; and some, as a cleft palate, are known to be occasionally inherited. It will suffice for our purpose to refer to the arrested brain-development of microcephalous idiots, as described in Vogt's memoir.[36] Their skulls are smaller, and the convolutions of the brain are less complex than in normal men. The frontal sinus, or the projection over the eye-brows, is largely developed, and the jaws are prognathous to an "*effrayant*" degree; so that these idiots somewhat resemble the lower types of mankind. Their intelligence, and most of their mental faculties, are extremely feeble. They cannot acquire the power of speech, and are wholly incapable of prolonged attention, but are much given to imitation. They are strong and remarkably active, continually gambolling and jumping about, and making grimaces. They often ascend stairs on all-fours; and are curiously fond of climbing up furniture or trees. We are thus reminded of the delight shewn by almost all boys in climbing trees; and this again reminds us how lambs and kids, originally alpine animals, delight to frisk on any hillock, however small. Idiots also resemble the lower animals in some other respects; thus several cases are recorded of their carefully smelling every mouthful of food before eating it. One idiot is described as often using his mouth in aid of his hands, whilst hunting for lice. They are often filthy in their habits, and have no sense of decency; and several cases have been published of their bodies being remarkably hairy.[37]

[36] 'Mémoire sur les Microcéphales,' 1867, pp. 50, 125, 169, 171, 184-198.

[37] Prof. Laycock sums up the character of brute-like idiots by calling them *theroid;* 'Journal of Mental Science,' July, 1863. Dr. Scott ('The Deaf

*Reversion.* — Many of the cases to be here given, might have been introduced under the last heading. When a structure is arrested in its development, but still continues growing, until it closely resembles a corresponding structure in some lower and adult member of the same group, it may in one sense be considered as a case of reversion. The lower members in a group give us some idea how the common progenitor was probably constructed; and it is hardly credible that a complex part, arrested at an early phase of embryonic development, should go on growing so as ultimately to perform its proper function, unless it had acquired such power during some earlier state of existence, when the present exceptional or arrested structure was normal. The simple brain of a microcephalous idiot, in as far as it resembles that of an ape, may in this sense be said to offer a case of reversion.[38] There are other cases which come more

[38] In my 'Variation of Animals under Domestication' (vol. ii. p. 57), I attributed the not very rare cases of supernumerary mammae in women to reversion. I was led to this as a probable conclusion, by the additional mammae being generally placed symmetrically on the breast; and more especially from one case, in which a single efficient mamma occurred in the inguinal region of a woman, the daughter of another woman with supernumerary mammae. But I now find (see, for instance, Prof. Preyer, 'Der Kampf um das Dasein,' 1869, s. 45) that *mammae erraticae* occur in other situations, as on the back, in the armpit, and on the thigh; the mammae in this latter instance having given so much milk that the child was thus nourished. The probability that the additional mammae are due to reversion is thus much weakened; nevertheless, it still seems to me probable, because two pairs are often found symmetrically on the breast; and of this I myself have received information in several cases. It is well known that some Lemurs normally have two pairs of mammae on the breast. Five cases have been recorded of the presence of more than a pair of mammae (of course rudimentary) in the male sex of mankind; see 'Journal of Anat. and Physiology,' 1872, p. 56, for a case given by Dr. Handyside, in which two brothers exhibited this peculiarity; see also a paper by Dr. Bartels, in 'Reichert's and du Bois-Reymond's Archiv.,' 1872, p. 304. In one of the cases alluded to by Dr. Bartels, a man bore five mammae, one being medial and placed above the navel; Meckel von Hemsbach thinks that this latter case is illustrated by

and Dumb,' 2nd edit., 1870, p. 10) has often observed the imbeciles smelling their food. See, on this same subject, and on the hairiness of idiots, Dr. Maudsley, 'Body and Mind,' 1870, pp. 46-51. Pinel has also given a striking case of hairiness in an idiot.

strictly under our present head of reversion. Certain structures, regularly occurring in the lower members of the group to which man belongs, occasionally make their appearance in him, though not found in the normal human embryo; or, if normally present in the human embryo, they become abnormally developed, although in a manner which is normal in the lower members of the group. These remarks will be rendered clearer by the following illustrations.

In various mammals the uterus graduates from a double organ with two distinct orifices and two passages, as in the marsupials, into a single organ, which is in no way double except from having a slight internal fold, as in the higher apes and man. The rodents exhibit a perfect series of gradations between

---

a medial mamma occurring in certain Cheiroptera. On the whole, we may well doubt if additional mammae would ever have been developed in both sexes of mankind, had not his early progenitors been provided with more than a single pair.

In the above work (vol. ii. p. 12), I also attributed, though with much hesitation, the frequent cases of polydactylism in men and various animals to reversion. I was partly led to this through Prof. Owen's statement, that some of the Ichthyopterygia possess more than five digits, and therefore, as I supposed, had retained a primordial condition; but Prof. Gegenbaur ('Jenaischen Zeitschrift,' B. v. Heft 3, s. 341), disputes Owen's conclusion. On the other hand, according to the opinion lately advanced by Dr. Günther, on the paddle of Ceratodus, which is provided with articulated bony rays on both sides of a central chain of bones, there seems no great difficulty in admitting that six or more digits on one side, or on both sides, might reappear through reversion. I am informed by Dr. Zouteveen that there is a case on record of a man having twenty-four fingers and twenty-four toes! I was chiefly led to the conclusion that the presence of supernumerary digits might be due to reversion from the fact that such digits, not only are strongly inherited, but, as I then believed, had the power of regrowth after amputation, like the normal digits of the lower vertebrata. But I have explained in the Second Edition of my Variation under Domestication why I now place little reliance on the recorded cases of such regrowth. Nevertheless it deserves notice, inasmuch as arrested development and reversion are intimately related processes; that various structures in an embryonic or arrested condition, such as a cleft palate, bifid uterus, &c., are frequently accompanied by polydactylism. This has been strongly insisted on by Meckel and Isidore Geoffroy St.-Hilaire. But at present it is the safest course to give up altogether the idea that there is any relation between the development of supernumerary digits and reversion to some lowly organized progenitor of man.

these two extreme states. In all mammals the uterus is developed from two simple primitive tubes, the inferior portions of which form the cornua; and it is in the words of Dr. Farre, "by the coalescence of the two cornua at their lower extremities that the body of the uterus is formed in man; while in those animals in which no middle portion or body exists, the cornua remain ununited. As the development of the uterus proceeds, the two cornua become gradually shorter, until at length they are lost, or, as it were, absorbed into the body of the uterus." The angles of the uterus are still produced into cornua, even in animals as high up in the scale as the lower apes and lemurs.

Now in women, anomalous cases are not very infrequent, in which the mature uterus is furnished with cornua, or is partially divided into two organs; and such cases, according to Owen, repeat "the grade of concentrative development," attained by certain rodents. Here perhaps we have an instance of a simple arrest of embryonic development, with subsequent growth and perfect functional development; for either side of the partially double uterus is capable of performing the proper office of gestation. In other and rarer cases, two distinct uterine cavities are formed, each having its proper orifice and passage.[39] No such stage is passed through during the ordinary development of the embryo; and it is difficult to believe, though perhaps not impossible, that the two simple, minute, primitive tubes should know how (if such an expression may be used) to grow into two distinct uteri, each with a well-constructed orifice and passage, and each furnished with numerous muscles, nerves, glands and vessels, if they had not formerly passed through a similar course of development, as in the case of existing marsupials. No one will pretend that so perfect a structure as the abnormal double uterus in woman could be the result of mere chance. But the principle of reversion, by which a long-lost structure is called back into

[39] See Dr. A. Farre's well-known article in the 'Cyclopaedia of Anatomy and Physiology,' vol. v. 1859, p. 642. Owen, 'Anatomy of Vertebrates,' vol. iii., 1868, p. 687. Professor Turner in 'Edinburgh Medical Journal,' February 1865.

existence, might serve as the guide for its full development, even after the lapse of an enormous interval of time.

Professor Canestrini, after discussing the foregoing and various analogous cases, arrives at the same conclusion as that just given. He adduces another instance, in the case of the malar bone,[40] which, in some of the Quadrumana and other mammals, normally consists of two portions. This is its condition in the human fœtus when two months old; and through arrested development, it sometimes remains thus in man when adult, more especially in the lower prognathous races. Hence Canestrini concludes that some ancient progenitor of man must have had this bone normally divided into two portions, which afterwards became fused together. In man the frontal bone consists of a single piece, but in the embryo, and in children, and in almost all the lower mammals, it consists of two pieces separated by a distinct suture. This suture occasionally persists more or less distinctly in man after maturity; and more frequently in ancient than in recent crania, especially, as Canestrini has observed, in those exhumed from the Drift, and belonging to the brachycephalic type. Here again he comes to the same conclusions as in the analogous case of the malar bones. In this, and other instances presently to be given, the cause of ancient races approaching the lower animals in certain characters more frequently than do the modern races, appears to be, that the latter stand

[40] 'Annuario della Soc. dei Naturalisti in Modena,' 1867, p. 83. Prof. Canestrini gives extracts on this subject from various authorities. Laurillard remarks, that as he has found a complete similarity in the form, proportions, and connection of the two malar bones in several human subjects and in certain apes, he cannot consider this disposition of the parts as simply accidental. Another paper on this same anomaly has been published by Dr. Saviotti in the 'Gazzetta delle Cliniche,' Turin, 1871, where he says that traces of the division may be detected in about two per cent. of adult skulls; he also remarks that it more frequently occurs in prognathous skulls, not of the Aryan race, than in others. See also G. Delorenzi on the same subject; 'Tre nuovi casi d'anomalia dell' osso malare,' Torino, 1872. Also, E. Morselli, 'Sopra una rara anomalia dell' osso malare,' Modena, 1872. Still more recently Gruber has written a pamphlet on the division of this bone. I give these references because a reviewer, without any grounds or scruples, has thrown doubts on my statements.

at a somewhat greater distance in the long line of descent from their early semi-human progenitors.

Various other anomalies in man, more or less analogous to the foregoing, have been advanced by different authors, as cases of reversion; but these seem not a little doubtful, for we have to descend extremely low in the mammalian series, before we find such structures normally present.[41]

In man, the canine teeth are perfectly efficient instruments for mastication. But their true canine character, as Owen[42] remarks, "is indicated by the conical form of the crown, which terminates in an obtuse point, is convex outward and flat or sub-concave within, at the base of which surface there is a feeble prominence. The conical form is best expressed in the Melanian races, especially the Australian. The canine is more deeply implanted, and by a stronger fang than the incisors." Nevertheless, this tooth no longer serves man as a special weapon for tearing his enemies or prey; it may, therefore, as far as its proper function is concerned, be considered as rudimentary. In every large collection of human skulls some may be found, as Häckel[43] observes, with the canine teeth projecting considerably beyond the others in the same manner as in the anthropomorphous apes, but in a less degree. In these cases, open spaces between the teeth in the one jaw are left for the reception of the canines of

[41] A whole series of cases is given by Isid. Geoffroy St.-Hilaire, 'Hist. des Anomalies,' tom. iii. p. 437. A reviewer ('Journal of Anat. and Physiology,' 1871, p. 366) blames me much for not having discussed the numerous cases, which have been recorded, of various parts arrested in their development. He says that, according to my theory, "every transient condition of an organ, during its development, is not only a means to an end, but once was an end in itself." This does not seem to me necessarily to hold good. Why should not variations occur during an early period of development, having no relation to reversion; yet such variations might be preserved and accumulated, if in any way serviceable, for instance, in shortening and simplifying the course of development? And again, why should not injurious abnormalities, such as atrophied or hypertrophied parts, which have no relation to a former state of existence, occur at an early period, as well as during maturity?

[42] 'Anatomy of Vertebrates,' vol. iii. 1868, p. 323.

[43] 'Generelle Morphologie,' 1866, B, ii. s. clv.

the opposite jaw. An inter-space of this kind in a Kaffir skull, figured by Wagner, is surprisingly wide.[44] Considering how few are the ancient skulls which have been examined, compared to recent skulls, it is an interesting fact that in at least three cases the canines project largely; and in the Naulette jaw they are spoken of as enormous.[45]

Of the anthropomorphous apes the males alone have their canines fully developed; but in the female gorilla, and in a less degree in the female orang, these teeth project considerably beyond the others; therefore the fact, of which I have been assured, that women sometimes have considerably projecting canines, is no serious objection to the belief that their occasional great development in man is a case of reversion to an ape-like progenitor. He who rejects with scorn the belief that the shape of his own canines, and their occasional great development in other men, are due to our early forefathers having been provided with these formidable weapons, will probably reveal, by sneering, the line of his descent. For though he no longer intends, nor has the power, to use these teeth as weapons, he will unconsciously retract his "snarling muscles" (thus named by Sir C. Bell),[46] so as to expose them ready for action, like a dog prepared to fight.

Many muscles are occasionally developed in man, which are proper to the Quadrumana or other mammals. Professor Vlacovich[47] examined forty male subjects, and found a muscle, called by him the ischio-pubic, in nineteen of them; in three others there was a ligament which represented this muscle; and in the remaining eighteen no trace of it. In only two out of thirty female subjects was this muscle developed on both sides, but in three others the rudimentary ligament was present. This muscle, therefore, appears to be much more common in the male than in the female sex; and on the belief in the descent of man

[44] Carl Vogt's 'Lectures on Man,' Eng. translat. 1864, p. 151.

[45] C. Carter Blake, on a jaw from La Naulette, 'Anthropolog. Review,' 1867, p. 295. Schaaffhausen, ibid. 1868, p. 426.

[46] 'The anatomy of Expression,' 1844, pp. 110, 131.

[47] Quoted by Prof. Canestrini in the 'Annuario,' &c., 1867, p. 90.

from some lower form, the fact is intelligible; for it has been dected in several of the lower animals, and in all of these it serves exclusively to aid the male in the act of reproduction.

Mr. J. Wood, in his valuable series of papers,[48] has minutely described a vast number of muscular variations in man, which resemble normal structures in the lower animals. The muscles which closely resemble those regularly present in our nearest allies, the Quadrumana, are too numerous to be here even specified. In a single male subject, having a strong bodily frame, and well-formed skull, no less than seven muscular variations were observed, all of which plainly represented muscles proper to various kinds of apes. This man, for instance, had on both sides of his neck a true and powerful *"levator claviculæ,"* such as is found in all kinds of apes, and which is said to occur in about one out of sixty human subjects.[49] Again, this man had "a special abductor of the metatarsal bone of the fifth digit, such as Professor Huxley and Mr. Flower have shewn to exist uniformly in the higher and lower apes." I will give only two additional cases; the *acromio-basilar* muscle is found in all mammals below man, and seems to be correlated with a quadrupedal gait,[50] and it occurs in about one out of sixty human subjects. In the lower extremities Mr. Bradley[51] found an *abductor ossis metatarsi quinti* in both feet of man; this muscle had not up to that time been recorded in mankind, but is always present in the anthro-

[48] These papers deserve careful study by any one who desires to learn how frequently our muscles vary, and in varying come to resemble those of the Quadrumana. The following references relate to the few points touched on in my text: 'Proc. Royal Soc.' vol. xiv. 1865, pp. 379-384; vol. xv, 1866, pp. 241, 242; vol. xv. 1867, p. 544; vol. xvi. 1868, p. 524. I may here add that Dr. Murie and Mr. St. George Mivart have shewn in their Memoir on the Lemuroidea ('Transact. Zoolog. Soc.' vol. vii. 1869, p. 96), how extraordinarily variable some of the muscles are in these animals, the lowest members of the Primates Gradations, also, in the muscles leading to structures found in animals still lower in the scale, are numerous in the Lemuroidea.

[49] See also Prof. Macalister in 'Proc. R. Irish Academy,' vol. x. 1868, p. 124.

[50] Mr. Champneys in 'Journal of Anat. and Phys.' Nov., 1871, p. 178.

[51] 'Journal of Anat. and Phys.' May, 1872, p. 421.

pomorphous apes. The muscles of the hands and arms — parts which are so eminently characteristic of man — are extremely liable to vary, so as to resemble the corresponding muscles in the lower animals.[52] Such resemblances are either perfect or imperfect; yet in the latter case they are manifestly of a transitional nature. Certain variations are more common in man, and others in woman, without our being able to assign any reason. Mr. Wood, after describing numerous variations, makes the following pregnant remark: "Notable departures from the ordinary type of muscular structures run in grooves or directions, which must be taken to indicate some unknown factor, of much importance to a comperhensive knowledge of general and scientific anatomy."[53]

That this unknown factor is reversion to a former state of existence may be admitted as in the highest degree probable.[54] It is quite incredible that a man should through mere accident abnormally resemble certain apes in no less than seven of his

[52] Prof. Macalister (ibid. p. 121) has tabulated his observations, and finds that muscular abnormalities are most frequent in the fore-arms, secondly, in the face, thirdly, in the foot, &c.

[53] The Rev. Dr. Haughton, after giving ('Proc. R. Irish Academy,' June 27, 1864, p. 715) a remarkable case of variation in the human *flexor pollicis longus,* adds, "This remarkable example shows that man may sometimes possess the arrangement of tendons of thumb and fingers characteristic of the macaque; but whether such a case should be regarded as a macaque passing upwards into a man, or a man passing downwards into a macaque, or as a congenital freak of nature, I cannot undertake to say." It is satisfactory to hear so capable an anatomist, and so embittered an opponent of evolutionism, admitting even the possibility of either of his first propositions. Prof. Macalister has also described ('Proc. R. Irish Acad.' vol. x. 1864, p. 138) variations in the *flexor pollicis longus,* remarkable from their relations to the same muscle in the Quadrumana.

[54] Since the first edition of this book appeared, Mr. Wood has published another memoir in the 'Phil. Transactions,' 1870, p. 83, on the varieties of the muscles of the human neck, shoulder, and chest. He here shows how extremely variable these muscles are, and how often and how closely the variations resemble the normal muscles of the lower animals. He sums up by remarking, "It will be enough for my purpose if I have succeeded in shewing the more important forms which, when occurring as varieties in the human subject, tend to exhibit in a sufficiently marked manner what may be considered as proofs and examples of the Darwinian principle of reversion, or law of inheritance, in this department of anatomical science."

muscles, if there had been no genetic connection between them. On the other hand, if man is descended from some ape-like creature, no valid reason can be assigned why certain muscles should not suddenly reappear after an interval of many thousand generations, in the same manner as with horses, asses, and mules, dark-coloured stripes suddenly reappear on the legs, and shoulders, after an interval of hundreds, or more probably of thousands of generations.

These various cases of reversion are so closely related to those of rudimentary organs given in the first chapter, that many of them might have been indifferently introduced either there or here. Thus a human uterus furnished with cornua may be said to represent, in a rudimentary condition, the same organ in its normal state in certain mammals. Some parts which are rudimentary in man, as the os coccyx in both sexes, and the mammæ in the male sex, are always present; whilst others, such as the supracondyloid foramen, only occasionally appear, and therefore might have been introduced under the head of reversion. These several reversionary structures, as well as the strictly rudimentary ones, reveal the descent of man from some lower form in an unmistakable manner.

*Correlated Variation.* — In man, as in the lower animals, many structures are so intimately related, that when one part varies so does another, without our being able, in most cases, to assign any reason. We cannot say whether the one part governs the other, or whether both are governed by some earlier developed part. Various monstrosities, as I. Geoffroy repeatedly insists, are thus intimately connected. Homologous structures are particularly liable to change together, as we see on the opposite sides of the body, and in the upper and lower extremities. Meckel long ago remarked, that when the muscles of the arm depart from their proper type, they almost always imitate those of the leg; and so, conversely, with the muscles of the legs. The organs of sight and hearing, the teeth and hair, the colour of the skin and of the hair, colour and constitution, are more or less correlated.[55] Professor Schaaffhausen first drew attention to the relation apparently existing between a muscular frame and the strongly-pronounced supra-orbital ridges, which are so characteristic of the lower races of man.

Besides the variations which can be grouped with more or less probability under the foregoing heads, there is a large class of variations which may be provisionally called spontaneous, for to our ignorance they appear to arise without any exciting cause. It can, however, be shewn that such variations, whether consisting of slight individual differences, or of strongly-marked and abrupt deviations of structure, depend much more on the constitution of the organism than on the nature of the conditions to which it has been subjected.[56]

*Rate of Increase.* — Civilised populations have been known under favourable conditions, as in the United States, to double their numbers in twenty-five years; and, according to a calculation, by Euler, this might occur in a little over twelve years.[57] At the former rate, the present population of the United States (thirty millions), would in 657 years cover the whole terraqueous globe so thickly, that four men would have to stand on each square yard of surface. The primary or fundamental check to the continued increase of man is the difficulty of gaining subsistence, and of living in comfort. We may infer that this is the case from what we see, for instance, in the United States, where subsistence is easy, and there is plenty of room. If such means were suddenly doubled in Great Britain, our number would be quickly doubled. With civilised nations this primary check acts chiefly by restraining marriages. The greater death-rate of in-

55 The authorities for these several statements are given in my 'Variation of Animals under Domestication,' vol. ii. pp. 320-335.

56 This whole subject has been discussed in chap. xxiii. vol. ii. of my 'Variation of Animals and Plants under Domestication.'

57 See the ever memorable 'Essay on the Principle of Population,' by the Rev. T. Malthus, vol. i. 1826, pp. 6, 517.

fants in the poorest classes is also very important; as well as the greater mortality, from various diseases, of the inhabitants of crowded and miserable houses, at all ages. The effects of severe epidemics and wars are soon counterbalanced, and more than counterbalanced, in nations placed under favourable conditions. Emigration also comes in aid as a temporary check, but, with the extremely poor classes, not to any great extent.

There is great reason to suspect, as Malthus has remarked, that the reproductive power is actually less in barbarous, than in civilised races. We know nothing positively on this head, for with savages no census has been taken; but from the concurrent testimony of missionaries, and of others who have long resided with such people, it appears that their families are usually small, and large ones rare. This may be partly accounted for, as it is believed, by the women suckling their infants during a long time; but it is highly probable that savages, who often suffer much hardships, and who do not obtain so much nutritious food as civilised men, would be actually less prolific. I have shewn in a former work,[58] that all our domesticated quadrupeds and birds, and all our cultivated plants, are more fertile than the corresponding species in a state of nature. It is no valid objection to this conclusion that animals suddenly supplied with an excess of food, or when grown very fat; and that most plants on sudden removal from very poor to very rich soil, are rendered more or less sterile. We might, therefore, expect that civilised men, who in one sense are highly domesticated, would be more prolific than wild men. It is also probable that the increased fertility of civilised nations would become, as with our domestic animals, an inherited character: it is at least known that with mankind a tendency to produce twins runs in families.[59]

Notwithstanding that savages appear to be less prolific than

[58] 'Variation of Animals and Plants under Domestication,' vol. ii. pp. 111-113, 163.

[59] Mr. Sedgwick, 'British and Foreign Medico-Chirurg. Review,' July, 1863, p. 170.

civilised people, they would no doubt rapidly increase if their numbers were not by some means rigidly kept down. The Santali, or hill-tribes of India, have recently afforded a good illustration of this fact; for, as shewn by Mr. Hunter,[60] they have increased at an extraordinary rate since vaccination has been introduced, other pestilences mitigated, and war sternly repressed. This increase, however, would not have been possible had not these rude people spread into the adjoining districts, and worked for hire. Savages almost always marry; yet there is some prudential restraint, for they do not commonly marry at the earliest possible age. The young men are often required to shew that they can support a wife; and they generally have first to earn the price with which to purchase her from her parents. With savages the difficulty of obtaining subsistence occasionally limits their number in a much more direct manner than with civilised people, for all tribes periodically suffer from severe famines. At such times savages are forced to devour much bad food, and their health can hardly fail to be injured. Many accounts have been published of their protruding stomachs and emaciated limbs after and during famines. They are then, also, compelled to wander much, and, as I was assured in Australia, their infants perish in large numbers. As famines are periodical, depending chiefly on extreme seasons, all tribes must fluctuate in number. They cannot steadily and regularly increase, as there is no artificial increase in the supply of food. Savages, when hard pressed, encroach on each other's territories, and war is the result; but they are indeed almost always at war with their neighbours. They are liable to many accidents on land and water in their search for food; and in some countries they suffer much from the larger beasts of prey. Even in India, districts have been depopulated by the ravages of tigers.

Malthus has discussed these several checks, but he does not lay stress enough on what is probably the most important of all, namely infanticide, especially of female infants and the habit of

[60] 'The Animals of Rural Bengal,' by W. W. Hunter, 1868, p. 259.

procuring abortion. These practices now prevail in many quarters of the world; and infanticide seems formerly to have prevailed, as Mr. M'Lennan[61] has shewn on a still more extensive scale. These practices appear to have originated in savages recognising the difficulty, or rather the impossibility of supporting all the infants that are born. Licentiousness may also be added to the foregoing checks; but this does not follow from failing means of subsistence; though there is reason to believe that in some cases (as in Japan) it has been intentionally encouraged as a means of keeping down the population.

If we look back to an extremely remote epoch, before man had arrived at the dignity of manhood, he would have been guided more by instinct and less by reason than are the lowest savages at the present time. Our early semi-human progenitors would not have practised infanticide or polyandry; for the instincts of the lower animals are never so perverted[62] as to lead them regularly to destroy their own offspring, or to be quite devoid of jealousy. There would have been no prudential restraint from marriage, and the sexes would have freely united at an early age. Hence the progenitors of man would have tended to increase rapidly; but checks of some kind, either periodical or constant, must have kept down their numbers, even more severely than with existing savages. What the precise nature of these checks were, we cannot say, any more than with most other animals. We know that horses and cattle, which are not

[61] 'Primitive Marriage,' 1865.

[62] A writer in the 'Spectator' (March 12th, 1871, p. 320) comments as follows on this passage: — "Mr. Darwin finds himself compelled to reintroduce a new doctrine of the fall of man. He shews that the instincts of the higher animals are far nobler than the habits of savage races of men, and he finds himself, therefore, compelled to re-introduce, — in a form of the substantial orthodoxy of which he appears to be quite unconscious, — and to introduce as a scientific hypothesis the doctrine that man's gain of *knowledge* was the cause of a temporary but long-enduring moral deterioration as indicated by the many foul customs, especially as to marriage, of savage tribes. What does the Jewish tradition of the moral degeneration of man through his snatching at a knowledge forbidden him by his highest instinct assert beyond this?"

extremely prolific animals, when first turned loose in South America, increased at an enormous rate. The elephant, the slowest breeder of all known animals, would in a few thousand years stock the whole world. The increase of every species of monkey must be checked by some means; but not, as Brehm remarks, by the attacks of beasts of prey. No one will assume that the actual power of reproduction in the wild horses and cattle of America, was at first in any sensible degree increased; or that, as each district became fully stocked, this same power was diminished. No doubt in this case, and in all others, many checks concur, and different checks under different circumstances; periodical dearths, depending on unfavourable seasons, being probably the most important of all. So it will have been with the early progenitors of man.

*Natural Selection.* — We have now seen that man is variable in body and mind; and that the variations are induced, either directly or indirectly, by the same general causes, and obey the same general laws, as with the lower animals. Man has spread widely over the face of the earth, and must have been exposed, during his incessant migration,[63] to the most diversified conditions. The inhabitants of Tierra del Fuego, the Cape of Good Hope, and Tasmania in the one hemisphere, and of the Arctic regions in the other, must have passed through many climates, and changed their habits many times, before they reached their present homes.[64] The early progenitors of man must also have tended, like all other animals, to have increased beyond their means of subsistence; they must, therefore, occasionally have been exposed to a struggle for existence, and consequently to the rigid law of natural selection. Beneficial variations of all kinds will thus, either occasionally or habitually, have been preserved and injurious ones eliminated. I do not refer to strongly-marked

[63] See some good remarks to this effect by W. Stanley Jevons, "A Deduction from Darwin's Theory," 'Nature,' 1869, p. 231.

[64] Latham, 'Man and his Migrations,' 1851, p. 135.

deviations of structure, which occur only at long intervals of time, but to mere individual differences. We know, for instance, that the muscles of our hands and feet, which determine our powers of movement, are liable, like those of the lower animals,[65] to incessant variability. If then the progenitors of man inhabiting any district, especially one undergoing some change in its conditions, were divided into two equal bodies, the one half which included all the individuals best adapted by their powers of movement for gaining subsistence, or for defending themselves, would on an average survive in greater numbers, and procreate more offspring than the other and less well endowed half.

Man in the rudest state in which he now exists is the most dominant animal that has ever appeared on this earth. He has spread more widely than any other highly organised form: and all others have yielded before him. He manifestly owes this immense superiority to his intellectual faculties, to his social habits, which lead him to aid and defend his fellows, and to his corporeal structure. The supreme importance of these characters has been proved by the final arbitrament of the battle for life. Through his powers of intellect, articulate language has been evolved; and on this his wonderful advancement has mainly depended. As Mr. Chauncey Wright remarks:[66] "a psychological analysis of the faculty of language shews, that even the smallest proficiency in it might require more brain power than the greatest proficiency in any other direction." He has invented and is able to use various weapons, tools, traps, &c., with which he defends himself, kills or catches prey, and otherwise obtains food. He has made rafts or canoes for fishing or crossing over to neighbouring fertile islands. He has discovered the art of making fire, by which

[65] Messrs. Murie and Mivart in their 'Anatomy of the Lemuroidea' ('Transact. Zoolog. Soc.' vol. vii. 1869, pp. 96-98) say, "some muscles are so irregular in their distribution that they cannot be well classed in any of the above groups." These muscles differ even on the opposite sides of the same individual.

[66] Limits of Natural Selection, 'North American Review,' Oct. 1870, p. 295.

hard and stringy roots can be rendered digestible, and poisonous roots or herbs innocuous. This discovery of fire, probably the greatest ever made by man, excepting language, dates from before the dawn of history. These several inventions, by which man in the rudest state has become so pre-eminent, are the direct results of the development of his powers of observation, memory, curiosity, imagination, and reason. I cannot, therefore, understand how it is that Mr. Wallace[67] maintains, that "natural selection could only have endowed the savage with a brain a little superior to that of an ape."

Although the intellectual powers and social habits of man are of paramount importance to him, we must not underrate the importance of his bodily structure, to which subject the remainder of this chapter will be devoted; the development of the intellectual and social or moral faculties being discussed in a later chapter.

Even to hammer with precision is no easy matter, as every one who has tried to learn carpentry will admit. To throw a stone with as true an aim as a Fuegian in defending himself, or in killing birds, requires the most consummate perfection in the correlated action of the muscles of the hand, arm, and shoulder, and, further, a fine sense of touch. In throwing a stone or spear, and in many other actions, a man must stand firmly on his feet; and this again demands the perfect co-adaptation of numerous

[67] 'Quarterly Review,' April 1869, p. 392. This subject is more fully discussed in Mr. Wallace's 'Contributions to the Theory of Natural Selection,' 1870, in which all the essays referred to in this work are republished. The 'Essay on Man,' has been ably criticised by Prof. Claparède, one of the most distinguished zoologists in Europe, in an article published in the 'Bibliothèque Universelle,' June 1870. The remark quoted in my text will surprise every one who has read Mr. Wallace's celebrated paper on 'The origin of Human Races deduced from the Theory of Natural Selection,' originally published in the 'Anthropological Review,' May 1864, p. clviii. I cannot here resist quoting a most just remark by Sir J. Lubbock ('Prehistoric Times,' 1865, p. 479) in reference to this paper, namely, that Mr. Wallace, "with characteristic unselfishness, ascribes it (i. e. the idea of natural selection) unreservedly to Mr. Darwin, although, as is well known, he struck out the idea independently, and published it, though not with the same elaboration, at the same time."

muscles. To chip a flint into the rudest tool, or to form a barbed spear or hook from a bone, demands the use of a perfect hand; for, as a most capable judge, Mr. Schoolcraft,[68] remarks, the shaping fragments of stone into knives, lances, or arrow-heads, shews "extraordinary ability and long practice." This is to a great extent proved by the fact the primeval men practised a division of labour; each man did not manufacture his own flint tools or rude pottery, but certain individuals appear to have devoted themselves to such work, no doubt receiving in exchange the produce of the chase. Archæologists are convinced that an enormous interval of time elapsed before our ancestors thought of grinding chipped flints into smooth tools. One can hardly doubt, that a man-like animal who possessed a hand and arm sufficiently perfect to throw a stone with precision, or to form a flint into a rude tool, could, with sufficient practice, as far as mechanical skill alone is concerned, make almost anything which a civilised man can make. The structure of the hand in this respect may be compared with that of the vocal organs, which in the apes are used for uttering various signal-cries, or, as in one genus, musical cadences; but in man the closely similar vocal organs have become adapted through the inherited effects of use for the utterance of articulate language.

Turning now to the nearest allies of men, and therefore to the best representatives of our early progenitors, we find that the hands of the Quadrumana are constructed on the same general pattern as our own, but are far less perfectly adapted for diversified uses. Their hands do not serve for locomotion so well as the feet of a dog; as may be seen in such monkeys as the chimpanzee and orang, which walk on the outer margins of the palms, or on the knuckles.[69] Their hands, however, are admirably adapted for climbing trees. Monkeys seize thin branches or

68 Quoted by Mr. Lawson Tait in his 'Law of Natural Selection,'— 'Dublin Quarterly Journal of Medical Science,' Feb. 1869. Dr. Keller is likewise quoted to the same effect.

69 Owen, 'Anatomy of Vertebrates,' vol. iii. p. 71.

ropes, with the thumb on one side and the fingers and palm on the other, in the same manner as we do. They can thus also lift rather large objects, such as the neck of a bottle, to their mouths. Baboons turn over stones, and scratch up roots with their hands. They seize nuts, insects, or other small objects with the thumb in opposition to the fingers, and no doubt they thus extract eggs and young from the nests of birds. American monkeys beat the wild oranges on the branches until the rind is cracked, and then tear it off with the fingers of the two hands. In a wild state they break open hard fruits with stones. Other monkeys open mussel-shells with the two thumbs. With their fingers they pull out thorns and burs, and hunt for each other's parasites. They roll down stones, or throw them at their enemies: nevertheless, they are clumsy in these various actions, and, as I have myself seen, are quite unable to throw a stone with precision.

It seems to me far from true that because "objects are grasped clumsily" by monkeys, "a much less specialised organ of prehension" would have served them[70] equally well with their present hands. On the contrary, I see no reason to doubt that more perfectly constructed hands would have been an advantage to them, provided that they were not thus rendered less fitted for climbing trees. We may suspect that a hand as perfect as that of man would have been disadvantageous for climbing; for the most arboreal monkeys in the world, namely, Ateles in America, Colobus in Africa, and Hylobates in Asia, are either thumbless, or their toes partially cohere, so that their limbs are converted into mere grasping hooks.[71]

As soon as some ancient member in the great series of the Primates came to be less arboreal, owing to a change in its man-

[70] 'Quarterly Review,' April 1869, p. 392.

[71] In *Hylobates syndactylus,* as the name expresses, two of the toes regularly cohere; and this, as Mr. Blyth informs me, is occasionally the case with the toes of *H. agilis, lar,* and *leuciscus.* Colobus is strictly arboreal and extraordinarily active (Brehm, 'Thierleben,' B. i. s. 50), but whether a better climber than the species of the allied genera, I do not know. It deserves notice that the feet of the sloths, the most arboreal animals in the world, are wonderfully hook-like.

ner of procuring subsistence, or to some change in the surrounding conditions, its habitual manner of progression would have been modified: and thus it would have been rendered more strictly quadrupedal or bipedal. Baboons frequent hilly and rocky districts, and only from necessity climb high trees;[72] and they have acquired almost the gait of a dog. Man alone has become a biped; and we can, I think, partly see how he has come to assume his erect attitude, which forms one of his most conspicuous characters. Man could not have attained his present dominant position in the world without the use of his hands, which are so admirably adapted to act in obedience to his will. Sir C. Bell[73] insists that "the hand supplies all instruments, and by its correspondence with the intellect gives him universal dominion." But the hands and arms could hardly have become perfect enough to have manufactured weapons, or to have hurled stones and spears with a true aim, as long as they were habitually used for locomotion and for supporting the whole weight of the body, or, as before remarked, so long as they were especially fitted for climbing trees. Such rough treatment would also have blunted the sense of touch, on which their delicate use largely depends. From these causes alone it would have been an advantage to man to become a biped; but for many actions it is indispensable that the arms and whole upper part of the body should be free; and he must for this end stand firmly on his feet. To gain this great advantage, the feet have been rendered flat; and the great toe has been peculiarly modified, though this has entailed the almost complete loss of its power of prehension. It accords with the principle of the division of physiological labour, prevailing throughout the animal kingdom, that as the hands became perfected for prehension, the feet should have become perfected for support and locomotion. With some savages, however, the foot has not altogether lost its prehensile power, as shewn by

[72] Brehm, 'Thierleben,' B. i. s. 80.

[73] "The Hand," &c. 'Bridgewater Treatise,' 1833, p. 38.

their manner of climbing trees, and of using them in other ways.[74]

If it be an advantage to man to stand firmly on his feet and to have his hands and arms free, of which, from his pre-eminent success in the battle of life, there can be no doubt, then I can see no reason why it should not have been advantageous to the progenitors of man to have become more and more erect or bipedal. They would thus have been better able to defend themselves with stones or clubs, to attack their prey, or otherwise to obtain food. The best built individuals would in the long run have succeeded best, and have survived in larger numbers. If the gorilla and a few allied forms had become extinct, it might have been argued, with great force and apparent truth, that an animal could not have been gradually converted from a quadruped into a biped, as all the individuals in an intermediate condition would have been miserably ill-fitted for progression. But we know (and this is well worthy of reflection) that the anthropomorphous apes are now actually in an intermediate condition; and no one doubts that they are on the whole well adapted for their conditions of life. Thus the gorilla runs with a sidelong shambling gait, but more commonly progresses by resting on its bent hands. The long-armed apes occasionally use their arms like crutches, swinging their bodies forward between them, and some kinds of Hylobates, without having been taught, can walk or run upright with tolerable quickness; yet they move awkwardly, and much less securely than man. We see, in short, in existing monkeys a manner of progression intermediate between that of a quadruped and a biped; but, as an unprejudiced judge[75]

[74] Häckel has an excellent discussion on the steps by which man became a biped: 'Natürliche Schöpfungsgeschichte,' 1868, s. 507. Dr. Büchner ('Conférences sur la Théorie Darwinienne,' 1869, p. 135) has given good cases of the use of the foot as a prehensile organ by man; and has also written on the manner of progression of the higher apes, to which I allude in the following paragraph: see also Owen ('Anatomy of Vertebrates,' vol. iii. p. 71) on this latter subject.

[75] Prof. Broca, La Constitution des Vertèbres caudales; 'La Revue d'Anthropologie,' 1872, p. 26, (separate copy).

insists, the anthropomorphous apes approach in structure more nearly to the bipedal than to the quadrupedal type.

As the progenitors of man became more and more erect, with their hands and arms more and more modified for prehension and other purposes, with their feet and legs at the same time transformed for firm support and progression, endless other changes of structure would have become necessary. The pelvis would have to be broadened, the spine peculiarly curved, and the head fixed in an altered position, all which changes have been attained by man. Prof. Schaaffhausen[76] maintains that "the powerful mastoid processes of the human skull are the result of his erect position;" and these processes are absent in the orang, chimpanzee, &c., and are smaller in the gorilla than in man. Various other structures, which appear connected with man's erect position, might here have been added. It is very difficult to decide how far these correlated modifications are the result of natural selection, and how far of the inherited effects of the increased use of certain parts, or of the action of one part on another. No doubt these means of change often co-operate: thus when certain muscles, and the crests of bone to which they are attached, become enlarged by habitual use, this shews that certain actions are habitually performed and must be serviceable. Hence the individuals which performed them best, would tend to survive in greater numbers.

The free use of the arms and hands, partly the cause and partly the result of man's erect position, appears to have led in an indirect manner to other modifications of structure. The early male forefathers of man were, as previously stated, probably furnished with great canine teeth; but as they gradually acquired the habit of using stones, clubs, or other weapons, for fighting with their enemies or rivals, they would use their jaws and teeth less and less. In this case, the jaws, together with the

[76] 'On the Primitive Form of the Skull,' translated in 'Anthropological Review,' Oct. 1868, p. 428. Owen ('Anatomy of Vertebrates,' vol. ii. 1866, p. 551) on the mastoid processes in the higher apes.

teeth, would become reduced in size, as we may feel almost sure from innumerable analogous cases. In a future chapter we shall meet with a closely parallel case, in the reduction or complete disappearance of the canine teeth in male ruminants, apparently in relation with the development of their horns; and in horses, in relation to their habit of fighting with their incisor teeth and hoofs.

In the adult male anthropomorphous apes, as Rütimeyer,[77] and others, have insisted, it is the effect on the skull of the great development of the jaw-muscles that causes it to differ so greatly in many respects from that of man, and has given to these animals "a truly frightful physiognomy." Therefore, as the jaws and teeth in man's progenitors gradually become reduced in size, the adult skull would have come to resemble more and more that of existing man. As we shall hereafter see, a great reduction of the canine teeth in the males would almost certainly affect the teeth of the females through inheritance.

As the various mental faculties gradually developed themselves the brain would almost certainly become larger. No one, I presume, doubts that the large proportion which the size of man's brain bears to his body, compared to the same proportion in the gorilla or orang, is closely connected with his higher mental powers. We meet with closely analogous facts with insects, for in ants the cerebral ganglia are of extraordinary dimensions, and in all the Hymenoptera these ganglia are many times larger than in the less intelligent orders, such as beetles.[78] On the other hand, no one supposes that the intellect of any two animals or of any two men can be accurately gauged by the cubic contents of their skulls. It is certain that there may be extraordinary mental activity with an extremely small absolute mass of nervous mat-

[77] 'Die Grenzen der Thierwelt, eine Betrachtung zu Darwin's Lehre,' 1868, s. 51.

[78] Dujardin, 'Annales des Sc. Nat.' 3rd series Zoolog. tom. xiv. 1850, p. 203. See also Mr. Lowne, 'Anatomy and Phys. of the *Musca vomitoria*,' 1870, p. 14. My son, Mr. F. Darwin, dissected for me the cerebral ganglia of the *Formica rufa*.

ter: thus the wonderfully diversified instincts, mental powers, and affections of ants are notorious, yet their cerebral ganglia are not so large as the quarter of a small pin's head. Under this point of view, the brain of an ant is one of the most marvellous atoms of matter in the world, perhaps more so than the brain of a man.

The belief that there exists in man some close relation between the size of the brain and the development of the intellectual faculties is supported by the comparison of the skulls of savage and civilised races, of ancient and modern people, and by the analogy of the whole vertebrate series. Dr. J. Barnard Davis has proved,[79] by many careful measurements, that the mean internal capacity of the skull in Europeans is 92.3 cubic inches; in Americans 87.5; in Asiatics 87.1; and in Australians only 81.9 cubic inches. Professor Broca[80] found that the nineteenth century skulls from graves in Paris were larger than those from vaults of the twelfth century, in the proportion of 1484 to 1426; and that the increased size, as ascertained by measurements, was exclusively in the frontal part of the skull—the seat of the intellectual faculties. Prichard is persuaded that the present inhabitants of Britain have "much more capacious braincases" than the ancient inhabitants. Nevertheless, it must be admitted that some skulls of very high antiquity, such as the famous one of Neanderthal, are well developed and capacious.[81] With respect to the lower animals, M. E. Lartet,[82] by comparing the crania of

79 'Philosophical Transactions,' 1869, p. 513.

80 'Les Sélections,' M. P. Broca, 'Revue d'Anthropologies,' 1873; see also, as quoted in C. Vogt's 'Lectures on Man,' Eng. Translat. 1864, pp. 88, 90. Prichard, 'Phys. Hist. of Mankind,' vol. i. 1838, p. 305.

81 In the interesting article just referred to, Prof. Broca has well remarked, that in civilised nations, the average capacity of the skull must be lowered by the preservation of a considerable number of individuals, weak in mind and body, who would have been promptly eliminated in the savage state. On the other hand, with savages, the average includes only the more capable individuals, who have been able to survive under extremely hard conditions of life. Broca thus explains the otherwise inexplicable fact, that the mean capacity of the skull of the ancient Troglodytes of Lozère is greater than that of modern Frenchmen.

82 'Comptes-rendus des Sciences,' &c., June 1, 1868.

tertiary and recent mammals belonging to the same groups, has come to the remarkable conclusion that the brain is generally larger and the convolutions are more complex in the more recent forms. On the other hand, I have shewn[83] that the brains of domestic rabbits are considerably reduced in bulk, in comparison with those of the wild rabbit or hare; and this may be attributed to their having been closely confined during many generations, so that they have exerted their intellect, instincts, senses and voluntary movements but little.

The gradually increasing weight of the brain and skull in man must have influenced the development of the supporting spinal column, more especially whilst he was becoming erect. As this change of position was being brought about, the internal pressure of the brain will also have influenced the form of the skull; for many facts shew how easily the skull is thus effected. Ethnologists believe that it is modified by the kind of cradle in which infants sleep. Habitual spasms of the muscles, and a cicatrix from a severe burn, have permanently modified the facial bones. In young persons whose heads have become fixed either sideways or backwards, owing to disease, one of the two eyes has changed its position, and the shape of the skull has been altered apparently by the pressure of the brain in a new direction.[84] I have shewn that with long-eared rabbits even so trifling a cause as the lopping forward of one ear drags forward almost every bone of the skull on that side; so that the bones on the opposite side no longer strictly correspond. Lastly, if any animal were to increase or diminish much in general size, without any change in its mental powers, or if the mental powers were to be

[83] 'The Variation of Animals and Plants under Domestication,' vol. i. pp. 124-129.

[84] Schaaffhausen gives from Blumenbach and Busch, the cases of the spasms and cicatrix, in 'Anthropolog. Review,' Oct. 1868, p. 420. Dr. Jarrold ('Anthropologia,' 1808, pp. 115, 116) adduces from Camper and from his own observations, cases of the modification of the skull from the head being fixed in an unnatural position. He believes that in certain trades, such as that of a shoemaker, where the head is habitually held forward, the forehead becomes more rounded and prominent.

much increased or diminished, without any great change in the size of the body, the shape of the skull would almost certainly be altered. I infer this from my observations on domestic rabbits, some kinds of which have become very much larger than the wild animal, whilst others have retained nearly the same size, but in both cases the brain has been much reduced relatively to the size of the body. Now I was at first much surprised on finding that in all these rabbits the skull had become elongated or dolichocephalic; for instance, of two skulls of nearly equal breadth, the one from a wild rabbit and the other from a large domestic kind, the former was 3.15 and the latter 4.3 inches in length.[85] One of the most marked distinctions in different races of men is that the skull in some is elongated, and in others rounded; and here the explanation suggested by the case of the rabbits may hold good; for Welcker finds that short "men incline more to brachycephaly, and tall men to dolichocephaly;"[86] and tall men may be compared with the larger and longer-bodied rabbits, all of which have elongated skulls, or are dolichocephalic.

From these several facts we can understand, to a certain extent, the means by which the great size and more or less rounded form of the skull have been acquired by man; and these are characters eminently distinctive of him in comparison with the lower animals.

Another most conspicuous difference between man and the lower animals is the nakedness of his skin. Whales and porpoises (Cetacea), dugongs (Sirenia) and the hippopotamus are naked; and this may be advantageous to them for gliding through the water; nor would it be injurious to them from the loss of warmth, as the species, which inhabit the colder regions, are protected by a thick layer of blubber, serving the same purpose as the fur of seals and otters. Elephants and rhinoceroses are

[85] 'Variation of Animals,' &c., vol. i. p. 117, on the elongation of the skull; p. 119, on the effect of the lopping of one ear.

[86] Quoted by Schaaffhausen, in 'Anthropolog. Review,' Oct. 1868, p. 419.

almost hairless; and as certain extinct species, which formerly lived under an Arctic climate, were covered with long wool or hair, it would almost appear as if the existing species of both genera had lost their hairy covering from exposure to heat. This appears the more probable, as the elephants in India which live on elevated and cool districts are more hairy[87] than those on the lowlands. May we then infer that man became divested of hair from having aboriginally inhabited some tropical land? That the hair is chiefly retained in the male sex on the chest and face, and in both sexes at the junction of all four limbs with the trunk, favours this inference — on the assumption that the hair was lost before man became erect; for the parts which now retain most hair would then have been most protected from the heat of the sun. The crown of the head, however, offers a curious exception, for at all times it must have been one of the most exposed parts, yet it is thickly clothed with hair. The fact, however, that the other members of the order of Primates, to which man belongs, although inhabiting various hot regions, are well clothed with hair, generally thickest on the upper surface,[88] is opposed to the supposition that man became naked through the action of the sun. Mr. Belt believes[89] that within the tropics it is an advantage to man to be destitute of hair, as he is thus enabled to free himself of the multitude of ticks (acari) and other parasites, with which he is often infested, and which sometimes cause ulceration. But whether this evil is of sufficient magnitude to

[87] Owen, 'Anatomy of Vertebrates,' vol. iii. p. 619.

[88] Isidore Geoffroy St.-Hilaire remarks ('Hist. Nat. Générale,' tom. ii. 1859, pp. 215-217) on the head of man being covered with long hair; also on the upper surfaces of monkeys and of other mammals being more thickly clothed than the lower surfaces. This has likewise been observed by various authors. Prof. P. Gervais ('Hist. Nat. des Mammifères,' tom. i. 1854, p. 28), however, states that in the Gorilla the hair is thinner on the back, where it is partly rubbed off, than on the lower surface.

[89] The 'Naturalist in Nicaragua,' 1874, p. 209. As some confirmation of Mr. Belt's view, I may quote the following passage from Sir W. Denison ('Varieties of Vice-Regal Life,' vol. i. 1870, p. 440): "It is said to be a practice with the Australians, when the vermin get troublesome, to singe themselves."

have led to the denudation of his body through natural selection, may be doubted, since none of the many quadrupeds inhabiting the tropics have, as far as I know, acquired any specialised means of relief. The view which seems to me the most probable is that man, or rather primarily woman, became divested of hair for ornamental purposes, as we shall see under Sexual Selection; and, according to this belief, it is not surprising that man should differ so greatly in hairiness from all other Primates, for characters, gained through sexual selection, often differ to an extraordinary degree in closely related forms.

According to a popular impression, the absence of a tail is eminently distinctive of man; but as those apes which come nearest to him are destitute of this organ, its disappearance does not relate exclusively to man. The tail often differs remarkably in length within the same genus: thus in some species of Macacus it is longer than the whole body, and is formed of twenty-four vertebræ; in others it consists of a scarcely visible stump, containing only three or four vertebræ. In some kinds of baboons there are twenty-five, whilst in the mandrill there are ten very small stunted caudal vertebræ, or, according to Cuvier,[90] sometimes only five. The tail, whether it be long or short, almost always tapers towards the end; and this, I presume, results from the atrophy of the terminal muscles, together with their arteries and nerves, through disuse, leading to the atrophy of the terminal bones. But no explanation can at present be given of the great diversity which often occurs in its length. Here, however, we are more specially concerned with the complete external disappearance of the tail. Professor Broca has recently shewn[91] that the tail in all quadrupeds consists of two portions, generally separated abruptly from each other; the basal portion consists of vertebræ, more or less perfectly channelled and furnished with

90 Mr. St. George Mivart, 'Proc. Zoolog. Soc.' 1865, pp. 562, 583. Dr. J. E. Gray, 'Cat. Brit. Mus.: 'Skeletons.' Owen, 'Anatomy of Vertebrates,' vol. ii. p. 517. Isidore Geoffroy, 'Hist. Nat. Gén.' tom. ii. p. 244.

91 'Revue d'Anthropologie,' 1872; 'La Constitution des Vertèbres caudales.'

apophyses like ordinary vertebræ; whereas those of the terminal portion are not channelled, are almost smooth, and scarcely resemble true vertebræ. A tail, though not externally visible, is really present in man and the anthropomorphous apes, and is constructed on exactly the same pattern in both. In the terminal portion the vertebræ, constituting the *os coccyx*, are quite rudimentary, being much reduced in size and number. In the basal portion, the vertebræ are likewise few, are united firmly together, and are arrested in development; but they have been rendered much broader and flatter than the corresponding vertebræ in the tails of other animals: they constitute what Broca calls the accessory sacral vertebræ. These are of functional importance by supporting certain internal parts and in other ways; and their modifications is directly connected with the erect or semi-erect attitude of man and the anthropomorphous apes. This conclusion is the more trustworthy, as Broca formerly held a different view, which he has now abandoned. The modification, therefore, of the basal caudal vertebræ in man and the higher apes may have been effected, directly or indirectly, through natural selection.

But what are we to say about the rudimentary and variable vertebræ of the terminal portion of the tail, forming the *os coccyx*? A notion which has often been, and will no doubt again be ridiculed, namely, that friction has had something to do with the disappearance of the external portion of the tail, is not so ridiculous as it at first appears. Dr. Anderson[92] states that the extremely short tail of *Macacus brunneus* is formed of eleven vertebræ, including the imbedded basal ones. The extremity is tendinous and contains no vertebræ; this is succeeded by five rudimentary ones, so minute that together they are only one line and a half in length, and these are permanently bent to one side in the shape of a hook. The free part of the tail, only a little above an inch in length, includes only four more small vertebræ. This short tail is carried erect; but about a quarter of its total length is doubled on to itself to the left; and this terminal part,

[92] 'Proc. Zoolog. Soc.,' 1872, p. 210.

which includes the hook-like portion, serves "to fill up the interspace between the upper divergent portion of the callosities;" so that the animal sits on it, and thus renders it rough and callous. Dr. Anderson thus sums up his observations: "These facts seem to me to have only one explanation; this tail, from its short size, is in the monkey's way when it sits down, and frequently becomes placed under the animal while it is in this attitude; and from the circumstance that it does not extend beyond the extremity of the ischial tuberosities, it seems as if the tail originally had been bent round by the will of the animal, into the interspace between the callosities, to escape being pressed between them and the ground, and that in time the curvature became permanent, fitting in of itself when the organ happens to be sat upon." Under these circumstances it is not surprising that the surface of the tail should have been roughened and rendered callous, and Dr. Murie,[93] who carefully observed this species in the Zoological Gardens, as well as three other closely allied forms with slightly longer tails, says that when the animal sits down, the tail "is necessarily thrust to one side of the buttocks; and whether long or short its root is consequently liable to be rubbed or chafed." As we now have evidence that mutilations occasionally produce an inherited effect,[94] it is not very improbable that in short-tailed monkeys, the projecting part of the tail, being functionally useless, should after many generations have become rudimentary and distorted, from being continually rubbed and chafed. We see the projecting part in this condition in the *Macacus brunneus*, and absolutely aborted in the *M. ecaudatus* and in several of the higher apes. Finally, then, as far as we can judge, the tail has disappeared in man and the anthropomorphous apes, owing to the

93 'Proc. Zoolog. Soc.,' 1872, p. 786.

94 I allude to Dr. Brown-Séquard's observations on the transmitted effect of an operation causing epilepsy in guinea-pigs, and likewise more recently on the analogous effects of cutting the sympathetic nerve in the neck. I shall hereafter have occasion to refer to Mr. Salvin's interesting case of the apparently inherited effects of mot-mots biting off the barbs of their own tail-feathers. See also on the general subject 'Variation of Animals and Plants under Domestication,' vol. ii. pp. 22-24.

terminal portion having been injured by friction during a long lapse of time; the basal and embedded portion having been reduced and modified, so as to become suitable to the erect or semi-erect position.

I have now endeavoured to shew that some of the most distinctive characters of man have in all probability been acquired, either directly, or more commonly indirectly, through natural selection. We should bear in mind that modifications in structure or constitution which do not serve to adapt an organism to its habits of life, to the food which it consumes, or passively to the surrounding conditions, cannot have been thus acquired. We must not, however, be too confident in deciding what modifications are of service to each being: we should remember how little we know about the use of many parts, or what changes in the blood or tissues may serve to fit an organism for a new climate or new kinds of food. Nor must we forget the principle of correlation, by which, as Isidore Geoffroy has shewn in the case of man, many strange deviations of structure are tied together. Independently of correlation, a change in one part often leads, through the increased or decreased use of other parts, to other changes of a quite unexpected nature. It is also well to reflect on such facts, as the wonderful growth of galls on plants caused by the poison of an insect, and on the remarkable changes of colour in the plumage of parrots when fed on certain fishes, or inoculated with the poison of toads;[95] for we can thus see that the fluids of the system, if altered for some special purpose, might induce other changes. We should especially bear in mind that modifications acquired and continually used during past ages for some useful purpose, would probably become firmly fixed, and might be long inherited.

Thus a large yet undefined extension may safely be given to the direct and indirect results of natural selection; but I now

[95] 'The Variation of Animals and Plants under Domestication,' vol. ii. pp. 280, 282.

admit, after reading the essay by Nägeli on plants, and the remarks by various authors with respect to animals, more especially those recently made by Professor Broca, that in the earlier editions of my 'Origin of Species' I perhaps attributed too much to the action of natural selection or the survival of the fittest. I have altered the fifth edition of the 'Origin' so as to confine my remarks to adaptive changes of structure; but I am convinced, from the light gained during even the last few years, that very many structures which now appear to us useless, will hereafter be proved to be useful, and will therefore come within the range of natural selection. Nevertheless, I did not formerly consider sufficiently the existence of structures, which, as far as we can at present judge, are neither beneficial nor injurious; and this I believe to be one of the greatest oversights as yet detected in my work. I may be permitted to say, as some excuse, that I had two distinct objects in view; firstly, to shew that species had not been separately created, and secondly, that natural selection had been the chief agent of change, though largely aided by the inherited effects of habit, and slightly by the direct action of the surrounding conditions. I was not, however, able to annul the influence of my former belief, then almost universal, that each species had been purposely created; and this led to my tacit assumption that every detail of structure, excepting rudiments, was of some special, though unrecognised, service. Any one with this assumption in his mind would naturally extend too far the action of natural selection, either during past or present times. Some of those who admit the principle of evolution, but reject natural selection, seem to forget, when criticising my book, that I had the above two objects in view; hence if I have erred in giving to natural selection great power, which I am very far from admitting, or in having exaggerated its power, which is in itself probable, I have at least, as I hope, done good service in aiding to overthrow the dogma of separate creations.

It is, as I can now see, probable that all organic beings, including man, possess peculiarities of structure, which neither are now, nor were formerly of any service to them, and which, therefore, are of no physiological importance. We know not what produces the numberless slight differences between the individuals of each species, for reversion only carries the problem a few steps backwards, but each peculiarity must have had its efficient cause. If these causes, whatever they may be, were to act more uniformly and energetically during a lengthened period (and against this no reason can be assigned), the result would probably be not a mere slight individual difference, but a well-marked and constant modification, though one of no physiological importance. Changed structures, which are in no way beneficial, cannot be kept uniform through natural selection, though the injurious will be thus eliminated. Uniformity of character would, however, naturally follow from the assumed uniformity of the exciting causes, and likewise from the free intercrossing of many individuals. During successive periods, the same organism might in this manner acquire successive modifications, which would be transmitted in a nearly uniform state as long as the exciting causes remained the same and there was free intercrossing. With respect to the exciting causes we can only say, as when speaking of so-called spontaneous variations, that they relate much more closely to the constitution of the varying organism, than to the nature of the conditions to which it has been subjected.

*Conclusion.* — In this chapter we have seen that as man at the present day is liable, like every other animal, to multiform individual differences or slight variations, so no doubt were the early progenitors of man; the variations being formerly induced by the same general causes, and governed by the same general and complex laws as at present. As all animals tend to multiply beyond their means of subsistence, so it must have been with the progenitors of man; and this would inevitably lead to a struggle for existence and to natural selection. The latter process would be greatly aided by the inherited effects of the increased use of parts, and these two processes would incessantly react on each other. It appears, also, as we shall hereafter see, that various unimportant characters have been acquired by man through sexual selection. An unexplained residuum of change must be left to the assumed uniform action of those unknown agencies, which occasionally induce strongly marked and abrupt deviations of structure in our domestic productions.

Judging from the habits of savages and of the greater number of the Quadrumana, primeval men, and even their ape-like progenitors, probably lived in society. With strictly social animals, natural selection sometimes acts on the individual, through the preservation of variations which are beneficial to the community. A community which includes a large number of well-endowed individuals increases in number, and is victorious over other less favoured ones; even although each separate member gains no advantage over the others of the same community. Associated insects have thus acquired many remarkable structures, which are of little or no service to the individual, such as the pollen-collecting apparatus, or the sting of the worker bee, or the great jaws of soldier-ants. With the higher social animals, I am not aware that any structure has been modified solely for the good of the community, though some are of secondary service to it. For instance, the horns of ruminants and the great canine teeth of baboons appear to have been acquired by the males as weapons for sexual strife, but they are used in defence of the herd or troop. In regard to certain mental powers the case, as we shall see in the fifth chapter, is wholly different; for these faculties have been chiefly, or even exclusively, gained for the benefit of the community, and the individuals thereof have at the same time gained an advantage indirectly.

It has often been objected to such views as the foregoing, that man is one of the most helpless and defenceless creatures in the world; and that during his early and less well-developed condition, he would have been still more helpless. The Duke of Argyll, for instance, insists[96] that "the human frame has diverged from the structure of brutes, in the direction of greater physical helplessness and weakness. That is to say, it is a divergence which of all others it is most impossible to ascribe to mere natural selection." He adduces the naked and unprotected state of the body, the absence of great teeth or claws for defence, the small strength and speed of man, and his slight power of discovering food or of avoiding danger by smell. To these deficiencies there might be added one still more serious, namely, that he cannot climb quickly, and so escape from enemies. The loss of hair would not have been a great injury to the inhabitants of a warm country. For we know that the unclothed Fuegians can exist under a wretched climate. When we compare the defenceless state of man with that of apes, we must remember that the great canine teeth with which the latter are provided, are possessed in their full development by the males alone, and are chiefly used by them for fighting with their rivals; yet the females, which are not thus provided, manage to survive.

In regard to bodily size or strength, we do not know whether man is descended from some small species, like the chimpanzee, or from one as powerful as the gorilla; and, therefore, we cannot say whether man has become larger and stronger, or smaller and weaker, than his ancestors. We should, however, bear in mind that an animal possessing great size, strength, and ferocity, and which, like the gorilla, could defend himself from all enemies, would not perhaps have become social: and this would most effectually have checked the acquirement of the higher mental qualities, such as sympathy and the love of his fellows. Hence it might have been an immense advantage to man to have sprung from some comparatively weak creature.

The small strength and speed of man, his want of natural weapons, &c., are more than counterbalanced, firstly, by his intellectual powers, through which he has formed for himself weapons, tools, &c., though still remaining in a barbarous state,

96 'Primeval Man,' 1869, p. 66.

and, secondly, by his social qualities which lead him to give and receive aid from his fellow-men. No country in the world abounds in a greater degree with dangerous beasts than Southern Africa; no country presents more fearful physical hardships than the Arctic regions; yet one of the puniest of races, that of the Bushmen, maintains itself in Southern Africa, as do the dwarfed Esquimaux in the Arctic regions. The ancestors of man were, no doubt, inferior in intellect, and probably in social disposition, to the lowest existing savages; but it is quite conceivable that they might have existed, or even flourished, if they had advanced in intellect, whilst gradually losing their brute-like powers, such as that of climbing trees, &c. But these ancestors would not have been exposed to any special danger, even if far more helpless and defenceless than any existing savages, had they inhabited some warm continent or large island, such as Australia, New Guinea, or Borneo, which is now the home of the orang. And natural selection arising from the competition of tribe with tribe, in some such large area as one of these, together with the inherited effects of habit, would, under favourable conditions, have sufficed to raise man to his present high position in the organic scale.

# The Mental Powers of Man and Animals

We have seen in the last two chapters that man bears in his bodily structure clear traces of his descent from some lower form; but it may be urged that, as man differs so greatly in his mental power from all other animals, there must be some error in this conclusion. No doubt the difference in this respect is enormous, even if we compare the mind of one of the lowest savages, who has no words to express any number higher than four, and who uses hardly any abstract terms for common objects or for the affections,[1] with that of the most highly organised ape. The difference would, no doubt, still remain immense, even if one of the higher apes had been improved or civilised as much as a dog has been in comparison with its parent-form, the wolf or jackal. The Fuegians rank amongst the lowest barbarians; but I was continually struck with surprise how closely the three natives on board H. M. S. "Beagle," who had lived some years in England,

[1] See the evidence on those points, as given by Lubbock, 'Prehistoric Times,' p. 354, &c.

and could talke a little English, resembled us in disposition and in most of our mental faculties. If no organic being excepting man had possessed any mental power, or if his powers had been of a wholly different nature from those of the lower animals, then we should never have been able to convince ourselves that our high faculties had been gradually developed. But it can be shewn that there is no fundamental difference of this kind. We must also admit that there is a much wider interval in mental power between one of the lowest fishes, as a lamprey or lancelet, and one of the higher apes, than between an ape and man; yet this interval is filled up by numberless gradations.

Nor is the difference slight in moral disposition between a barbarian, such as the man described by the old navigator Byron, who dashed his child on the rocks for dropping a basket of sea-urchins, and a Howard or Clarkson; and in intellect, between a savage who uses hardly any abstract terms, and a Newton or Shakespeare. Differences of this kind between the highest men of the highest races and the lowest savages, are connected by the finest gradations. Therefore it is possible that they might pass and be developed into each other.

My object in this chapter is to shew that there is no fundamental difference between man and the higher mammals in their mental faculties. Each division of the subject might have been extended into a separate essay, but must here be treated briefly. As no classification of the mental powers has been universally accepted, I shall arrange my remarks in the order most convenient for my purpose; and will select those facts which have struck me most, with the hope that they may produce some effect on the reader.

With respect to animals very low in the scale, I shall give some additional facts under Sexual Selection, shewing that their mental powers are much higher than might have been expected. The variability of the faculties in the individuals of the same species is an important point for us, and some few illustrations will here be given. But it would be superfluous to enter into

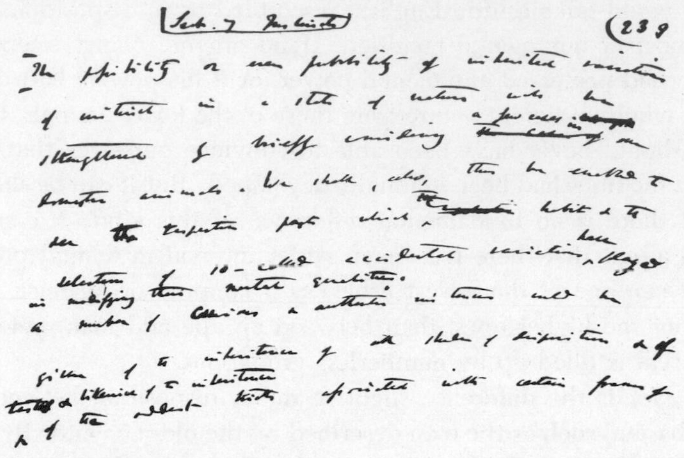

Facsimile of a manuscript page in the handwriting of Charles Darwin

many details on this head, for I have found on frequent enquiry, that it is the unanimous opinion of all those who have long attended to animals of many kinds, including birds, that the individuals differ greatly in every mental characteristic. In what manner the mental powers were first developed in the lowest organisms, is as hopeless an enquiry as how life itself first originated. These are problems for the distant future, if they are ever to be solved by man.

As man possesses the same senses as the lower animals, his fundamental intuitions must be the same. Man has also some few instincts in common, as that of self-preservation, sexual love, the love of the mother for her new-born offspring, the desire possessed by the latter to suck, and so forth. But man, perhaps, has somewhat fewer instincts than those possessed by the animals which come next to him in the series. The orang in the Eastern islands, and the chimpanzee in Africa, build platforms on which they sleep; and, as both species follow the same habit, it might be argued that this was due to instinct, but we cannot feel sure that it is not the result of both animals having similar wants, and possessing similar powers of reasoning. These apes, as we may assume, avoid the many poisonous fruits of the tropics, and man has no such knowledge: but as our domestic animals, when taken to foreign lands, and when first turned out in the spring, often eat poisonous herbs, which they afterwards avoid, we cannot feel sure that the apes do not learn from their own experience or from that of their parents what fruits to select. It is, however, certain, as we shall presently see, that apes have an instinctive dread of serpents, and probably of other dangerous animals.

The fewness and the comparative simplicity of the instincts in the higher animals are remarkable in contrast with those of the lower animals. Cuvier maintained that instinct and intelligence stand in an inverse ratio to each other; and some have thought that the intellectual faculties of the higher animals have been gradually developed from their instincts. But Pouchet, in an interesting essay,[2] has shewn that no such inverse ratio really exists. Those insects which possess the most wonderful instincts are certainly the most intelligent. In the vertebrate series, the least intelligent members, namely fishes and amphibians, do not possess complex instincts; and amongst mammals the animal most remarkable for its instincts, namely the beaver, is highly intelligent, as will be admitted by every one who has read Mr. Morgan's excellent work.[3]

Although the first dawnings of intelligence, according to Mr. Herbert Spencer,[4] have been developed through the multiplication and co-ordination of reflex actions, and although many of the simpler instincts graduate into reflex actions, and can hardly be distinguished from them, as in the case of young animals sucking, yet the more complex instincts seem to have originated

[2] 'L'instinct chez les Insectes,' 'Revue des Deux Mondes,' Feb. 1870, p. 690.

[3] 'The American Beaver and His Works,' 1868.

[4] 'The Principles of Psychology,' 2nd edit. 1870, pp. 418-443.

independently of intelligence. I am, however, very far from wishing to deny that instinctive actions may lose their fixed and untaught character, and be replaced by others performed by the aid of the free will. On the other hand, some intelligent actions, after being performed during several generations, become converted into instincts and are inherited, as when birds on oceanic islands learn to avoid man. These actions may then be said to be degraded in character, for they are no longer performed through reason or from experience. But the greater number of the more complex instincts appear to have been gained in a wholly different manner, through the natural selection of variations of simpler instinctive actions. Such variations appear to arise from the same unknown causes acting on the cerebral organisation, which induce slight variations or individual differences in other parts of the body; and these variations, owing to our ignorance, are often said to arise spontaneously. We can, I think, come to no other conclusion with respect to the origin of the more complex instincts, when we reflect on the marvellous instincts of sterile worker-ants and bees, which leave no offspring to inherit the effects of experience and of modified habits.

Although, as we learn from the above-mentioned insects and the beaver, a high degree of intelligence is certainly compatible with complex intincts, and although actions, at first learnt voluntarily can soon through habit be performed with the quickness and certainty of a reflex action, yet it is not improbable that there is a certain amount of interference between the development of free intelligence and of instinct, — which latter implies some inherited modification of the brain. Little is known about the functions of the brain, but we can perceive that as the intellectual powers become highly developed, the various parts of the brain must be connected by very intricate channels of the freest intercommunication; and as a consequence each separate part would perhaps tend to be less well fitted to answer to particular sensations or associations in a definite and inherited — that is instinctive — manner. There seems even to exist some relation between a low degree of intelligence and a strong tendency to the formation of fixed, though not inherited habits; for as a sagacious physician remarked to me, persons who are slightly imbecile tend to act in everything by routine or habit; and they are rendered much happier if this is encouraged.

I have thought this digression worth giving, because we may easily underrate the mental powers of the higher animals, and especially of man, when we compare their actions founded on the memory of past events, on foresight, reason, and imagination, with exactly similar actions instinctively performed by the lower animals; in this latter case the capacity of performing such actions has been gained, step by step, through the variability of the mental organs and natural selection, without any conscious intelligence on the part of the animal during each successive generation. No doubt, as Mr. Wallace has argued,[5] much of the intelligent work done by man is due to imitation and not to reason; but there is this great difference between his actions and many of those performed by the lower animals, namely, that man cannot, on his first trial, make, for instance, a stone hatchet or a canoe, through his power of imitation. He has to learn his work by practice; a beaver, on the other hand, can make its dam or canal, and a bird its nest, as well, or nearly as well, and a spider its wonderful web, quite as well,[6] the first time it tries as when old and experienced.

To return to our immediate subject: the lower animals, like man, manifestly feel pleasure and pain, happiness and misery. Happiness is never better exhibited than by young animals, such as puppies, kittens, lambs, &c., when playing together, like our own children. Even insects play together, as has been described by that excellent observer, P. Huber,[7] who saw ants chasing and pretending to bite each other, like so many puppies.

[5] 'Contributions to the Theory of Natural Selection,' 1870, p. 212.

[6] For the evidence on this head, see Mr. J. Traherne Moggridge's most interesting work, 'Harvesting Ants and Trap-door Spiders,' 1873, pp. 126, 128.

[7] 'Recherches sur les Moeurs des Fourmis,' 1810, p. 173.

The fact that the lower animals are excited by the same emotions as ourselves is so well established, that it will not be necessary to weary the reader by many details. Terror acts in the same manner on them as on us, causing the muscles to tremble, the heart to palpitate, the sphincters to be relaxed, and the hair to stand on end. Suspicion, the offspring of fear, is eminently characteristic of most wild animals. It is, I think, impossible to read the account given by Sir E. Tennent, of the behaviour of the female elephants, used as decoys, without admitting that they intentionally practise deceit, and well know what they are about. Courage and timidity are extremely variable qualities in the individuals of the same species, as is plainly seen in our dogs. Some dogs and horses are ill-tempered, and easily turn sulky; others are good-tempered; and these qualities are certainly inherited. Every one knows how liable animals are to furious rage, and how plainly they shew it. Many, and probably true, anecdotes have been published on the long-delayed and artful revenge of various animals. The accurate Rengger, and Brehm[8] state that the American and African monkeys which they kept tame, certainly revenged themselves. Sir Andrew Smith, a zoologist whose scrupulous accuracy was known to many persons, told me the following story of which he was himself an eye-witness; at the Cape of Good Hope an officer had often plagued a certain baboon, and the animal, seeing him approaching one Sunday for parade, poured water into a hole and hastily made some thick mud, which he skilfully dashed over the officer as he passed by, to the amusement of many bystanders. For long afterwards the baboon rejoiced and triumphed whenever he saw his victim.

The love of a dog for his master is notorious; as an old writer quaintly says,[9] "A dog is the only thing on this earth that luvs you more than he luvs himself."

[8] All the following statements, given on the authority of these two naturalists, are taken from Rengger's 'Naturgesch. der Säugethiere von Paraguay,' 1830, s. 41-57, and from Brehm's 'Thierleben,' B. i. s. 10-87.

In the agony of death a dog has been known to caress his master, and every one has heard of the dog suffering under vivisection, who licked the hand of the operator; this man, unless the operation was fully justified by an increase of our knowledge, or unless he had a heart of stone, must have felt remorse to the last hour of his life.

As Whewell[10] has well asked, "who that reads the touching instances of maternal affection, related so often of the women of all nations, and of the females of all animals, can doubt that the principle of action is the same in the two cases?" We see maternal affection exhibited in the most trifling details; thus Rengger observed an American monkey (a Cebus) carefully driving away the flies which plagued her infant; and Duvaucel saw a Hylobates washing the faces of her young ones in a stream. So intense is the grief of female monkeys for the loss of their young, that it invariably caused the death of certain kinds kept under confinement by Brehm in N. Africa. Orphan monkeys were always adopted and carefully guarded by the other monkeys, both males and females. One female baboon had so capacious a heart that she not only adopted young monkeys of other species, but stole young dogs and cats, which she continually carried about. Her kindness, however, did not go so far as to share her food with her adopted offspring, at which Brehm was surprised, as his monkeys always divided everything quite fairly with their own young ones. An adopted kitten scratched his affectionate baboon, who certainly had a fine intellect, for she was much astonished at being scratched, and immediately examined the kitten's feet, and without more ado bit off the claws.[11] In the Zoological Gardens, I heard from the keeper that

[9] Quoted by Dr. Lauder Lindsay, in his 'Physiology of Mind in the Lower Animals;' 'Journal of Mental Science,' April 1871, p. 38.

[10] 'Bridgewater Treatise,' p. 263.

[11] A critic, without any grounds ('Quarterly Review,' July, 1871, p. 72), disputes the possibility of this act as described by Brehm, for the sake of discrediting my work. Therefore I tried, and found that I could readily seize with my own teeth the sharp little claws of a kitten nearly five weeks old.

an old baboon (*C. chacma*) had adopted a Rhesus monkey; but when a young drill and mandrill were placed in the cage, she seemed to perceive that these monkeys, though distinct species, were her nearer relatives, for she at once rejected the Rhesus and adopted both of them. The young Rhesus, as I saw, was greatly discontented at being thus rejected, and it would, like a naughty child, annoy and attack the young drill and mandrill whenever it could do so with safety; this conduct exciting great indignation in the old baboon. Monkeys will also, according to Brehm, defend their masters when attacked by any one, as well as dogs to whom they are attached, from the attacks of other dogs. But we here trench on the subjects of sympathy and fidelity, to which I shall recur. Some of Brehm's monkeys took much delight in teasing a certain old dog whom they disliked, as well as other animals, in various ingenious ways.

Most of the more complex emotions are common to the higher animals and ourselves. Every one has seen how jealous a dog is of his master's affection, if lavished on any other creature; and I have observed the same fact with monkeys. This shews that animals not only love, but have desire to be loved. Animals manifestly feel emulation. They love approbation or praise; and a dog carrying a basket for his master exhibits in a high degree self-complacency or pride. There can, I think, be no doubt that a dog feels shame, as distinct from fear, and something very like modesty when begging too often for food. A great dog scorns the snarling of a little dog, and this may be called magnanimity. Several observers have stated that monkeys certainly dislike being laughed at; and they sometimes invent imaginary offences. In the Zoological Gardens I saw a baboon who always got into a furious rage when his keeper took out a letter or book and read it aloud to him; and his rage was so violent that, as I witnessed on one occasion, he bit his own leg till the blood flowed. Dogs shew what may be fairly called a sense of humour, as distinct from mere play; if a bit of stick or other such object be thrown to one, he will often carry it away for a short distance; and then squatting down with it on the ground close before him, will wait until his master comes quite close to take it away. The dog will then seize it and rush away in triumph, repeating the same manœuvre, and evidently enjoying the practical joke.

We will now turn to the more intellectual emotions and faculties, which are very important, as forming the basis for the development of the higher mental powers. Animals manifestly enjoy excitement, and suffer from ennui, as may be seen with dogs, and, according to Rengger, with monkeys. All animals feel *Wonder*, and many exhibit *Curiosity*. They sometimes suffer from this latter quality, as when the hunter plays antics and thus attracts them; I have witnessed this with deer, and so it is with the wary chamois, and with some kinds of wild-ducks. Brehm gives a curious account of the instinctive dread, which his monkeys exhibited, for snakes; but their curiosity was so great that they could not desist from occasionally satiating their horror in a most human fashion, by lifting up the lid of the box in which the snakes were kept. I was so much surprised at this account, that I took a stuffed and coiled-up snake into the monkey-house at the Zoological Gardens, and the excitement thus caused was one of the most curious spectacles which I ever beheld. Three species of Cercopithecus were the most alarmed; they dashed about their cages, and uttered sharp signal cries of danger, which were understood by the other monkeys. A few young monkeys and one old Anubis baboon alone took no notice of the snake. I then placed the stuffed specimen on the ground in one of the larger compartments. After a time all the monkeys collected round it in a large circle, and staring intently, presented a most ludicrous appearance. They became extremely nervous; so that when a wooden ball, with which they were familiar as a plaything, was accidentally moved in the straw, under which it was partly hidden, they all instantly started away. These monkeys behaved very differently when a dead fish, a mouse,[12] a living

[12] I have given a short account of their behaviour on this occasion in my 'Expression of the Emotions,' p. 43.

turtle, and other new objects were placed in their cages; for though at first frightened, they soon approached, handled and examined them. I then placed a live snake in a paper bag, with the mouth loosely closed, in one of the larger compartments. One of the monkeys immediately approached, cautiously opened the bag a little, peeped in, and instantly dashed away. Then I witnessed what Brehm has described, for monkey after monkey, with head raised high and turned on one side, could not resist taking a momentary peep into the upright bag, at the dreadful object lying quietly at the bottom. It would almost appear as if monkeys had some notion of zoological affinities, for those kept by Brehm exhibited a strange, though mistaken, instinctive dread of innocent lizards and frogs. An orang, also, has been known to be much alarmed at the first sight of a turtle.[13]

The principle of *Imitation* is strong in man, and especially, as I have myself observed, with savages. In certain morbid states of the brain this tendency is exaggerated to an extraordinary degree: some hemiplegic patients and others, at the commencement of inflammatory softening of the brain, unconsciously imitate every word which is uttered, whether in their own or in a foreign language, and every gesture or action which is performed near them.[14] Desor[15] has remarked that no animal voluntarily imitates an action performed by man, until in the ascending scale we come to monkeys, which are well known to be ridiculous mockers. Animals, however, sometimes imitate each other's actions: thus two species of wolves, which had been reared by dogs, learned to bark, as does sometimes the jackal,[16] but whether this can be called voluntary imitation is another question. Birds imitate the songs of their parents, and sometimes of other birds; and parrots are notorious imitators of any sound which they often

[13] W. C. L. Martin, 'Nat. Hist. of Mammalia,' 1841, p. 405.

[14] Dr. Bateman 'On Aphasia,' 1870, p. 110.

[15] Quoted by Vogt, 'Mémoire sur les Microcéphales,' 1867, p. 168.

[16] 'The Variation of Animals and Plants under Domestication,' vol. i. p. 27.

hear. Dureau de la Malle gives an account[17] of a dog reared by a cat, who learned to imitate the well-known action of a cat licking her paws, and thus washing her ears and face; this was also witnessed by the celebrated naturalist Audouin. I have received several confirmatory accounts; in one of these, a dog had not been suckled by a cat, but had been brought up with one, together with kittens, and had thus acquired the above habit, which he ever afterwards practised during his life of thirteen years. Dureau de la Malle's dog likewise learnt from the kittens to play with a ball by rolling it about with his fore paws, and springing on it. A correspondent assures me that a cat in his house used to put her paws into jugs of milk having too narrow a mouth for her head. A kitten of this cat soon learned the same trick, and practised it ever afterwards, whenever there was an opportunity.

The parents of many animals, trusting to the principle of imitation in their young, and more especially to their instinctive or inherited tendencies, may be said to educate them. We see this when a cat brings a live mouse to her kittens; and Dureau de la Malle has given a curious account (in the paper above quoted) of his observations on hawks which taught their young dexterity, as well as judgment of distances, by first dropping through the air dead mice and sparrows, which the young generally failed to catch, and then bringing them live birds and letting them loose.

Hardly any faculty is more important for the intellectual progress of man than *Attention*. Animals clearly manifest this power, as when a cat watches by a hole and prepares to spring on its prey. Wild animals sometimes become so absorbed when thus engaged, that they may be easily approached. Mr. Bartlett has given me a curious proof how variable this faculty is in monkeys. A man who trains monkeys to act in plays, used to purchase common kinds from the Zoological Society at the price of five pounds for each; but he offered to give double the price, if he might keep three or four of them for a few days, in order

17 'Annales des Sc. Nat.' (1st Series), tom. xxii. p. 397.

to select one. When asked how he could possibly learn so soon, whether a particular monkey would turn out a good actor, he answered that it all depended on their power of attention. If when he was talking and explaining anything to a monkey, its attention was easily distracted, as by a fly on the wall or other trifling object, the case was hopeless. If he tried by punishment to make an inattentive monkey act, it turned sulky. On the other hand, a monkey which carefully attended to him could always be trained.

It is almost superfluous to state that animals have excellent *Memories* for persons and places. A baboon at the Cape of Good Hope, as I have been informed by Sir Andrew Smith, recognised him with joy after an absence of nine months. I had a dog who was savage and averse to all strangers, and I purposely tried his memory after an absence of five years and two days. I went near the stable where he lived, and shouted to him in my old manner; he shewed no joy, but instantly followed me out walking, and obeyed me, exactly as if I had parted with him only half an hour before. A train of old associations, dormant during five years, had thus been instantaneously awakened in his mind. Even ants, as P. Huber[18] has clearly shewn, recognised their fellow-ants belonging to the same community after a separation of four months. Animals can certainly by some means judge of the intervals of time between recurrent events.

The *Imagination* is one of the highest prerogatives of man. By this faculty he unites former images and ideas, independently of the will, and thus creates brilliant and novel results. A poet, as Jean Paul Richter remarks,[19] "who must reflect whether he shall make a character say yes or no — to the devil with him; he is only a stupid corpse." Dreaming gives us the best notion of this power; as Jean Paul again says, "The dream is an involuntary art of poetry." The value of the products of our imagination

18 'Les Moeurs des Fourmis,' 1810, p. 150.

19 Quoted in Dr. Maudsley's 'Physiology and Pathology of Mind,' 1868, pp. 19, 220.

depends of course on the number, accuracy, and clearness of our impressions, on our judgment and taste in selecting or rejecting the involuntary combinations, and to a certain extent on our power of voluntarily combining them. As dogs, cats, horses, and probably all the higher animals, even birds[20] have vivid dreams, and this is shewn by their movements and the sounds uttered, we must admit that they possess some power of imagination. There must be something special, which causes dogs to howl in the night, and especially during moonlight, in that remarkable and melancholy manner called baying. All dogs do not do so; and, according to Houzeau,[21] they do not then look at the moon, but at some fixed point near the horizon. Houzeau thinks that their imaginations are disturbed by the vague outlines of the surrounding objects, and conjure up before them fantastic images: if this be so, their feelings may almost be called superstitious.

Of all the faculties of the human mind, it will, I presume, be admitted that *Reason* stands at the summit. Only a few persons now dispute that animals possess some power of reasoning. Animals may constantly be seen to pause, deliberate, and resolve. It is a significant fact, that the more the habits of any particular animal are studied by a naturalist, the more he attributes to reason and the less to unlearnt instincts.[22] In future chapters we shall see that some animals extremely low in the scale apparently display a certain amount of reason. No doubt it is often difficult to distinguish between the power of reason and that of instinct. For instance, Dr. Hayes, in his work on 'The Open Polar Sea,' repeatedly remarks that his dogs, instead of continuing to draw the sledges in a compact body, diverged and separated when they came to thin ice, so that their weight might be more evenly distributed. This was often the first warning which the travellers

[20] Dr. Jerdon, 'Birds of India,' vol. i. 1862, p. xxi. Houzeau says that his parakeets and canary-birds dreamt: 'Facultés Mentales,' tom. ii. p. 136.

[21] 'Facultés Mentales des Animaux,' 1872, tom. ii. p. 181.

[22] Mr. L. H. Morgan's work on 'The American Beaver,' 1868, offers a good illustration of this remark. I cannot help thinking, however, that he goes too far in underrating the power of instinct.

received that the ice was becoming thin and dangerous. Now, did the dogs act thus from the experience of each individual, or from the example of the older and wiser dogs, or from an inherited habit, that is from instinct? This instinct, may possibly have arisen since the time, long ago, when dogs were first employed by the natives in drawing their sledges; or the Arctic wolves, the parent-stock of the Esquimaux dog, may have acquired an instinct impelling them not to attack their prey in a close pack, when on thin ice.

We can only judge by the circumstances under which actions are performed, whether they are due to instinct, or to reason, or to the mere association of ideas: this latter principle, however, is intimately connected with reason. A curious case has been given by Prof. Möbius,[23] of a pike, separated by a plate of glass from an adjoining aquarium stocked with fish, and who often dashed himself with such violence against the glass in trying to catch the other fishes, that he was sometimes completely stunned. The pike went on thus for three months, but at last learnt caution, and ceased to do so. The plate of glass was then removed, but the pike would not attack these particular fishes, though he would devour others which were afterwards introduced; so strongly was the idea of a violent shock associated in his feeble mind with the attempt on his former neighbours. If a savage, who had never seen a large plate-glass window, were to dash himself even once against it, he would for a long time afterwards associate a shock with a window-frame; but very differently from the pike, he would probably reflect on the nature of the impediment, and be cautious under analogous circumstances. Now with monkeys, as we shall presently see, a painful or merely a disagreeable impression, from an action once performed, is sometimes sufficient to prevent the animal from repeating it. If we attribute this difference between the monkey and the pike solely to the association of ideas being so much stronger and more persistent in the one than the other, though the pike often re-

[23] 'Die Bewegungen der Thiere,' &c., 1873, p. 11.

ceived much the more severe injury, can we maintain in the case of man that a similar difference implies the possession of a fundamentally different mind?

Houzeau relates[24] that, whilst crossing a wide and arid plain in Texas, his two dogs suffered greatly from thirst, and that between thirty and forty times they rushed down the hollows to search for water. These hollows were not valleys, and there were no trees in them, or any other difference in the vegetation, and as they were absolutely dry there could have been no smell of damp earth. The dogs behaved as if they knew that a dip in the ground offered them the best chance of finding water, and Houzeau has often witnessed the same behaviour in other animals.

I have seen, as I daresay have others, that when a small object is thrown on the ground beyond the reach of one of the elephants in the Zoological Gardens, he blows through his trunk on the ground beyond the object, so that the current reflected on all sides may drive the object within his reach. Again a well-known ethnologist, Mr. Westropp, informs me that he observed in Vienna a bear deliberately making with his paw a current in some water, which was close to the bars of his cage, so as to draw a piece of floating bread within his reach. These actions of the elephant and bear can hardly be attributed to instinct or inherited habit, as they would be of little use to an animal in a state of nature. Now, what is the difference between such actions, when performed by an uncultivated man, and by one of the higher animals?

The savage and the dog have often found water at a low level, and the coincidence under such circumstances has become associated in their minds. A cultivated man would perhaps make some general proposition on the subject; but from all that we know of savages it is extremely doubtful whether they would do so, and a dog certainly would not. But a savage, as well as a dog, would search in the same way, though frequently disap-

[24] 'Facultés Mentales des Animaux,' 1872, tom. ii. p. 265.

pointed; and in both it seems to be equally an act of reason, whether or not any general proposition on the subject is consciously placed before the mind.[25] The same would apply to the elephant and the bear making currents in the air or water. The savage would certainly neither know nor care by what law the desired movements were effected; yet his act would be guided by a rude process of reasoning, as surely as would a philosopher in his longest chain of deductions. There would no doubt be this difference between him and one of the higher animals, that he would take notice of much slighter circumstances and conditions, and would observe any connection between them after much less experience, and this would be of paramount importance. I kept a daily record of the actions of one of my infants, and when he was about eleven months old, and before he could speak a single word, I was continually struck with the greater quickness, with which all sorts of objects and sounds were associated together in his mind, compared with that of the most intelligent dogs I ever knew. But the higher animals differ in exactly the same way in this power of association from those low in the scale, such as the pike, as well as in that of drawing inferences and of observation.

The promptings of reason, after very short experience, are well shewn by the following actions of American monkeys, which stand low in their order. Rengger, a most careful observer, states that when he first gave eggs to his monkeys in Paraguay, they smashed them, and thus lost much of their contents; afterwards they gently hit one end against some hard body, and picked off the bits of shell with their fingers. After cutting themselves only *once* with any sharp tool, they would not touch it again, or would handle it with the greatest caution. Lumps of sugar were often given them wrapped up in paper; and Rengger sometimes put a live wasp in the paper, so that in hastily unfolding it they got

[25] Prof. Huxley has analysed with admirable clearness the mental steps by which a man, as well as a dog, arrives at a conclusion in a case analogous to that given in my text. See his article, 'Mr. Darwin's Critics,' in the 'Contemporary Review,' Nov. 1871, p. 462, and in his 'Critiques and Essays,' 1873, p. 279.

stung; after this had *once* happened, they always first held the packet to their ears to detect any movement within.[26]

The following cases relate to dogs. Mr. Colquhoun[27] winged two wild-ducks, which fell on the further side of a stream; his retriever tried to bring over both at once, but could not succeed; she then, though never before known to ruffle a feather, deliberately killed one, brought over the other, and returned for the dead bird. Col. Hutchinson relates that two partridges were shot at once, one being killed, the other wounded; the latter ran away, and was caught by the retriever, who on her return came across the dead bird; "she stopped, evidently greatly puzzled, and after one or two trials, finding she could not take it up without permitting the escape of the winged bird, she considered a moment, then deliberately murdered it by giving it a severe crunch, and afterwards brought away both together. This was the only known instance of her ever having wilfully injured any game." Here we have reason though not quite perfect, for the retriever might have brought the wounded bird first and then returned for the dead one, as in the case of the two wild-ducks. I give the above cases, as resting on the evidence of two independent witnesses, and because in both instances the retrievers, after deliberation, broke through a habit which is inherited by them (that of not killing the game retrieved), and because they shew how strong their reasoning faculty must have been to overcome a fixed habit.

I will conclude by quoting a remark by the illustrious Humboldt.[28] "The muleteers in S. America say, 'I will not give you the mule whose step is easiest, but *la mas racional,* — the one that reasons best;' " and as he adds, "this popular expression, dictated by long experience, combats the system of animated machines,

[26] Mr. Belt, in his most interesting work, 'The Naturalist in Nicaragua,' 1874 (p. 119), likewise describes various actions of a tamed Cebus, which, I think, clearly shew that this animal possessed some reasoning power.

[27] 'The Moor and the Loch,' p. 45. Col. Hutchinson on 'Dog Breaking,' 1850, p. 46.

[28] 'Personal Narrative,' Eng. translat., vol. iii. p. 106.

better perhaps than all the arguments of speculative philosophy." Nevertheless some writers even yet deny that the higher animals possess a trace of reason; and they endeavour to explain away, by what appears to be mere verbiage,[29] all such facts as those above given.

It has, I think, now been shewn that man and the higher animals, especially the Primates, have some few instincts in common. All have the same senses, intuitions, and sensations,—similar passions, affections, and emotions, even the more complex ones, such as jealousy, suspicion, emulation, gratitude, and magnanimity; they practise deceit and are revengeful; they are sometimes susceptible to ridicule, and even have a sense of humour; they feel wonder and curiosity; they possess the same faculties of imitation, attention, deliberation, choice, memory, imagination, the association of ideas, and reason, though in very different degrees. The individuals of the same species graduate in intellect from absolute imbecility to high excellence. They are also liable to insanity, though far less often than in the case of man.[30] Nevertheless, many authors have insisted that man is divided by an insuperable barrier from all the lower animals in his mental faculties. I formerly made a collection of above a score of such aphorisms, but they are almost worthless, as their wide difference and number prove the difficulty, if not the impossibility, of the attempt. It has been asserted that man alone is capable of progressive improvement; that he alone makes use of tools or fire, domesticates other animals, or possesses property; that no

[29] I am glad to find that so acute a reasoner as Mr. Leslie Stephen ('Darwinism and Divinity, Essays on Free-thinking,' 1873, p. 80), in speaking of the supposed impassable barrier between the minds of man and the lower animals, says, "The distinctions, indeed, which have been drawn, seem to us to rest upon no better foundation than a great many other metaphysical distinctions; that is, the assumption that because you can give two things different names, they must therefore have different natures. It is difficult to understand how anybody who has ever kept a dog, or seen an elephant, can have any doubt as to an animal's power of performing the essential process of reasoning."

[30] See 'Madness in Animals,' by Dr. W. Lauder Lindsay, in 'Journal of Mental Science,' July 1871.

animal has the power of abstraction, or of forming general concepts, is self-conscious and comprehends itself, that no animal employs language; that man alone has a sense of beauty, is liable to caprice, has the feeling of gratitude, mystery, &c.; believes in God, or is endowed with a conscience. I will hazard a few remarks on the more important and interesting of these points.

Archbishop Sumner formerly maintained[31] that man alone is capable of progressive improvement. That he is capable of incomparably greater and more rapid improvement than is any other animal, admits of no dispute; and this is mainly due to his power of speaking and handing down his acquired knowledge. With animals, looking first to the individual, every one who has had any experience in setting traps, knows that young animals can be caught much more easily than old ones; and they can be much more easily approached by an enemy. Even with respect to old animals, it is impossible to catch many in the same place and in the same kind of trap, or to destroy them by the same kind of poison; yet it is improbable that all should have partaken of the poison, and impossible that all should have been caught in a trap. They must learn caution by seeing their brethren caught or poisoned. In North America, where the fur-bearing animals have long been pursued, they exhibit, according to the unanimous testimony of all observers, an almost incredible amount of sagacity, caution and cunning; but trapping has been there so long carried on, that inheritance may possibly have come into play. I have received several accounts that when telegraphs are first set up in any district, many birds kill themselves by flying against the wires, but that in the course of a very few years they learn to avoid this danger, by seeing, as it would appear, their comrades killed.[32]

If we look to successive generations, or to the race, there is no doubt that birds and other animals gradually both acquire

[31] Quoted by Sir C. Lyell, 'Antiquity of Man,' p. 497.

[32] For additional evidence, with detaails, see M. Houzeau, 'Les Facultés Mentales,' tom. ii. 1872, p. 147.

and lose caution in relation to man or other enemies;[33] and this caution is certainly in chief part an inherited habit or instinct, but in part the result of individual experience. A good observer, Leroy,[34] states, that in districts where foxes are much hunted, the young, on first leaving their burrows, are incontestably much more wary than the old ones in districts where they are not much disturbed.

Our domestic dogs are descended from wolves and jackals,[35] and though they may not have gained in cunning, and may have lost in wariness and suspicion, yet they have progressed in certain moral qualities, such as in affection, trust-worthiness, temper, and probably in general intelligence. The common rat has conquered and beaten several other species throughout Europe, in parts of North America, New Zealand, and recently in Formosa, as well as on the mainland of China. Mr. Swinhoe,[36] who describes these two latter cases, attributes the victory of the common rat over the large *Mus coninga* to its superior cunning; and this latter quality may probably be attributed to the habitual exercise of all its faculties in avoiding extirpation by man, as well as to nearly all the less cunning or weak-minded rats having been continuously destroyed by him. It is, however, possible that the success of the common rat may be due to its having possessed greater cunning than its fellow-species, before it became associated with man. To maintain, independently of any direct evidence, that no animal during the course of ages has progressed in intellect or other mental faculties, is to beg the question of the evolution of species. We have seen that, according to Lartet, existing mammals belonging to several orders have larger brains than their ancient tertiary prototypes.

[33] See, with respect to birds on oceanic islands, my 'Journal of Researches during the voyage of the "Beagle," ' 1845, p. 398.

[34] 'Lettres Phil. sur l'Intelligence des Animaux,' nouvelle édit. 1802, p. 86.

[35] See the evidence on this head in chap. i. vol. i. 'On the Variation of Animals and Plants under Domestication.'

[36] 'Proc. Zoolog. Soc.' 1864, p. 186.

It has often been said that no animal uses any tool; but the chimpanzee in a state of nature cracks a native fruit, somewhat like a walnut, with a stone.[37] Rengger[38] easily taught an American monkey thus to break open hard palm-nuts; and afterwards of its own accord, it used stones to open other kinds of nuts, as well as boxes. It thus also removed the soft rind of fruit that had a disagreeable flavour. Another monkey was taught to open the lid of a large box with a stick, and afterwards it used the stick as a lever to move heavy bodies; and I have myself seen a young orang put a stick into a crevice, slip his hand to the other end, and use it in the proper manner as a lever. The tamed elephants in India are well known to break off branches of trees and use them to drive away the flies; and this same act has been observed in an elephant in a state of nature.[39] I have seen a young orang, when she thought she was going to be whipped, cover and protect herself with a blanket or straw. In these several cases stones and sticks were employed as implements; but they are likewise used as weapons. Brehm[40] states, on the authority of the well-known traveller Schimper, that in Abyssinia when the baboons belonging to one species (*C. gelada*) descend in troops from the mountains to plunder the fields, they sometimes encounter troops of another species (*C. hamadryas*), and then a fight ensues. The Geladas roll down great stones, which the Hamadryas try to avoid, and then both species, making a great uproar, rush furiously against each other. Brehm, when, accompanying the Duke of Coburg-Gotha, aided in an attack with firearms on a troop of baboons in the pass of Mensa in Abyssinia. The baboons in return rolled so many stones down the mountain, some as large as a man's head, that the attackers had to beat a hasty retreat; and the pass was actually closed for a time against the caravan. It deserves notice that these baboons thus acted in concert. Mr.

[37] Savage and Wyman in 'Boston Journal of Nat. Hist.' vol. iv. 1843-44, p. 383.

[38] 'Saugethiere von Paraguay,' 1830, s. 51-56.

[39] The 'Indian Field,' March 4, 1871.

[40] 'Thierleben,' B. i. s. 79, 82.

Wallace[41] on three occasions saw female orangs, accompanied by their young, "breaking off branches and the great spiny fruit of the Durian tree, with every appearance of rage; causing such a shower of missiles as effectually kept us from approaching too near the tree." As I have repeatedly seen, a chimpanzee will throw any object at hand at a person who offends him; and the before-mentioned baboon at the Cape of Good Hope prepared mud for the purpose.

In the Zoological Gardens, a monkey, which had weak teeth, used to break open nuts with a stone; and I was assured by the keepers that after using the stone, he hid it in the straw, and would not let any other monkey touch it. Here, then, we have the idea of property; but this idea is common to every dog with a bone, and to most or all birds with their nests.

The Duke of Argyll[42] remarks, that the fashioning of an implement for a special purpose is absolutely peculiar to man; and he considers that this forms an immeasurable gulf between him and the brutes. This is no doubt a very important distinction; but there appears to me much truth in Sir J. Lubbock's suggestion,[43] that when primeval man first used flint-stones for any purpose, he would have accidentally splintered them, and would then have used the sharp fragments. From this step it would be a small one to break the flints on purpose, and not a very wide step to fashion them rudely. This latter advance, however, may have taken long ages, if we may judge by the immense interval of time which elapsed before the men of the neolithic period took to grinding and polishing their stone tools. In breaking the flints, as Sir J. Lubbock likewise remarks, sparks would have been emitted, and in grinding them heat would have been evolved: thus the two usual methods of "obtaining fire may have originated." The nature of fire would have been known in the many volcanic regions where lava occasionally flows through

41 'The Malay Archipelago,' vol. i. 1869, p. 87.

42 'Primeval Man,' 1869, pp. 145, 147.

43 'Prehistoric Times,' 1865, p. 473, &c.

forests. The anthropomorphous apes, guided probably by instinct, build for themselves temporary platforms; but as many instincts are largely controlled by reason, the simpler ones, such as this of building a platform, might readily pass into a voluntary and conscious act. The orang is known to cover itself at night with the leaves of the Pandanus; and Brehm states that one of his baboons used to protect itself from the heat of the sun by throwing a straw-mat over its head. In these several habits, we probably see the first steps towards some of the simpler arts, such as rude architecture and dress, as they arose amongst the early progenitors of man.

*Abstraction, General Conceptions, Self-consciousness, Mental Individuality.* — It would be very difficult for any one with even much more knowledge than I possess, to determine how far animals exhibit any traces of these high mental powers. This difficulty arises from the impossibility of judging what passes through the mind of an animal; and again, the fact that writers differ to a great extent in the meaning which they attribute to the above terms, causes a further difficulty. If one may judge from various articles which have been published lately, the greatest stress seems to be laid on the supposed entire absence in animals of the power of abstraction, or of forming general concepts. But when a dog sees another dog at a distance, it is often clear that he perceives that it is a dog in the abstract; for when he gets nearer his whole manner suddenly changes, if the other dog be a friend. A recent writer remarks, that in all such cases it is a pure assumption to assert that the mental act is not essentially of the same nature in the animal as in man. If either refers what he perceives with his senses to a mental concept, then so do both.[44] When I say to my terrier, in an eager voice (and I have made the trial many times), "Hi, hi, where is it?" she at once takes it as a sign that something is to be hunted, and generally first looks quickly all around, and then rushes into the

[44] Mr. Hookham, in a letter to Prof. Max Müller, in the 'Birmingham News,' May 1873.

nearest thicket, to scent for any game, but finding nothing, she looks up into any neighbouring tree for a squirrel. Now do not these actions clearly shew that she had in her mind a general idea or concept that some animal is to be discovered and hunted?

It may be freely admitted that no animal is self-conscious, if by this term it is implied, that he reflects on such points, as whence he comes or whither he will go, or what is life and death, and so forth. But how can we feel sure that an old dog with an excellent memory and some power of imagination, as shewn by his dreams, never reflects on his past pleasures or pains in the chase? And this would be a form of self-consciousness. On the other hand, as Büchner[45] has remarked, how little can the hard-worked wife of a degraded Australian savage, who uses very few abstract words, and cannot count above four, exert her self-consciousness, or reflect on the nature of her own existence. It is generally admitted, that the higher animals possess memory, attention, association, and even some imagination and reason. If these powers, which differ much in different animals, are capable of improvement, there seems no great improbability in more complex faculties, such as the higher forms of abstraction, and self-consciousness, &c., having been evolved through the development and combination of the simpler ones. It has been urged against the views here maintained that it is impossible to say at what point in the ascending scale animals have become capable of abstraction, &c.; but who can say at what age this occurs in our young children? We see at least that such powers are developed in children by imperceptible degrees.

That animals retain their mental individuality is unquestionable. When my voice awakened a train of old associations in the mind of the before-mentioned dog, he must have retained his mental individuality, although every atom of his brain had probably undergone change more than once during the interval of five years. This dog might have brought forward the argument

[45] 'Conférences sur la Théorie Darwinienne,' French translat. 1869, p. 132.

lately advanced to crush all evolutionists, and said, "I abide amid all mental moods and all material changes. . . . The teaching that atoms leave their impressions as legacies to other atoms falling into the places they have vacated is contradictory of the utterance of consciousness, and is therefore false; but it is the teaching necessitated by evolutionism, consequently the hypothesis is a false one."[46]

*Language.*—This faculty has justly been considered as one of the chief distinctions between man and the lower animals. But man, as a highly competent judge, Archbishop Whately remarks, "is not the only animal that can make use of language to express what is passing in his mind, and can understand, more or less, what is so expressed by another."[47] In Paraguay the *Cebus azaræ* when excited utters at least six distinct sounds, which excite in other monkeys similar emotions.[48] The movements of the features and gestures of monkeys are understood by us, and they partly understand ours, as Rengger and others declare. It is a more remarkable fact that the dog, since being domesticated, has learnt to bark[49] in at least four or five distinct tones. Although barking is a new art, no doubt the wild parent-species of the dog expressed their feelings by cries of various kinds. With the domesticated dog we have the bark of eagerness, as in the chase; that of anger, as well as growling; the yelp or howl of despair, as when shut up; the baying at night; the bark of joy, as when starting on a walk with his master; and the very distinct one of demand or supplication, as when wishing for a door or window to be opened. According to Houzeau, who paid particular attention to the subject, the domestic fowl utters at least a dozen significant sounds.[50]

The habitual use of articulate language is, however, peculiar

[46] The Rev. Dr. J. M'Cann, 'Anti-Darwinism,' 1869, p. 13.
[47] Quoted in 'Anthropological Revue,' 1864, p. 158.
[48] Rengger, ibid. s. 45.
[49] See my 'Variation of Animals and Plans under Domestication,' vol. i. p. 27.
[50] 'Facultés Mentales des Animaux,' tom. ii. 1872, p. 346-349.

to man; but he uses, in common with the lower animals, inarticulate cries to express his meaning, aided by gestures and the movements of the muscles of the face.[51] This especially holds good with the more simple and vivid feelings, which are but little connected with our higher intelligence. Our cries of pain, fear, surprise, anger, together with their appropriate actions, and the murmur of a mother to her beloved child are more expressive than any words. That which distinguishes man from the lower animals is not the understanding of articulate sounds, for, as every one knows, dogs understand many words and sentences. In this respect they are at the same stage of development as infants, between the ages of ten and twelve months, who understand many words and short sentences, but cannot yet utter a single word. It is not the mere articulation which is our distinguishing character, for parrots and other birds possess this power. Nor is it the mere capacity of connecting definite sounds with definite ideas; for it is certain that some parrots, which have been taught to speak, connect unerringly words with things, and persons with events.[52] The lower animals differ from man solely in his almost infinitely larger power of associating together the most diversified sounds and ideas; and this obviously depends on the high development of his mental powers.

[51] See a discussion on this subject in Mr. E. B. Tylor's very interesting work, 'Researches into the Early History of Mankind,' 1865, chaps. ii. to iv.

[52] I have received several detailed accounts to this effect. Admiral Sir B. J. Sullivan, whom I know to be a careful observer, assures me that an African parrot, long kept in his father's house, invariably called certain persons of the household, as well as visitors, by their names. He said "good morning" to every one at breakfast, and "good night" to each as they left the room at night, and never reversed these salutations. To Sir B. J. Sullivan's father, he used to add to the "good morning" a short sentence, which was never once repeated after his father's death. He scolded violently a strange dog which came into the room through the open window; and he scolded another parrot (saying "you naughty polly") which had got out of its cage, and was eating apples on the kitchen table. See also, to the same effect, Houzeau on parrots, 'Facultés Mentales,' tom. ii. p. 309. Dr. A. Moschkau informs me that he knew a starling which never made a mistake in saying in German "good morning" to persons arriving, and "good bye, old fellow," to those departing. I could add several other such cases.

As Horne Tooke, one of the founders of the noble science of philology, observes, language is an art, like brewing or baking; but writing would have been a better simile. It certainly is not a true instinct, for every language has to be learnt. It differs, however, widely from all ordinary arts, for man has an instinctive tendency to speak, as we see in the babble of our young children; whilst no child has an instinctive tendency to brew, bake, or write. Moreover, no philologist now supposes that any language has been deliberately invented; it has been slowly and unconsciously developed by many steps.[53] The sounds uttered by birds offer in several respects the nearest analogy to language, for all the members of the same species utter the same instinctive cries expressive of their emotions; and all the kinds which sing, exert their power instinctively; but the actual song, and even the call-notes, are learnt from their parents or foster-parents. These sounds, as Daines Barrington[54] has proved, "are no more innate than language is in man." The first attempts to sing "may be compared to the imperfect endeavour in a child to babble." The young males continue practising, or as the bird-catchers say, "recording," for ten or eleven months. Their first essays show hardly a rudiment of the future song; but as they grow older we can perceive what they are aiming at; and at last they are said "to sing their song round." Nestlings which have learnt the song of a distinct species, as with the canary-birds educated in the Tyrol, teach and transmit their new song to their offspring. The slight natural differences of song in the same species inhabiting different districts may be appositely compared, as Barrington remarks, "to provincial dialects;" and the songs of allied, though

[53] See some good remarks on this head by Prof. Whitney, in his 'Oriental and Linguistic Studies,' 1873, p. 354. He observes that the desire of communication between man is the living force, which, in the development of language, "works both consciously and unconsciously; consciously as regards the immediate end to be attained; unconsciously as regards the further consequences of the act."

[54] Hon. Daines Barrington in 'Philosoph. Transactions,' 1773, p. 262. See also Dureau de la Malle, in 'Ann. des Sc. Nat.' 3rd series, Zoolog. tom. x. p. 119.

distinct species may be compared with the languages of distinct races of man. I have given the foregoing details to shew that an instinctive tendency to acquire an art is not peculiar to man.

With respect to the origin of articulate language, after having read on the one side the highly interesting works of Mr. Hensleigh Wedgwood, the Rev. F. Farrar, and Prof. Schleicher,[55] and the celebrated lectures of Prof. Max Müller on the other side, I cannot doubt that language owes its origin to the imitation and modification of various natural sounds, the voices of other animals, and man's own instinctive cries, aided by signs and gestures. When we treat of sexual selection we shall see that primeval man, or rather some early progenitor of man, probably first used his voice in producing true musical cadences, that is in singing, as do some of the gibbon-apes at the present day; and we may conclude from a widely-spread analogy, that this power would have been especially exerted during the courtship of the sexes,—would have expressed various emotions, such as love, jealousy, triumph,—and would have served as a challenge to rivals. It is, therefore, probable that the imitation of musical cries by articulate sounds may have given rise to words expressive of various complex emotions. The strong tendency in our nearest allies, the monkeys, in microcephalous idiots,[56] and in the barbarous races of mankind, to imitate whatever they hear deserves notice, as bearing on the subject of imitation. Since monkeys certainly understand much that is said to them by man, and when wild, utter signal-cries of danger to their fellows;[57] and since fowls give distinct warnings for danger on the ground, or in the sky

[55] 'On the Origin of Language,' by H. Wedgwood, 1866. 'Chapters on Language,' by the Rev. F. W. Farrar, 1865. These works are most interesting. See also 'De la Phys. et de Parole,' par Albert Lemoine, 1865, p. 190. The work on this subject, by the late Prof. Aug. Schleicher, has been translated by Dr. Bikkers into English, under the title of 'Darwinism tested by the Science of Language,' 1869.

[56] Vogt, 'Mémoire sur les Microcéphales,' 1867, p. 169. With respect to savages, I have given some facts in my 'Journal of Researches,' &c., 1845, p. 206.

[57] See clear evidence on this head in the two works so often quoted, by Brehm and Rengger.

from hawks (both, as well as a third cry, intelligible to dogs),[58] may not some unusually wise ape-like animal have imitated the growl of a beast of prey, and thus told his fellow-monkeys the nature of the expected danger? This would have been a first step in the formation of a language.

As the voice was used more and more, the vocal organs would have been strengthened and perfected through the principle of the inherited effects of use; and this would have reacted on the power of speech. But the relation between the continued use of language and the development of the brain, has no doubt been far more important. The mental powers in some early progenitor of man must have been more highly developed than in any existing ape, before even the most imperfect form of speech could have come into use; but we may confidently believe that the continued use and advancement of this power would have reacted on the mind itself, by enabling and encouraging it to carry on long trains of thought. A complex train of thought can no more be carried on without the aid of words, whether spoken or silent, than a long calculation without the use of figures or algebra. It appears, also, that even an ordinary train of thought almost requires, or is greatly facilitated by some form of language, for the dumb, deaf, and blind girl, Laura Bridgman, was observed to use her fingers whilst dreaming.[59] Nevertheless, a long succession of vivid and connected ideas may pass through the mind without the aid of any form of language, as we may infer from the movements of dogs during their dreams. We have, also, seen that animals are able to reason to a certain extent, manifestly without the aid of language. The intimate connection between the brain, as it is now developed in us, and the faculty of speech, is well shewn by those curious cases of brain-disease in which speech is specially affected, as when the power to remember substantives is lost, whilst other words can be correctly

58 Houzeau gives a very curious account of his observations on this subject in his 'Facultés Mentales des Animaux,' tom. ii. p. 348.

59 See remarks on this head by Dr. Maudsley, 'The Physiology and Pathology of Mind,' 2nd edit. 1868, p. 199.

used, or where substantives of a certain class, or all except the initial letters of substantives and proper names are forgotten.[60] There is no more improbability in the continued use of the mental and vocal organs leading to inherited changes in their structure and functions, than in the case of hand-writing, which depends partly on the form of the hand and partly on the disposition of the mind; and handwriting is certainly inherited.[61]

Several writers, more especially Prof. Max Müller,[62] have lately insisted that the use of language implies the power of forming general concepts; and that as no animals are supposed to possess this power, an impassable barrier is formed between them and man.[63] With respect to animals, I have already endeavoured to shew that they have this power, at least in a rude and incipient degree. As far as concerns infants of from ten to eleven months old, and deaf-mutes, it seems to me incredible, that they should be able to connect certain sounds with certain general ideas as quickly as they do, unless such ideas were already formed in their minds. The same remark may be extended to the more in-

[60] Many curious cases have been recorded. See, for instance, Dr. Bateman 'On Aphasia,' 1870, p. 27, 31, 53, 100, &c. Also, 'Inquiries Concerning the Intellectual Powers,' by Dr. Abercrombie, 1838, p. 150.

[61] 'The Variation of Animals and Plants under Domestication,' vol. ii. p. 6.

[62] Lectures on 'Mr. Darwin's Philosophy of Languages,' 1873.

[63] The judgment of a distinguished philologist, such as Prof. Whitney, will have far more weight on this point than anything that I can say. He remarks ('Oriental and Linguistic Studies,' 1873, p. 297), in speaking of Bleek's views: "Because on the grand scale language is the necessary auxiliary of thought, indispensable to the development of the power of thinking, to the distinctness and variety and complexity of cognitions to the full mastery of consciousness; therefore he would fain make thought absolutely impossible without speech, identifying the faculty with its instrument. He might just as reasonably assert that the human hand cannot act without a tool. With such a doctrine to start from, he cannot stop short of Müller's worst paradoxes, that an infant (*in fans,* not speaking) is not a human being, and that deaf-mutes do not become possessed of reason until they learn to twist their fingers into imitation of spoken words." Max Müller gives in italics ('Lectures on Mr. Darwin's Philosophy of Language,' 1873, third lecture) the following aphorism: "There is no thought without words, as little as there are words without thought." What a strange definition must here be given to the word thought!

telligent animals; as Mr. Leslie Stephen observes,[64] "A dog frames a general concept of cats or sheep, and knows the corresponding words as well as a philosopher. And the capacity to understand is as good a proof of vocal intelligence, though in an inferior degree, as the capacity to speak."

Why the organs now used for speech should have been originally perfected for this purpose, rather than any other organs, it is not difficult to see. Ants have considerable powers of intercommunication by means of their antennæ, as shewn by Huber, who devotes a whole chapter to their language. We might have used our fingers as efficient instruments, for a person with practice can report to a deaf man every word of a speech rapidly delivered at a public meeting; but the loss of our hands, whilst thus employed, would have been a serious inconvenience. As all the higher mammals possess vocal organs, constructed on the same general plan as ours, and used as a means of communication, it was obviously probable that these same organs would be still further developed if the power of communication had to be improved; and this has been effected by the aid of adjoining and well adapted parts, namely the tongue and lips.[65] The fact of the higher apes not using their vocal organs for speech, no doubt depends on their intelligence not having been sufficiently advanced. The possession by them of organs, which with long-continued practice might have been used for speech, although not thus used, is paralleled by the case of many birds which possess organs fitted for singing, though they never sing. Thus, the nightingale and crow have vocal organs similarly constructed, these being used by the former for diversified song, and by the latter only for croaking.[66] If it be asked why apes have

[64] 'Essays on Free-thinking,' &c., 1873, p. 82.

[65] See some good remarks to this effect by Dr. Maudsley, 'The Physiology and Pathology of Mind,' 1868, p. 199.

[66] Macgillivray, 'Hist. of British Birds,' vol. ii. 1839, p. 29. An excellent observer, Mr. Blackwall, remarks that the magpie learns to pronounce single words, and even short sentences, more readily than almost any other British bird; yet, as he adds, after long and closely investigating its habits, he has never known it, in a state of nature, to display any unusual capacity for imitation. 'Researches in Zoology,' 1834, p. 158.

not had their intellects developed to the same degree as that of man, general causes only can be assigned in answer, and it is unreasonable to expect any thing more definite, considering our ignorance with respect to the successive stages of development through which each creature has passed.

The formation of different languages and of distinct species, and the proofs that both have been developed through a gradual process, are curiously parallel.[67] But we can trace the formation of many words further back than that of species, for we can perceive how they actually arose from the imitation of various sounds. We find in distinct languages striking homologies due to community of descent, and analogies due to a similar process of formation. The manner in which certain letters or sounds change when others change is very like correlated growth. We have in both cases the reduplication of parts, the effects of long-continued use, and so forth. The frequent presence of rudiments, both in languages and in species, is still more remarkable. The letter *m* in the word *am*, means *I;* so that in the expression *I am*, a superfluous and useless rudiment has been retained. In the spelling also of words, letters often remain as the rudiments of ancient forms of pronunciation. Languages, like organic beings, can be classed in groups under groups; and they can be classed either naturally according to descent, or artificially by other characters. Dominant languages and dialects spread widely, and lead to the gradual extinction of other tongues. A language, like a species, when once extinct, never, as Sir C. Lyell remarks, reappears. The same language never has two birth-places. Distinct languages may be crossed or blended together.[68] We see variability in every tongue, and new words are continually cropping up; but as there is a limit to the powers of the memory, single words, like whole

[67] See the very interesting parallelism between the development of species and languages, given by Sir C. Lyell in 'The Geolog. Evidences of the Antiquity of Man,' 1863, chap. xxiii.

[68] See remarks to this effect by the Rev. F. W. Farrar, in an interesting article, entitled 'Philology and Darwinism,' in 'Nature,' March 24th, 1870, p. 528.

languages, gradually became extinct. As Max Müller[69] has well remarked: — "A struggle for life is constantly going on amongst the words and grammatical forms in each language. The better, the shorter, the easier forms are constantly gaining the upper hand, and they owe their success to their own inherent virtue." To these more important causes of the survival of certain words, mere novelty and fashion may be added; for there is in the mind of man a strong love for slight changes in all things. The survival or preservation of certain favoured words in the struggle for existence is natural selection.

The perfectly regular and wonderfully complex construction of the languages of many barbarous nations has often been advanced as a proof, either of the divine origin of these languages, or of the high art and former civilisation of their founders. Thus F. von Schlegel writes: "In those languages which appear to be at the lowest grade of intellectual culture, we frequently observe a very high and elaborate degree of art in their grammatical structure. This is especially the case with the Basque and the Lapponian, and many of the American languages."[70] But it is assuredly an error to speak of any language as an art, in the sense of its having been elaborately and methodically formed. Philologists now admit that conjugations, declensions, &c., originally existed as distinct words, since joined together; and as such words express the most obvious relations between objects and persons, it is not surprising that they should have been used by the men of most races during the earliest ages. With respect to perfection, the following illustration will best shew how easily we may err: a Crinoid sometimes consists of no less than 150,000 pieces of shell.[71] all arranged with perfect symmetry in radiating lines; but a naturalist does not consider an animal of this kind as more perfect than a bilateral one with comparatively few parts, and with none of these parts alike, excepting on the opposite sides of

69 'Nature,' January 6th, 1870, p. 257.

70 Quoted by C. S. Wake, 'Chapters on Man,' 1868, p. 101.

71 Buckland, 'Bridgewater Treatise,' p. 411.

the body. He justly considers the differentiation and specialisation of organs as the test of perfection. So with languages: the most symmetrical and complex ought not to be ranked above irregular, abbreviated, and bastardised languages, which have borrowed expressive words and useful forms of construction from various conquering, conquered, or immigrant races.

From these few and imperfect remarks I conclude that the extremely complex and regular construction of many barbarous languages, is no proof that they owe their origin to a special act of creation.[72] Nor, as we have seen, does the faculty of articulate speech in itself offer any insuperable objection to the belief that man has been developed from some lower form.

*Sense of Beauty.* — This sense has been declared to be peculiar to man. I refer here only to the pleasure given by certain colours, forms, and sounds, and which may fairly be called a sense of the beautiful; with cultivated men such sensations are, however, intimately associated with complex ideas and trains of thought. When we behold a male bird elaborately displaying his graceful plumes or splendid colours before the female, whilst other birds, not thus decorated, make no such display, it is impossible to doubt that she admires the beauty of her male partner. As women everywhere deck themselves with these plumes, the beauty of such ornaments cannot be disputed. As we shall see later, the nests of humming-birds, and the playing passages of bower-birds are tastefully ornamented with gaily-coloured objects; and this shews that they must receive some kind of pleasure from the sight of such things. With the great majority of animals, however, the taste for the beautiful is confined, as far as we can judge, to the attractions of the opposite sex. The sweet strains poured forth by many male birds during the season of love, are certainly admired by the females, of which fact evidence will hereafter be given. If female birds had been incapable of appreciating the beautiful colours, the ornaments,

[72] See some good remarks on the simplification of languages, by Sir J. Lubbock, 'Origin of Civilisation,' 1870, p. 278.

and voices of their male partners, all the labour and anxiety exhibited by the latter in displaying their charms before the females would have been thrown away; and this it is impossible to admit. Why certain bright colours should excite pleasure cannot, I presume, be explained, any more than why certain flavours and scents are agreeable; but habit has something to do with the result, for that which is at first unpleasant to our senses, ultimately becomes pleasant, and habits are inherited. With respect to sounds, Helmholtz has explained to a certain extent on physiological principles, why harmonies and certain cadences are agreeable. But besides this, sounds frequently recurring at irregular intervals are highly disagreeable, as every one will admit who has listened at night to the irregular flapping of a rope on board ship. The same principle seems to come into play with vision, as the eye prefers symmetry or figures with some regular recurrence. Patterns of this kind are employed by even the lowest savages as ornaments; and they have been developed through sexual selection for the adornment of some male animals. Whether we can or not give any reason for the pleasure thus derived from vision and hearing, yet man and many of the lower animals are alike pleased by the same colours, graceful shading and forms, and the same sounds.

The taste for the beautiful, at least as far as female beauty is concerned, is not of a special nature in the human mind; for it differs widely in the different races of man, and is not quite the same even in the different nations of the same race. Judging from the hideous ornaments, and the equally hideous music admired by most savages, it might be urged that their æsthetic faculty was not so highly developed as in certain animals, for instance, as in birds. Obviously no animal would be capable of admiring such scenes as the heavens at night, a beautiful landscape, or refined music; but such high tastes are acquired through culture, and depend on complex associations; they are not enjoyed by barbarians or by uneducated persons.

Many of the faculties, which have been of inestimable service to man for his progressive advancement, such as the powers of the imagination, wonder, curiosity, an undefined sense of beauty, a tendency to imitation, and the love of excitement or novelty, could hardly fail to lead to capricious changes of customs and fashions. I have alluded to this point, because a recent writer[73] has oddly fixed on Caprice "as one of the most remarkable and typical differences between savages and brutes." But not only can we partially understand how it is that man is from various conflicting influences rendered capricious, but that the lower animals are, as we shall hereafter see, likewise capricious in their affections, aversions, and sense of beauty. There is also reason to suspect that they love novelty, for its own sake.

*Belief in God — Religion.* — There is no evidence that man was aboriginally endowed with the ennobling belief in the existence of an Omnipotent God. On the contrary there is ample evidence, derived not from hasty travellers, but from men who have long resided with savages, that numerous races have existed, and still exist, who have no idea of one or more gods, and who have no words in their languages to express such an idea.[74] The question is of course wholly distinct from that higher one, whether there exists a Creator and Ruler of the universe; and this has been answered in the affirmative by some of the highest intellects that have ever existed.

If, however, we include under the term "religion" the belief in unseen or spiritual agencies, the case is wholly different; for this belief seems to be universal with the less civilised races. Nor is it difficult to comprehend how it arose. As soon as the important faculties of the imagination, wonder, and curiosity, together with some power of reasoning, had become partially developed, man would naturally crave to understand what was

[73] 'The Spectator,' Dec. 4th, 1869, p. 1430.

[74] See an excellent article on this subject by the Rev. F. W. Farrar, in the 'Anthropological Review,' Aug. 1864, p. ccxvii. For further facts see Sir J. Lubbock, 'Prehistoric Times,' 2nd edit. 1869, p. 564; and especially the chapters on Religion in his 'Origin of Civilisation,' 1870.

passing around him, and would have vaguely speculated on his own existence. As Mr. M'Lennan[75] has remarked, "Some explanation of the phenomena of life, a man must feign for himself, and to judge from the universality of it, the simplest hypothesis, and the first to occur to men, seems to have been that natural phenomena are ascribable to the presence in animals, plants, and things, and in the forces of nature, of such spirits prompting to action as men are conscious they themselves possess." It is also probable, as Mr. Tylor has shewn, that dreams may have first given rise to the notion of spirits; for savages do not readily distinguish between subjective and objective impressions. When a savage dreams, the figures which appear before him are believed to have come from a distance, and to stand over him; or "the soul of the dreamer goes out on its travels, and comes home with a remembrance of what it has seen."[76] But until the faculties of imagination, curiosity, reason, &c., had been fairly well developed in the mind of man, his dreams would not have led him to believe in spirits, any more than in the case of a dog.

The tendency in savages to imagine that natural objects and agencies are animated by spiritual or living essences, is perhaps illustrated by a little fact which I once noticed: my dog, a full-

[75] 'The Worship of Animals and Plants,' in the 'Fortnightly Review,' Oct. 1, 1869, p. 422.

[76] Tylor, 'Early History of Mankind,' 1865, p. 6. See also the three striking chapters on the Development of Religion, in Lubbock's 'Origin of Civilisation,' 1870. In a like manner Mr. Herbert Spencer, in his ingenious essay in the 'Fortnightly Review' (May 1st, 1870, p. 535), accounts for the earliest forms of religious belief throughout the world, by man being led through dreams, shadows, and other causes, to look at himself as a double essence, corporeal and spiritual. As the spiritual being is supposed to exist after death and to be powerful, it is propitiated by various gifts and ceremonies, and its aid invoked. He then further shews that names or nicknames given from some animal or other object, to the early progenitors or founders of a tribe, are supposed after a long interval to represent the real progenitor of the tribe; and such animal or object is then naturally believed still to exist as a spirit, is held sacred, and worshipped as a god. Nevertheless I cannot but suspect that there is a still earlier and ruder stage, when anything which manifests power or movement is thought to be endowed with some form of life, and with mental faculties analogous to our own.

grown and very sensible animal, was lying on the lawn during a hot and still day; but at a little distance a slight breeze occasionally moved an open parasol, which would have been wholly disregarded by the dog, had any one stood near it. As it was, every time that the parasol slightly moved, the dog growled fiercely and barked. He must, I think, have reasoned to himself in a rapid and unconscious manner, that movement without any apparent cause indicated the presence of some strange living agent, and that no stranger had a right to be on his territory.

The belief in spiritual agencies would easily pass into the belief in the existence of one or more gods. For savages would naturally attribute to spirits the same passions, the same love of vengeance or simplest form of justice, and the same affections which they themselves feel. The Fuegians appear to be in this respect in an intermediate condition, for when the surgeon on board the "Beagle" shot some young ducklings as specimens, York Minster declared in the most solemn manner, "Oh, Mr. Bynoe, much rain, much snow, blow much;" and this was evidently a retributive punishment for wasting human food. So again he related how, when his brother killed a "wild man," storms long raged, much rain and snow fell. Yet we could never discover that the Fuegians believed in what we should call a God, or practised any religious rites; and Jemmy Button, with justifiable pride, stoutly maintained that there was no devil in his land. This latter assertion is the more remarkable, as with savages the belief in bad spirits is far more common than that in good ones.

The feeling of religious devotion is a highly complex one, consisting of love, complete submission to an exalted and mysterious superior, a strong sense of dependence,[77] fear, reverence, gratitude, hope for the future, and perhaps other elements. No being could experience so complex an emotion until advanced in his intellectual and moral faculties to at least a moderately high level. Nevertheless, we see some distant approach to this state of

[77] See an able article on the 'Physical Elements of Religion,' by Mr. L. Owen Pike, in 'Anthropolog. Review,' April, 1870, p. lxiii.

mind in the deep love of a dog for his master, associated with complete submission, some fear, and perhaps other feelings. The behaviour of a dog when returning to his master after an absence, and, as I may add, of a monkey to his beloved keeper, is widely different from that towards their fellows. In the latter case the transports of joy appear to be somewhat less, and the sense of equality is shewn in every action. Professor Braubach goes so far as to maintain that a dog looks on his master as on a god.[78]

The same high mental faculties which first led man to believe in unseen spiritual agencies, then in fetishism, polytheism, and ultimately in monotheism, would infallibly lead him, as long as his reasoning powers remained poorly developed, to various strange superstitions and customs. Many of these are terrible to think of — such as the sacrifice of human beings to a blood-loving god; the trial of innocent persons by the ordeal of poison or fire; witchcraft, &c. — yet it is well occasionally to reflect on these superstitions, for they shew us what an infinite debt of gratitude we owe to the improvement of our reason, to science, and to our accumulated knowledge. As Sir J. Lubbock[79] has well observed, "it is not too much to say that the horrible dread of unknown evil hangs like a thick cloud over savage life, and embitters every pleasure." These miserable and indirect consequences of our highest faculties may be compared with the incidental and occasional mistakes of the instincts of the lower animals.

[78] 'Religion, Moral, &c., der Darwin'schen Art-Lehre,' 1869, s. 53. It is said (Dr. W. Lauder Lindsay, 'Journal of Mental Science,' 1871, p. 43), that Bacon long ago, and the poet Burns, held the same notion.

[79] 'Prehistoric Times,' 2nd edit. p. 571. In this work (p. 571) there will be found an excellent account of the many strange and capricious customs of savages.

# *The Expression of the Emotions in Man and Animals*[56]

I have now described, to the best of my ability, the chief expressive actions in man, and in some few of the lower animals. I have also attempted to explain the origin or development of these actions through . . . three principles. . . . The first of these principles is, that movements which are serviceable in gratifying some desire, or in relieving some sensation, if often repeated, become so habitual that they are performed, whether or not of any service, whenever the same desire or sensation is felt, even in a very weak degree.

Our second principle is that of antithesis. The habit of voluntarily performing opposite movements under opposite impulses has become firmly established in us by the practice of our whole lives. Hence, if certain actions have been regularly performed, in accordance with our first principle, under a certain frame of mind, there will be a strong and involuntary tendency to the performance of directly opposite actions, whether or not these are of any use, under the excitement of an opposite frame of mind.

Our third principle is the direct action of the excited nervous system on the body, independently of the will, and independently, in large part, of habit. Experience shows that nerve-force is generated and set free whenever the cerebro-spinal system is excited. The direction which this nerve-force follows is necessarily determined by the lines of connection between the nerve-cells, with each other and with various parts of the body. But the direction is likewise much influenced by habit; inasmuch as nerve-force passes readily along accustomed channels.

The frantic and senseless actions of an enraged man may be attributed in part to the undirected flow of nerve-force, and in part to the effects of habit, for these actions often vaguely represent the act of striking. They thus pass into gestures included under our first principle; as when an indignant man unconsciously throws himself into a fitting attitude for attacking his opponent, though without any intention of making an actual attack. We see also the influence of habit in all the emotions and sensations which are called exciting; for they have assumed this character from having habitually led to energetic action; and action affects, in an indirect manner, the respiratory and circulatory system; and the latter reacts on the brain. Whenever these emotions or sensations are even slightly felt by us, though they may not at the time lead to any exertion, our whole system is nevertheless disturbed through the force of habit and association. Other emotions and sensations are called depressing, because they have not habitually led to energetic action, excepting just at first, as in the case of extreme pain, fear, and grief, and they have ultimately caused complete exhaustion; they are consequently expressed chiefly by negative signs and by prostration. Again, there are other emotions, such as that of affection, which do not commonly lead to action of any kind, and consequently are not exhibited by any strongly marked outward signs. Affection indeed, in as far as it is a pleasurable sensation, excites the ordinary signs of pleasure.

On the other hand, many of the effects due to the excitement of the nervous system seem to be quite independent of the flow of nerve-force along the channels which have been rendered habitual by former exertions of the will. Such effects, which often reveal the state of mind of the person thus affected, cannot at present be explained; for instance, the change of colour in the hair from extreme terror or grief, — the cold sweat and the trembling of the muscles from fear, — the modified secretions of the intestinal canal, — and the failure of certain glands to act.

Notwithstanding that much remains unintelligible in our present subject, so many expressive movements and actions can be explained to a certain extent through the above three principles, that we may hope hereafter to see all explained by these or by closely analogous principles.

Actions of all kinds, if regularly accompanying any state of the mind, are at once recognized as expressive. These may consist of movements of any part of the body, as the wagging of a dog's tail, the shrugging of a man's shoulders, the erection of the hair, the exudation of perspiration, the state of the capillary circulation, laboured breathing, and the use of the vocal or other sound-producing instruments. Even insects express anger, terror, jealousy, and love by their stridulation. With man the respiratory organs are of especial importance in expression, not only in a direct, but in a still higher degree in an indirect manner.

Few points are more interesting in our present subject than the extraordinary complex chain of events which lead to certain expressive movements. Take, for instance, the oblique eyebrows of a man suffering from grief or anxiety. When infants scream loudly from hunger or pain, the circulation is affected, and the eyes tend to become gorged with blood: consequently the muscles surrounding the eyes are strongly contracted as a protection: this action, in the course of many generations, has become firmly fixed and inherited: but when, with advancing years and culture, the habit of screaming is partially repressed, the muscles round the eyes still tend to contract, whenever even slight distress is felt: of these muscles, the pyramidals of the nose are less under the control of the will than are the others, and their contraction can be checked only by that of the central fasciæ of the frontal muscle: these latter fasciæ draw up the inner ends of the eyebrows, and wrinkle the forehead in a peculiar manner, which we instantly recognize as the expression of grief or anxiety. Slight movements, such as these just described, or the scarcely perceptible drawing down of the corners of the mouth, are the last remnants or rudiments of strongly marked and intelligible movements. They are as full of significance to us in regard to expression, as are ordinary rudiments to the naturalist in the classification and genealogy of organic beings.

That the chief expressive actions, exhibited by man and by the lower animals, are now innate or inherited, — that is, have not been learnt by the individual, — is admitted by every one. So little has learning or imitation to do with several of them that they are from the earliest days and throughout life quite beyond our control; for instance, the relaxation of the arteries of the skin in blushing, and the increased action of the heart in anger. We may see children, only two or three years old, and even those born blind, blushing from shame; and the naked scalp of a very young infant reddens from passion. Infants scream from pain directly after birth, and all their features then assume the same form as during subsequent years. These facts alone suffice to show that many of our most important expressions have not been learnt; but it is remarkable that some, which are certainly innate, require practice in the individual, before they are performed in a full and perfect manner; for instance, weeping and laughing. The inheritance of most of our expressive actions explains the fact that those born blind display them, as I hear from the Rev. R. H. Blair, equally well with those gifted with eyesight. We can thus also understand the fact that the young and the old of widely different races, both with man and animals, express the same state of mind by the same movements.

We are so familiar with the fact of young and old animals

Charles Darwin in 1880

displaying their feelings in the same manner, that we hardly perceive how remarkable it is that a young puppy should wag its tail when pleased, depress its ears and uncover its canine teeth when pretending to be savage, just like an old dog; or that a kitten should arch its little back and erect its hair when frightened and angry, like an old cat. When, however, we turn to less common gestures in ourselves, which we are accustomed to look at as artificial or conventional, — such as shrugging the shoulders, as a sign of impotence, or the raising the arms with open hands and extended fingers, as a sign of wonder, — we feel perhaps too much surprise at finding that they are innate. That these and some other gestures are inherited, we may infer from their being performed by very young children, by those born blind, and by the most widely distinct races of man. We should also bear in mind that new and highly peculiar tricks, in association with certain states of the mind, are known to have arisen in certain individuals, and to have been afterwards transmitted to their offspring, in some cases, for more than one generation.

Certain other gestures, which seem to us so natural that we might easily imagine that they were innate, apparently have been learnt like the words of a language. This seems to be the case with the joining of the uplifted hands, and the turning up of the eyes, in prayer. So it is with kissing as a mark of affection; but this is innate, in so far as it depends on the pleasure derived from contact with a beloved person. The evidence with respect to the inheritance of nodding and shaking the head, as signs of affirmation and negation, is doubtful; for they are not universal, yet seem too general to have been independently acquired by all the individuals of so many races.

We will now consider how far the will and consciousness have come into play in the development of the various movements of expression. As far as we can judge, only a few expressive movements, such as those just referred to, are learnt by each individual; that is, were consciously and voluntarily performed during the early years of life for some definite object, or in imitation of others, and then became habitual. The far greater number of the movements of expression, and all the more important ones, are, as we have seen, innate or inherited; and such cannot be said to depend on the will of the individual. Nevertheless, all those included under our first principle were at first voluntarily performed for a definite object, — namely, to escape some danger, to relieve some distress, or to gratify some desire. For instance, there can hardly be a doubt that the animals which fight with their teeth, have acquired the habit of drawing back their ears closely to their heads, when feeling savage, from their progenitors having voluntarily acted in this manner in order to protect their ears from being torn by their antagonists; for those animals which do not fight with their teeth do not thus express a savage state of mind. We may infer as highly probable that we ourselves have acquired the habit of contracting the muscles round the eyes, whilst crying gently, that is, without the utterance of any loud sound, from our progenitors, especially during infancy, having experienced, during the act of screaming, an uncomfortable sensation in their eyeballs. Again, some highly expressive movements result from the endeavour to check or prevent other expressive movements; thus the obliquity of the eyebrows and the drawing down of the corners of the mouth follow from the endeavour to prevent a screaming-fit from coming on, or to check it after it has come on. Here it is obvious that the consciousness and will must at first have come into play; not that we are conscious in these or in other such cases what muscles are brought into action, any more than when we perform the most ordinary voluntary movements.

With respect to the expressive movements due to the principle of antithesis, it is clear that the will has intervened, though in a remote and indirect manner. So again with the movements coming under our third principle; these, in as far as they are influenced by nerve-force readily passing along habitual channels, have been determined by former and repeated exertions of the will. The effects indirectly due to this latter agency are often combined in a complex manner, through the force of habit and associations, with those directly resulting from the excitement of the cerebro-spinal system. This seems to be the case with the increased action of the heart under the influence of any strong emotion. When an animal erects its hair, assumes a threatening attitude, and utters fierce sounds, in order to terrify an enemy, we see a curious combination of movements which were originally voluntary with those that are involuntary. It is, however, possible that even strictly involuntary actions, such as the erection of the hair, may have been affected by the mysterious power of the will.

Some expressive movements may have arisen spontaneously, in association with certain states of the mind, like the tricks lately referred to, and afterwards been inherited. But I know of no evidence rendering this view probable.

The power of communication between the members of the same tribe by means of language has been of paramount importance in the development of man; and the force of language is much aided by the expressive movements of the face and body. We perceive this at once when we converse on an important subject with any person whose face is concealed. Nevertheless there are no grounds, as far as I can discover, for believing that any muscle has been developed or even modified exclusively for the sake of expression. The vocal and other sound-producing organs, by which various expressive noises are produced, seem to form a partial exception; but I have elsewhere attempted to show that these organs were first developed for sexual purposes, in order that one sex might call or charm the other. Nor can I discover grounds for believing that any inherited movement, which now serves as a means of expression, was at first voluntarily and consciously performed for this special purpose, — like some of the gestures and the finger-language used by the deaf and dumb. On the contrary, every true or inherited movement of expression seems to have had some natural and independent origin. But when once acquired, such movements may be voluntarily and consciously employed as a means of communication. Even infants, if carefully attended to, find out at a very early age that their screaming brings relief, and they soon voluntarily practise it. We may frequently see a person voluntarily raising his eyebrows to express surprise, or smiling to express pretended satisfaction and acquiescence. A man often wishes to make certain gestures conspicuous or demonstrative, and will raise his extended arms with widely opened fingers above his head, to show astonishment, or lift his shoulders to his ears, to show that he cannot or will not do something. The tendency to such movements will be strengthened or increased by their being thus voluntarily and repeatedly performed; and the effects may be inherited.

It is perhaps worth consideration whether movements at first used only by one or a few individuals to express a certain state of mind may not sometimes have spread to others, and ultimately have become universal, through the power of conscious and unconscious imitation. That there exists in man a strong tendency to imitation, independently of the conscious will, is certain. This is exhibited in the most extraordinary manner in certain brain diseases, especially at the commencement of inflammatory softening of the brain, and has been called the "echo sign." Patients thus affected imitate, without understanding, every absurd gesture which is made, and every word which is uttered near them, even in a foreign language.[1] In the case of animals, the jackal and wolf have learnt under confinement to imitate the barking of the dog. How the barking of the dog, which serves to express various emotions and desires, and which is so remarkable from having been acquired since the animal was domesticated, and from being inherited in different degrees by different breeds, was first learnt, we do not know; but may we not suspect that imitation has had something to do with its

[1] See the interesting facts given by Dr. Bateman on 'Aphasia,' 1870, p. 110.

acquisition, owing to dogs having long lived in strict association with so loquacious an animal as man?

In the course of the foregoing remarks and throughout this volume, I have often felt much difficulty about the proper application of the terms, will, consciousness, and intention. Actions, which were at first voluntary, soon became habitual, and at last hereditary, and may then be performed even in opposition to the will. Although they often reveal the state of the mind, this result was not at first either intended or expected. Even such words as that "certain movements serve as a means of expression" are apt to mislead, as they imply that this was their primary purpose or object. This, however, seems rarely or never to have been the case; the movements having been at first either of some direct use, or the indirect effect of the excited state of the sensorium. An infant may scream either intentionally or instinctively to show that it wants food; but it has no wish or intention to draw its features into the peculiar form which so plainly indicates misery; yet some of the most characteristic expressions exhibited by man are derived from the act of screaming, as has been explained.

Although most of our expressive actions are innate or instinctive, as is admitted by everyone, it is a different question whether we have any instinctive power of recognizing them. This has generally been assumed to be the case; but the assumption has been strongly controverted by M. Lemoine.[2] Monkeys soon learn to distinguish, not only the tones of voice of their masters, but the expression of their faces, as is asserted by a careful observer.[3] Dogs well know the difference between caressing and threatening gesture or tones; and they seem to recognize a compassionate tone. But as far as I can make out, after repeated trials, they do not understand any movement confined to the features, excepting a smile or laugh; and this they appear, at least in some cases, to recognize. This limited amount of knowledge has probably been gained, both by monkeys and dogs,

[2] 'La Physionomie et la Parole,' 1865, pp. 103, 118.

[3] Rengger, 'Naturgeschichte der Säugethiere von Paraguay,' 1830, s. 55.

through their associating harsh or kind treatment with our actions; and the knowledge certainly is not instinctive. Children, no doubt, would soon learn the movements of expression in their elders in the same manner as animals learn those of man. Moreover, when a child cries or laughs, he knows in a general manner what he is doing and what he feels; so that a very small exertion of reason would tell him what crying or laughing meant in others. But the question is, do our children acquire their knowledge of expression solely by experience through the power of association and reason?

As most of the movements of expression must have been gradually acquired, afterwards becoming instinctive, there seems to be some degree of *à priori* probability that their recognition would likewise have become instinctive. There is, at least, no greater difficulty in believing this than in admitting that, when a female quadruped first bears young, she knows the cry of distress of her offspring, or than in admitting that many animals instinctively recognize and fear their enemies; and of both these statements there can be no reasonable doubt. It is however extremely difficult to prove that our children instinctively recognize any expression. I attended to this point in my first-born infant, who could not have learnt anything by associating with other children, and I was convinced that he understood a smile and received pleasure from seeing one, answering it by another, at much too early an age to have learnt anything by experience. When this child was about four months old, I made in his presence many odd noises and strange grimaces, and tried to look savage; but the noises, if not too loud, as well as the grimaces, were all taken as good jokes; and I attributed this at the time to their being preceded or accompanied by smiles. When five months old, he seemed to understand a compassionate expression and tone of voice. When a few days over six months old, his nurse pretended to cry, and I saw that his face instantly assumed a melancholy expression, with the corners of the mouth strongly depressed; now this child could rarely have seen any other child crying, and never a grown-up person crying, and I should doubt whether at so early an age he could have reasoned on the subject. Therefore it seems to me that an innate feeling must have told him that the pretended crying of his nurse expressed grief; and this through the instinct of sympathy excited grief in him.

M. Lemoine argues that, if man possessed an innate knowledge of expression, authors and artists would not have found it so difficult, as is notoriously the case, to describe and depict the characteristic signs of each particular state of mind. But this does not seem to me a valid argument. We may actually behold the expression changing in an unmistakable manner in a man or animal, and yet be quite unable, as I know from experience, to analyse the nature of the change. In the two photographs given by Duchenne of the same old man, almost every one recognized that the one represented a true, and the other a false smile; but I have found it very difficult to decide in what the whole amount of difference consists. It has often struck me as a curious fact that so many shades of expression are instantly recognized without any conscious process of analysis on our part. No one, I believe, can clearly describe a sullen or sly expression; yet many observers are unanimous that these expressions can be recognized in the various races of man. Almost everyone to whom I showed Duchenne's photograph of the young man with oblique eyebrows at once declared that it expressed grief or some such feeling; yet probably not one of these persons, or one out of a thousand persons, could beforehand have told anything precise about the obliquity of the eyebrows with their inner ends puckered, or about the rectangular furrows on the forehead. So it is with many other expressions, of which I have had practical experience in the trouble requisite in instructing others what points to observe. If, then, great ignorance of details does not prevent our recognizing with certainty and promptitude various expressions, I do not see how this ignorance can be advanced as an argument that our knowledge, though vague and general, is not innate.

I have endeavoured to show in considerable detail that all

the chief expressions exhibited by man are the same throughout the world. This fact is interesting, as it affords a new argument in favour of the several races being descended from a single parent-stock, which must have been almost completely human in structure, and to a large extent in mind, before the period at which the races diverged from each other. No doubt similar structures, adapted for the same purpose, have often been independently acquired through variation and natural selection by distinct species; but this view will not explain close similarity between distinct species in a multitude of unimportant details. Now if we bear in mind the numerous points of structure having no relation to expression, in which all the races of man closely agree, and then add to them the numerous points, some of the highest importance and many of the most trifling value, on which the movements of expression directly or indirectly depend, it seems to me improbable in the highest degree that so much similarity, or rather identity of structure, could have been acquired by independent means. Yet this must have been the case if the races of man are descended from several aboriginally distinct species. It is far more probable that the many points of close similarity in the various races are due to inheritance from a single parent-form, which had already assumed a human character.

It is a curious, though perhaps an idle speculation, how early in the long line of our progenitors the various expressive movements, now exhibited by man, were successively acquired. The following remarks will at least serve to recall some of the chief points discussed in this volume. We may confidently believe that laughter, as a sign of pleasure or enjoyment, was practised by our progenitors long before they deserved to be called human; for very many kinds of monkeys, when pleased, utter a reiterated sound, clearly analogous to our laughter, often accompanied by vibratory movements of their jaws or lips, with the corners of the mouth drawn backwards and upwards, by the wrinkling of the cheeks, and even by the brightening of the eyes.

We may likewise infer that fear was expressed from an extremely remote period, in almost the same manner as it now is by man; namely, by trembling, the erection of the hair, cold perspiration, pallor, widely opened eyes, the relaxation of most of the muscles, and by the whole body cowering downwards or held motionless.

Suffering, if great, will from the first have caused screams or groans to be uttered, the body to be contorted, and the teeth to be ground together. But our progenitors will not have exhibited those highly expressive movements of the features which accompany screaming and crying until their circulatory and respiratory organs, and the muscles surrounding the eyes, had acquired their present structure. The shedding of tears appears to have originated through reflex action from the spasmodic contraction of the eyelids, together perhaps with the eyeballs becoming gorged with blood during the act of screaming. Therefore weeping probably came on rather late in the line of our descent; and this conclusion agrees with the fact that our nearest allies, the anthropomorphous apes, do not weep. But we must here exercise some caution, for as certain monkeys, which are not closely related to man, weep, this habit might have been developed long ago in a sub-branch of the group from which man is derived. Our early progenitors, when suffering from grief or anxiety, would not have made their eyebrows oblique, or have drawn down the corners of their mouth, until they had acquired the habit of endeavouring to restrain their screams. The expression, therefore, of grief and anxiety is eminently human.

Rage will have been expressed at a very early period by threatening or frantic gestures, by the reddening of the skin, and by glaring eyes, but not by frowning. For the habit of frowning seems to have been acquired chiefly from the corrugators being the first muscles to contract round the eyes, whenever during infancy pain, anger, or distress is felt, and there consequently is a near approach to screaming; and partly from a frown serving as a shade in difficult and intent vision. It seems probable that this shading action would not have become habitual until man had assumed a completely upright position, for monkeys do not frown when exposed to a glaring light. Our early progenitors, when enraged, would probably have exposed their teeth more freely than does man, even when giving full vent to his rage, as with the insane. We may, also, feel almost certain that they would have protruded their lips, when sulky or disappointed, in a greater degree than is the case with our own children, or even with the children of existing savage races.

Our early progenitors, when indignant or moderately angry, would not have held their heads erect, opened their chests, squared their shoulders, and clenched their fists, until they had acquired the ordinary carriage and upright attitude of man, and had learnt to fight with their fists or clubs. Until this period had arrived the antithetical gesture of shrugging the shoulders, as a sign of impotence or of patience, would not have been developed. From the same reason astonishment would not then have been expressed by raising the arms with open hands and extended fingers. Nor, judging from the actions of monkeys, would astonishment have been exhibited by a widely opened mouth; but the eyes would have been opened and the eyebrows arched. Disgust would have been shown at a very early period by movements round the mouth, like those of vomiting, — that is, if the view which I have suggested respecting the source of the expression is correct, namely, that our progenitors had the power, and used it, of voluntarily and quickly rejecting any food from their stomachs which they disliked. But the more refined manner of showing contempt or disdain, by lowering the eyelids, or turning away the eyes and face, as if the despised person were not worth looking at, would not probably have been acquired until a much later period.

Of all expressions, blushing seems to be the most strictly human; yet it is common to all or nearly all the races of man, whether or not any change of colour is visible in their skin. The relaxation of the small arteries of the surface, on which blushing depends, seems to have primarily resulted from earnest attention directed to the appearance of our own persons, especially of our faces, aided by habit, inheritance, and the ready flow of nerve-force along accustomed channels; and afterwards to have been extended by the power of association to self-attention directed to moral conduct. It can hardly be doubted that many animals are capable of appreciating beautiful colours and even forms, as is shown by the pains which the individuals of one sex take in displaying their beauty before those of the opposite sex. But it does not seem possible that any animal, until its mental powers had been developed to an equal or nearly equal degree with those of man, would have closely considered and been sensitive about its own personal appearance. Therefore we may conclude that blushing originated at a very late period in the long line of our descent.

From the various facts just alluded to, and given in the course of this volume, it follows that, if the structure of our organs of respiration and circulation had differed in only a slight degree from the state in which they now exist, most of our expressions would have been wonderfully different. A very slight change in the course of the arteries and veins which run to the head, would probably have prevented the blood from accumulating in our eyeballs during violent expiration; for this occurs in extremely few quadrupeds. In this case we should not have displayed some of our most characteristic expressions. If man had breathed water by the aid of external branchiæ (though the idea is hardly conceivable), instead of air through his mouth and nostrils, his features would not have expressed his feelings much more efficiently than now do his hands or limbs. Rage and disgust, however, would still have been shown by movements about the lips and mouth, and the eyes would have become brighter or duller according to the state of the circulation. If our ears had remained movable, their movements would have been highly expressive, as is the case with all the animals which fight with their teeth; and we may infer that our early progenitors thus fought, as we still uncover the canine tooth on one side when we sneer at or defy any one, and we uncover all our teeth when furiously enraged.

The movements of expression in the face and body, whatever their origin may have been, are in themselves of much importance for our welfare. They serve as the first means of communication between the mother and her infant; she smiles approval, and thus encourages her child on the right path, or frowns disapproval. We readily perceive sympathy in others by their expression; our sufferings are thus mitigated and our pleasures increased; and mutual good feeling is thus strengthened. The movements of expression give vividness and energy to our spoken words. They reveal the thoughts and intentions of others more truly than do words, which may be falsified. Whatever amount of truth the so-called science of physiognomy may contain, appears to depend, as Haller long ago remarked,[4] on different persons bringing into frequent use different facial muscles, according to their dispositions; the development of these muscles being perhaps thus increased, and the lines or furrows on the face, due to their habitual contraction, being thus rendered deeper and more conspicuous. The free expression by outward signs of an emotion intensifies it. On the other hand, the repression, as far as this is possible, of all outward signs softens our emotions.[5] He who gives way to violent gestures will increase his rage; he who does not control the signs of fear will experience fear in a greater degree; and he who remains passive when overwhelmed with grief loses his best chance of recovering elasticity of mind. These results follow partly from the intimate relation which exists between almost all the emotions and their outward manifestations; and partly from the direct influence of exertion on the heart, and consequently on the brain. Even the simulation of an emotion tends to arouse it in our minds. Shake-

4 Quoted by Moreau, in his edition of Lavater, 1820, tom. iv. p. 211.

5 Gratiolet ('De la Physionomie,' 1865, p. 66) insists on the truth of this conclusion.

speare, who from his wonderful knowledge of the human mind ought to be an excellent judge, says: —

> "Is it not monstrous that this player here,
> But in a fiction, in a dream of passion,
> Could force his soul so to his own conceit,
> That, from her working, all his visage wann'd;
> Tears in his eyes, distraction in 's aspect,
> A broken voice, and his whole function suiting
> With forms to his conceit? And all for nothing!"
>
> *Hamlet*, act ii, sc. 2.

We have seen that the study of the theory of expression confirms to a certain limited extent the conclusion that man is derived from some lower animal form, and supports the belief of the specific or sub-specific unity of the several races; but as far as my judgment serves, such confirmation was hardly needed. We have also seen that expression in itself, or the language of the emotions, as it has sometimes been called, is certainly of importance for the welfare of mankind. To understand, as far as possible, the source or origin of the various expressions which may be hourly seen on the faces of the men around us, not to mention our domesticated animals, ought to possess much interest for us. From these several causes, we may conclude that the philosophy of our subject has well deserved the attention which it has already received from several excellent observers, and that it deserves still further attention, especially from any able physiologist.

# *On the Importance of Earthworms*[57]

Worms have played a more important part in the history of the world than most persons would at first suppose. In almost all humid countries they are extraordinarily numerous, and for their size possess great muscular power. In many parts of England a weight of more than ten tons (10,516 kilogrammes) of dry earth annually passes through their bodies and is brought to the surface on each acre of land; so that the whole superficial bed of vegetable mould passes through their bodies in the course of every few years. From the collapsing of the old burrows the mould is in constant though slow movement, and the particles composing it are thus rubbed together. By these means fresh surfaces are continually exposed to the action of the carbonic acid in the soil, and of the humus-acids which appear to be still more efficient in the decomposition of rocks. The generation of the humus-acids is probably hastened during the digestion of the many half-decayed leaves which worms consume. Thus the particles of earth, forming the superficial mould, are subjected to conditions eminently favourable for their decomposition and disintegration. Moreover, the particles of the softer rocks suffer some amount of mechanical trituration in the muscular gizzards of worms, in which small stones serve as mill-stones.

The finely levigated castings, when brought to the surface in a moist condition, flow during rainy weather down any moderate slope; and the smaller particles are washed far down even a gently inclined surface. Castings when dry often crumble into small pellets and these are apt to roll down any sloping surface. Where the land is quite level and is covered with herbage, and where climate is humid so that much dust cannot be blown away, it appears at first sight impossible that there should be any appreciable amount of sub-aerial denudation; but worm-castings are blown, especially whilst moist and viscid, in one uniform direction by the prevalent winds which are accompanied by rain. By these several means the superficial mould is prevented from accumulating to a great thickness; and a thick bed of mould checks in many ways the disintegration of the underlying rocks and fragments of rocks.

The removal of worm-castings by the above means leads to results which are far from insignificant. . . .

Archeologists ought to be grateful to worms, as they protect and preserve for an indefinitely long period every object, not liable to decay, which is dropped on the surface of the land, by burying it beneath their castings. Thus, also, many elegant and curious tesselated pavements and other ancient remains have been preserved; though no doubt the worms have in these cases been largely aided by earth washed and blown from adjoining land, especially when cultivated. The old tesselated pavements have, however, often suffered by having subsided unequally from being unequally undermined by the worms. Even old massive walls may be undermined and subside; and no building is in this respect safe, unless the foundations lie 6 or 7 feet beneath the surface, at a depth at which worms cannot work. It is probable that many monoliths and some old walls have fallen down from having been undermined by worms.

## PUNCH'S VOICE OF THE STARS.

### FOR AUGUST.

THIS is the month of Virgo. Pic-nics and river parties will be very popular. Most of the stars will now be in the provinces, consequently the London theatres will be under-let to speculators. Mars enters the scales on the 18th, and are found much heavier. This will be favourable to manufacturers of Anti-Fat, and other remedies for removing corpulency. The Crown Prince of GERMANY gains by the transit of Jupiter, which is now sent to him post paid direct from the head-office. The Emperor of AUSTRIA, if he has not bought a new hat since the commencement of the year, may now be expected to supply the omission in his outfit.

INFANTRY, BUT NOT FOOT.—Children in Arms.

## PUNCH'S VOICE OF THE STARS.

### FOR SEPTEMBER.

As Saturn halts in 26' 11′ of Taurus, *id est*, exactly on the place of the Solar Eclipse (8·26' 15′) of last May, several birds may be expected to be shot in England on the 1st. A per-centage of these birds will be called partridges. Persia will have a bad time of it. People living in Krim Tartary or Margate, should be careful to avoid catching cold on or about the 16th. BISMARCK will be seen smoking during this month. Should the Sun be in good aspect with the Moon on the 22nd, his highness will drink a glass of beer. Certain acquaintances of Mr. MARWOOD will find this month unfavourable to their health.

CON. FOR CASUISTS.—Can a man be said to indulge in the lie circumstantial when he lies at full length ?

"Man is but a Worm"

Worms prepare the ground in an excellent manner for the growth of fibrous-rooted plants and for seedlings of all kinds. They periodically expose the mould to the air, and sift it so that no stones larger than the particles which they can swallow are left in it. They mingle the whole intimately together, like a gardener who prepares fine soil for his choicest plants. In this state it is well fitted to retain moisture and to absorb all soluble substances, as well as the process for nitrification. The bones of dead animals, the harder parts of insects, the shells of land-molluscs, leaves, twigs, &c., are before long buried beneath the accumulated castings of worms, and are thus brought into a more or less decayed state within reach of the roots of plants. Worms likewise drag an infinite number of dead leaves and other parts of plants into their burrows, partly for the sake of plugging them up and partly as food.

The leaves which are dragged into the burrows as food, after being torn into the finest shreds, partially digested, and saturated with intestinal and urinary secretions, are commingled with much earth. This earth forms the dark coloured, rich humus which almost everywhere covers the surface of the land with a fairly well-defined layer or mantle. . . .

Worms are poorly provided with sense-organs, for they cannot be said to see, although they can just distinguish between light and darkness; they are completely deaf, and have only a feeble power of smell; the sense of touch alone is well developed. They can therefore learn little about the outside world, and it is surprising that they should exhibit some skill in lining their burrows with their castings and with leaves, and in the case of some species in piling up their castings into tower-like constructions. But it is far more surprising that they should apparently exhibit some degree of intelligence instead of a mere blind instinctive impulse, in their manner of plugging up the mouths of their burrows. They act in nearly the same manner as would a man, who had to close a cylindrical tube with different kinds of leaves, . . . paper, &c., for they commonly seize such objects by their pointed ends. But with thin objects a certain number are drawn in by their broader ends. They do not act in the same unvarying manner in all cases, as do most of the lower animals; for instance, they do not drag in leaves by their foot-stalks, unless the basal part of the blade is as narrow as the apex, or narrower than it.

When we behold a wide, turf-covered expanse, we should remember that its smooth-ness, on which so much of its beauty depends, is mainly due to all the inequalities having been slowly levelled by the worms. It is a marvellous reflection that the whole of the superficial mould over any such expanse has passed, and will again pass, every few years through the bodies of worms. The plough is one of the most ancient and most valuable of man's inventions; but long before he existed the land was in fact regularly ploughed, and still continues to be thus ploughed by earthworms. It may be doubted whether there are many other animals which have played so important a part in the history of the world, as have these lowly organised creatures. Some other animals, however, still more lowly organized, namely corals, have done far more conspicuous work in having constructed innumerable reefs and islands in the great oceans; but these are almost confined to the tropical zones.

# Thomas Henry Huxley on the *Origin of Species*[58]

Many of you will be familiar with the aspect of this small green-covered book. It is a copy of the first edition of the "Origin of Species," and bears the date of its production. . . .

Those whose memories carry them back to the publication of the "Origin of Species" will remember that the infant was remarkably lively, and that a great number of excellent persons mistook its manifestations of a vigorous individuality for mere naughtiness; in fact there was a very pretty turmoil about its cradle. My recollections of the period are particularly vivid; for, having conceived a tender affection for a child of what appeared to me to be such remarkable promise, I acted for some time in the capacity of a sort of under-nurse, and thus came in for my share of the storms which threatened the very life of the young creature. For some years it was undoubtedly warm work; but considering how exceedingly unpleasant the apparition of the new-comer must have been to those who did not fall in love with him at first sight, I think it is to the credit of our age that the war was not fiercer, and that the more bitter and unscrupulous forms of opposition died away as soon as they did.

I speak of this period as of something past and gone, possessing merely an historical, I had almost said an antiquarian interest. For, during the second decade of the existence of the "Origin of Species," opposition, though by no means dead, assumed a different aspect. On the part of all those who had any reason to respect themselves, it assumed a thoroughly respectful character. By this time, the dullest began to perceive that the child was not likely to perish of any congenital weakness or infantile disorder, but was growing into a stalwart personage, upon whom mere goody scoldings and threatenings with the birch-rod were quite thrown away.

In fact, those who have watched the progress of science within the last ten years will bear me out to the full, when I assert that there is no field of biological inquiry in which the influence of the "Origin of Species" is not traceable; the foremost men of science in every country are either avowed champions of its leading doctrines, or at any rate abstain from opposing them; a host of young and ardent investigators seek for and find inspiration and guidance in Mr. Darwin's great work; and the general doctrine of evolution, to one side of which it gives expression, obtains, in the phenomena of biology, a firm base of operations whence it may conduct its conquest of the whole realm of Nature.

History warns us, however, that it is the customary fate of new truths to begin as heresies and to end as superstitions; and, as matters now stand, it is hardly rash to anticipate that, in another twenty years, the new generation, educated under the influences of the present day, will be in danger of accepting the main doctrines of the "Origin of Species," with as little reflection, and it may be with as little justification, as so many of our contemporaries, twenty years ago, rejected them.

Against any such a consummation let us all devoutly pray; for the scientific spirit is of more value than its products, and irrationally held truths may be more harmful than reasoned errors. Now the essence of the scientific spirit is criticism. It tells us

Thomas Henry Huxley

that whenever a doctrine claims our assent we should reply, Take it if you can compel it. The struggle for existence holds as much in the intellectual as in the physical world. A theory is a species of thinking, and its right to exist is coextensive with its power of resisting extinction by its rivals.

From this point of view, it appears to me that it would be but a poor way of celebrating the Coming of Age of the "Origin of Species," were I merely to dwell upon the facts, undoubted and remarkable as they are, of its far-reaching influence and of the great following of ardent disciples who are occupied in spreading and developing its doctrines. Mere insanities and inanities have before now swollen to portentous size in the course of twenty years. Let us rather ask this prodigious change in opinion to justify itself: let us inquire whether anything has happened since 1859, which will explain, on rational grounds, why so many are worshipping that which they burned, and burning that which they worshipped. It is only in this way that we shall acquire the means of judging whether the movement we have witnessed is a mere eddy of fashion, or truly one with the irreversible current of intellectual progress, and, like it, safe from retrogressive reaction.

Every belief is the product of two factors: the first is the state of the mind to which the evidence in favour of that belief is presented; and the second is the logical cogency of the evidence itself. In both these respects, the history of biological science during the last twenty years appears to me to afford an ample explanation of the change which has taken place; and a brief consideration of the salient events of that history will enable us to understand why, if the "Origin of Species" appeared now, it would meet with a very different reception from that which greeted it in 1859.

One-and-twenty years ago, in spite of the work commenced by Hutton and continued with rare skill and patience by Lyell, the dominant view of the past history of the earth was catastrophic. Great and sudden physical revolutions, wholesale creations and extinctions of living beings, were the ordinary machinery of the geological epic brought into fashion by the misapplied genius of Cuvier. It was gravely maintained and taught that the end of every geological epoch was signalised by a cataclysm, by which every living being on the globe was swept away, to be replaced by a brand-new creation when the world returned to quiescence. A scheme of nature which appeared to be modelled on the likeness of a succession of rubbers of whist, at the end of each of which the players upset the table and called for a new pack, did not seem to shock anybody.

I may be wrong, but I doubt if, at the present time, there is a single responsible representative of these opinions left. The progress of scientific geology has elevated the fundamental principle of uniformitarianism, that the explanation of the past is to be sought in the study of the present, into the position of an axiom; and the wild speculations of the catastrophists, to which we all listened with respect a quarter of a century ago, would hardly find a single patient hearer at the present day. No physical geologist now dreams of seeking, outside the range of known natural causes, for the explanation of anything that happened millions of years ago, any more than he would be guilty of the like absurdity in regard to current events.

The effect of this change of opinion upon biological speculation is obvious. For, if there have been no periodical general physical catastrophes, what brought about the assumed general extinctions and re-creations of life which are the corresponding biological catastrophes? And, if no such interruptions of the ordinary course of nature have taken place in the organic, any more than in the inorganic, world, what alternative is there to the admission of evolution?

The doctrine of evolution in biology is the necessary result of the logical application of the principles of uniformitarianism to the phenomena of life. Darwin is the natural successor of

Hutton and Lyell, and the "Origin of Species" the logical sequence of the "Principles of Geology."

The fundamental doctrine of the "Origin of Species," as of all forms of the theory of evolution applied to biology, is "that the innumerable species, genera, and families of organic beings with which the world is peopled have all descended, each within its own class or group, from common parents, and have all been modified in the course of descent."[1]

And, in view of the facts of geology, it follows that all living animals and plants "are the lineal descendants of those which lived long before the Silurian epoch."[2]

It is an obvious consequence of this theory of descent with modification, as it is sometimes called, that all plants and animals, however different they may now be, must, at one time or other, have been connected by direct or indirect intermediate gradations, and that the appearance of isolation presented by various groups of organic beings must be unreal.

No part of Mr. Darwin's work ran more directly counter to the prepossessions of naturalists twenty years ago than this. And such prepossessions were very excusable, for there was undoubtedly a great deal to be said, at that time, in favour of the fixity of species and of the existence of great breaks, which there was no obvious or probable means of filling up, between various groups of organic beings.

For various reasons, scientific and unscientific, much had been made of the hiatus between man and the rest of the higher mammalia, and it is no wonder that issue was first joined on this part of the controversy. I have no wish to revive past and happily forgotten controversies; but I must state the simple fact that the distinctions in the cerebral and other characters, which were so hotly affirmed to separate man from all other animals in 1860, have all been demonstrated to be non-existent, and that the contrary doctrine is now universally accepted and taught.

[1] *Origin of Species,* ed. 1, p. 457.

[2] *Origin of Species,* p. 458.

But there were other cases in which the wide structural gaps asserted to exist between one group of animals and another were by no means fictitious; and, when such structural breaks were real, Mr. Darwin could account for them only by supposing that the intermediate forms which once existed had become extinct. In a remarkable passage he says —

"We may thus account even for the distinctness of whole classes from each other — for instance, of birds from all other vertebrate animals — by the belief that many animal forms of life have been utterly lost, through which the early progenitors of birds were formerly connected with the early progenitors of the other vertebrate classes."[3]

Adverse criticism made merry over such suggestions as these. Of course it was easy to get out of the difficulty by supposing extinction; but where was the slightest evidence that such intermediate forms between birds and reptiles as the hypothesis required ever existed? And then probably followed a tirade upon this terrible forsaking of the paths of "Baconian induction."

But the progress of knowledge has justified Mr. Darwin to an extent which could hardly have been anticipated. In 1862, the specimen of *Archæopteryx*, which, until the last two or three years, has remained unique, was discovered; and it is an animal which, in its feathers and the greater part of its organisation, is a veritable bird, while, in other parts, it is as distinctly reptilian.

In 1868, I had the honour of bringing under your notice, . . . the results of investigations made, up to that time, into the anatomical characters of certain ancient reptiles, which showed the nature of the modifications in virtue of which the type of the quadrupedal reptile passed into that of a bipedal bird; and abundant confirmatory evidence of the justice of the conclusions which I then laid before you has since come to light.

In 1875, the discovery of the toothed birds of the cretaceous formation in North America by Professor Marsh completed the series of transitional forms between birds and reptiles, and re-

[3] *Origin of Species,* p. 431.

moved Mr. Darwin's proposition that "many animal forms of life have been utterly lost, through which the early progenitors of birds were formerly connected with the early progenitors of the other vertebrate classes," from the region of hypothesis to that of demonstrable fact.

In 1859, there appeared to be a very sharp and clear hiatus between vertebrated and invertebrated animals, not only in their structure, but, what was more important, in their development. I do not think that we even yet know the precise links of connection between the two; but the investigations of Kowalewsky and others upon the development of *Amphioxus* and of the *Tunicata* prove, beyond a doubt, that the differences which were supposed to constitute a barrier between the two are non-existent. There is no longer any difficulty in understanding how the vertebrate type may have arisen from invertebrate, though the full proof of the manner in which the transition was actually effected may still be lacking.

Again, in 1859, there appeared to be a no less sharp separation between the two great groups of flowering and flowerless plants. It is only subsequently that the series of remarkable investigations inaugurated by Hofmeister has brought to light the extraordinary and altogether unexpected modifications of the reproductive apparatus in the *Lycopodiaceœ,* the *Rhizocarpeæ,* and the *Gymnospermeæ,* by which the ferns and the mosses are gradually connected with the Phanerogamic division of the vegetable world.

So, again, it is only since 1859 that we have acquired that wealth of knowledge of the lowest forms of life which demonstrates the futility of any attempt to separate the lowest plants from the lowest animals, and shows that the two kingdoms of living ntaure have a common borderland which belongs to both, or to neither.

Thus it will be observed that the whole tendency of biological investigation, since 1859, has been in the direction of removing the difficulties which the apparent breaks in the series created at that time; and the recognition of gradation is the first step towards the acceptance of evolution.

As another great factor in bringing about the change of opinion which has taken place among naturalists, I count the astonishing progress which has been made in the study of embryology. Twenty years ago, not only were we devoid of any accurate knowledge of the mode of development of many groups of animals and plants, but the methods of investigation were rude and imperfect. At the present time, there is no important group of organic beings the development of which has not been carefully studied; and the modern methods of hardening and section-making enable the embryologist to determine the nature of the process, in each case, with a degree of minuteness and accuracy which is truly astonishing to those whose memories carry them back to the beginnings of modern histology. And the results of these embryological investigations are in complete harmony with the requirements of the doctrine of evolution. The first beginnings of all the higher forms of animal life are similar, and however diverse their adult conditions, they start from a common foundation. Moreover, the process of development of the animal or the plant from its primary egg, or germ, is a true process of evolution — a progress from almost formless to more or less highly organized matter, in virtue of the properties inherent in that matter.

To those who are familiar with the process of development, all *à priori* objections to the doctrine of biological evolution appear childish. Any one who has watched the gradual formation of a complicated animal from the protoplasmic mass, which constitutes the essential element of a frog's or a hen's egg, has had under his eyes sufficient evidence that a similar evolution of the whole animal world from the like foundation is, at any rate, possible.

Yet another product of investigation has largely contributed to the removal of the objections to the doctrine of evolution current in 1859. It is the proof afforded by successive discoveries that Mr. Darwin did not overestimate the imperfection of the geological record. No more striking illustration of this is needed than a comparison of our knowledge of the mammalia fauna of the Tertiary epoch in 1859 with its present condition. M. Gaudry's researches on the fossils of Pikermi were published in 1868, those of Messrs. Leidy, Marsh, and Cope, on the fossils of the Western Territories of America, have appeared almost wholly since 1870, those of M. Filhol on the phosphorites of Quercy in 1878. The general effect of these investigations has been to introduce to us a multitude of extinct animals, the existence of which was previously hardly suspected; just as if zoologists were to become acquainted with a country, hitherto unknown, as rich in novel forms of life as Brazil or South Africa once were to Europeans. Indeed, the fossil fauna of the Western Territories of America bid fair to exceed in interest and importance all other known Tertiary deposits put together; and yet, with the exception of the case of the American tertiaries, these investigations have extended over very limited areas; and, at Pikermi, were confined to an extremely small space.

Such appear to me to be the chief events in the history of the progress of knowledge during the last twenty years, which account for the changed feeling with which the doctrine of evolution is at present regarded by those who have followed the advance of biological science, in respect of those problems which bear indirectly upon that doctrine.

But all this remains mere secondary evidence. It may remove dissent, but it does not compel assent. Primary and direct evidence in favour of evolution can be furnished only by palæontology. The geological record, so soon as it approaches completeness, must, when properly questioned, yield either an affirmative or a negative answer: if evolution has taken place, there will its mark be left; if it has not taken place, there will lie its refutation.

What was the state of matters in 1859? Let us hear Mr. Darwin, who may be trusted always to state the case against himself as strongly as possible.

"On this doctrine of the extermination of an infinitude of connecting links between the living and extinct inhabitants of the world, and at each successive period between the extinct and still older species, why is not every geological formation charged with such links? Why does not every collection of fossil remains afford plain evidence of the gradation and mutation of the forms of life? We meet with no such evidence, and this is the most obvious and plausible of the many objections which may be urged against my theory."[4]

Nothing could have been more useful to the opposition than this characteristically candid avowal, twisted as it immediately was into an admission that the writer's views were contradicted by the facts of palæontology. But, in fact, Mr. Darwin made no such admission. What he says in effect is, not that palæontological evidence is against him, but that it is not distinctly in his favour; and, without attempting to attenuate the fact, he accounts for it by the scantiness and the imperfection of that evidence.

What is the state of the case now, when, as we have seen, the amount of our knowledge respecting the mammalia of the Tertiary epoch is increased fifty-fold, and in some directions even approaches completeness?

Simply this, that, if the doctrine of evolution had not existed, palæontologists must have invented it, so irresistibly is it forced upon the mind by the study of the remains of the Tertiary mammalia which have been brought to light since 1859.

Among the fossils of Pikermi, Gaudry found the successive stages by which the ancient civets passed into the more modern hyænas; through the Tertiary deposits of Western America, Marsh tracked the successive forms by which the ancient stock of the horse has passed into its present form; and innumerable less complete indications of the mode of evolution of other groups of the higher mammalia have been obtained. In the remarkable memoir on the phosphorites of Quercy, to which I have referred, M. Filhol describes no fewer than seventeen va-

[4] *Origin of Species*, ed. 1, p. 463.

rieties of the genus *Cynodictis*, which fill up all the interval between the viverine animals and the bear-like dog *Amphicyon;* nor do I know any solid ground of objection to the supposition that, in this *Cynodictis-Amphicyon* group, we have the stock whence all the Viveridæ Felidæ, Hyænidæ, Canidæ, and perhaps the Procyonidæ and Ursidæ, of the present fauna have been evolved. On the contrary, there is a great deal to be said in favour.

In the course of summing up his results, M. Filhol observes: —

"During the epoch of the phosphorites, great changes took place in animal forms, and almost the same types as those which now exist became defined from one another.

"Under the influence of natural conditions of which we have no exact knowledge, though traces of them are discoverable, species have been modified in a thousand ways: races have arisen which, becoming fixed, have thus produced a corresponding number of secondary species."

In 1859, language of which this is an unintentional paraphrase, occurring in the "Origin of Species," was scouted as wild speculation; at present, it is a sober statement of the conclusions to which an acute and critically-minded investigator is led by large and patient study of the facts of palæontology. I venture to repeat what I have said before, that so far as the animal world is concerned, evolution is no longer a speculation, but a statement of historical fact. It takes its place alongside of those accepted truths which must be reckoned with by philosophers of all schools.

# *Notes*

1. Charles Darwin, *On the Origin of Species by Means of Natural Selection, or the Preservation of Favoured Races in the Struggle for Life* (London: John Murray, 1859).

2. Charles Darwin, *Journal of Researches into the Geology and Natural History of the Various Countries Visited by H. M. S. Beagle* (London: Henry Colburn, 1839; facsimile reprint, New York: Hafner Publishing Co., 1952).

3. Alfred Russel Wallace, *Darwinism* (London: Macmillan and Co., 1923), p. 9.

4. Josiah Royce, *The Spirit of Modern Philosophy* (Boston and New York: Houghton Mifflin Co., 1893), p. 202.

5. Nora Barlow (ed.), *The Autobiography of Charles Darwin 1809-1882* (London: Collins, 1958), pp. 167-219.

6. Francis Darwin (ed.), *The Life and Letters of Charles Darwin* (3 vols.; London: John Murray, 1887), I, 56, 48. Hereinafter cited as *Letters.*

7. *Letters,* I, 186-188, 169, 182.

8. *Letters,* I, 221n.

9. Nora Barlow (ed.), *Charles Darwin and the Voyage of the Beagle* (London: Pilot Press, 1945), pp. 1-2, 7-39, 149-268.

10. *Letters,* I, 276.

11. *Letters,* II, 371. Italics in original.

12. Charles Darwin, *The Foundations of the Origin of Species, A Sketch Written in 1842,* ed. Francis Darwin (Cambridge: The University Press, 1909). *Letters,* II, 16-18.

13. *Letters,* II, 85.

14. *Letters,* II, 68.

15. *Letters,* II, 168.

16. *Letters,* I, 87-88.

17. Bert James Loewenberg, *Darwin, Wallace, and the Theory of Natural Selection* (Cambridge: Arlington Books, 1958). *Letters,* II, 116.

18. *Letters,* I, 88.

19. *Letters,* II, 220.

20. *Letters,* II, 205; III, 42, 152.

21. *Letters,* III, 254.

22. *Letters,* III, 59.

23. *Letters,* II, 35.

24. Charles Darwin, *The Variation of Animals and Plants under Domestication* (2 vols; London: John Murray, 1868), II, 357-404. *Letters,* III, 80. Francis Darwin (ed.), *More Letters of Charles Darwin* (2 vols; London: John Murray, 1903), I, 300.

25. *Letters,* III, 96, 98-99.

26. *Letters,* III, 91.

27. *Letters,* III, 98-99.

28. Charles Darwin, *The Descent of Man, and Selection in Relation to Sex* (2 vols; London: John Murray, 1871), I, 5. Charles Darwin, *The Expression of the Emotions in Man and Animals* (London: John Murray, 1872), pp. 2, 12. *Letters,* III, 96, 233.

29. *Letters,* III, 373-376.

30. *Letters,* II, 360, 138.

31. *Letters,* III, 175, 181, 183, 184, 212, 254-359.

32. *Letters,* III, 370.

33. Charles Darwin, *The Formation of Vegetable Mould Through the Action of Earth-Worms* (London: John Murray, 1881).

34. *Letters,* III, 218.

35. H. E. Litchfield (ed.), *Emma Darwin Wife of Charles Darwin, A Century of Family Letters* (2 vols; Cambridge: privately printed at The University Press, 1904), II, 327.

36. Litchfield, *Emma Darwin,*

II, 316, 230, 240, 247, 276, 279, 299, 298, 302, 314, 318. *Letters,* I, 300.

37. *Letters,* II, 300.

38. *Letters,* II, 228.

39. *Letters,* II, 352.

40. *Letters,* III, 164; I, 89; II, 349-351.

41. *Letters,* II, 315n.

42. *Letters,* II, 314.

43. *More Letters,* I, 283.

44. *More Letters,* I, 327-328; I, 217-218.

45. Ernst Krause, *Erasmus Darwin,* trans. W. S. Dallas (London: John Murray, 1879). This selection is taken from the long prefatory notice by Charles Darwin, pp. 1-58.

46. *Letters,* I, 11-20.

47. *Letters,* I, 26-67.

48. *Letters,* I, 192-193; 193-194; 195-196; 196-197; 198-199.

49. Barlow, *Darwin and the Beagle,* pp. 79-81.

50. Darwin, *Journal of Researches,* Everyman Library, New York: E. P. Dutton, 1955, pp. 357-386.

51. Litchfield, *Emma Darwin,* I, 382-383; 383-384; 384; 385.

52. Litchfield, *Emma Darwin,* I, 413-414; 415; 416-417; 418-420; 436-437; 438-439; 439-440; II, 10.

53. Loewenberg, *Darwin, Wallace,* pp. 41-80.

54. The selections from the *Origin of Species* are from the sixth and final edition, 1872. Ch. IV, pp. 62-105; Ch. VI, pp. 133-167; Ch. XV, pp. 404-429.

55. The selections from *The Descent of Man* are from the second, revised, one-volume edition, 1874, Modern Library reprint. Random House, New York: n.d. Ch. II, pp. 413-444; Ch. III, pp. 445-470; Ch. XXI, pp. 909-920.

56. Darwin, *Expression of the Emotions,* Ch. XIV, pp. 348-367.

57. Darwin, *Vegetable Mould,* pp. 305-313.

58. Thomas Henry Huxley, "The Coming of Age of the 'Origin of Species,'" [1889] *Darwiniana* (New York: D. Appleton and Co., 1896), pp. 227-243. *Letters,* II, 179-204.